Forget Your Troubles
Just Dance

Gaybrielle LeeAnn

Gaybrielle LeeAnn Dixon
www.gaybrielleleeann.com

ISBN: 978-0-9989943-2-1

I would like to acknowledge and thank God first and foremost for giving me the words to write this book and simply showing favor on me in everything I have done.

My parents, for instilling in me the morals and values that make up the woman I am today.

My family, for always encouraging me through the good and the bad times.

For everyone who played a part in my story, thank you. It wouldn't be what it is without you.

Lastly, everyone who has believed in me and supported me from the very beginning. There is so much more to come.

Thank you.

This book is dedicated to my baby sister Genesis.

I pray you always keep your head high. I strive to do my best every day in life because I know you look up to me and I want nothing more than to make you proud. You are so beautiful and intelligent and I can't wait to see you surpass me because then I'll know I did my job as your big sister. Always remember Jeremiah 29:11, "For I know the plans I have for you," declares the Lord. "Plans to prosper you and not to harm you, plans to give you hope and a future."

I love you.

CONTENTS

Part I

Be

Strong

Joshua 1:9KJV "Have not I commanded thee? Be strong and of good courage; be not affrighted, neither be thou dismayed: For Jehovah thy God is with thee withersoever thou goest."

Chapter 1

Loud Lies versus Calm Confirmations

"She won't last! She can't remember nothing," are the words I watched come out of my dance teacher's mouth as my mom yelled back and forth with her while tears flowed down my face. Only ten years old and my world was crushed! Who knew someone so young could feel so much pain. Pain from seeing someone I learned from have so much hate in their voice towards me. Pain from seeing the woman whom I came from have so much hurt in her eyes from listening to someone speak negatively about her first born. Many would have thought being a part of a church dance group would be uplifting and drama free. While I couldn't speak on every church, THIS one wasn't it. As my mother said her last words in defense for me, she turned to me with tears in her eyes only I could see and said, "Let's go." I hesitated. I didn't want to leave simply because I didn't want to miss out. But I was young and didn't understand what was best for me. Wanting to be a part and not being able to, was such a sting to my heart. I felt as though if everyone could like me, maybe life would be easier. Who would possibly think at that age the opposite of that would make you more sustainable in society? She snatched my arm, leading me out of the bathroom into the foyer where some of the other dancers and their mothers watched and wondered what the problem was. They knew, but all they could do was stare and form their own opinions privately. I looked no one in the eyes as tears rolled down my face. The real fight was me worrying about what everyone else was thinking. I was struggling between feeling hurt and embarrassed. I guess whatever emotion suited that moment is what it was.

The car ride home was quiet; quiet, but tense. I looked over only to find a tear sitting in the bed of my mother's eye, but she refused to let it drop. She was so strong. I started to regret the emotions I displayed because it wasn't strength. But what was strength? How was I supposed to be strong? How was I supposed to know if I fulfilled the very emotion meant for such a moment, or even how to understand my mom, who truly showed it. I knew she didn't want me to see her cry because she didn't want me crying.

When I got home my dad was waiting in the kitchen. "How was practice baby girl?" He always called me baby girl. I loved that. I ran to him and started crying in his arms. My mom said nothing, just walked straight to their room. He said in one still tone after her "Baby." No response. He watched her walk away and shut the room door behind her. He pulled me forward, looked me in my eyes and said, "What is going on?" I took one look in his eyes. That's all it took. It was always something about my daddy's eyes. When he looked at me, I couldn't hold myself together and fell right back into his arms crying my eyes out. He took one big sigh and looked up to God. He held me for a moment, as if God revealed to him exactly what it was. "Go clean yourself up." He walked to his room and shut the door. I went to my room and pressed my ear to the wall in hopes I could hear something, anything. I got nothing. I knew ma was in good hands though. He always put a smile on her face.

About an hour later they called me to the family dining room table. I sat up in my bed rolling my eyes. I hated family meetings. What was about to happen was expected. I came out of my room slowly, dragging my feet on the ground every step. I knew I was going to hear something I didn't want to hear. As I sat down, dad crossed his fingers, looked at me and said,

"Your mom and I have decided to take you out of the dance group right now."

"I don't want to!" I begged. It didn't work.

Their minds were made up. Who was I kidding? I knew I didn't need to be there at that time. I knew deep down inside of me I wasn't ready to face whatever it was before me and my parents knew it too. As my mom held my shoulders, I looked up at her with a faint innocent expression and tears in my eyes. She didn't say anything, but I saw reassurance in her eyes. I looked back to my dad. He grabbed my hand, and with a smile on his face and his one dimple coming through his cheek he said,

"God is going to work this thing out for your good, you'll see."

My mom pulled on my shoulder saying, "I want you to be strong sweetie, and stop doing all that crying."

And with that said, my dad went into a prayer. That meant it was all said and done. There would be no more talk about it. I walked back to my room, still somewhat dejected, but not defeated. For some reason I knew it was the start of something. I didn't know what it was, but at such a young age I knew something had just begun for me. The one word that rang in my head all night was strong. Strong. Why did it keep coming up? Was I missing something? To my knowledge, at my age, how much strength was I required to display?

Little did I know a few years later I would rejoin the team. I didn't know how it was going to go for me this time around, but what I did know was I was ready to begin the journey and my story that God would later reveal to me. The instructor hadn't changed. It was like reliving the same person you thought would've gotten it together. It seemed to be 10%

5

ministry, 90% entertainment. She formed the team she wanted, and I was coming into it. Was I welcomed? I wish I could say I was, but the truth became more and more evident with every practice and every performance. I would come to practice and the rest of the team, along with the instructor would come in all at once having already practiced together at someone's house. I was around thirteen now. I was smart enough to know when someone did and did not want me around. I got the picture. It was evident. I didn't fit amongst them. That was partially okay with me. "Stay strong sweetie and stop all that crying." The words of my mother echoing. They constantly rang in my head. As they all walked in, the instructor would say, "Catch on to what you missed" as if it was my fault. I didn't know what was new. I tried my hardest to tune out the sly remarks the girls would make about their private practice, but it was so hard. "Girl! It was so funny when you messed up on that part." "We had so much space in your living room, we gotta have a sleepover." Every single word, statement, and remark sent a sharp pain to my heart. I pushed hard and remained levelheaded amid them, but I cried after every practice. Every practice my mother would pick me up and she could see the tears forming in my eyes. I know she told me to "stop all that crying" but at this point, I didn't believe anyone could truly understand what I was facing. I would tuck my head over where she couldn't see and pinch myself so I wouldn't let a tear drop in front of her. I knew if she saw just one she was going to raise hell at not only them, but me too. One tear and I was out. She didn't like seeing me this way, but her knowing I didn't want to quit kept her from speaking her mind in the moment. I couldn't wait to get home to let it all out in the privacy of my room. Why me? It seemed it would only get worse.

Come performance night they were teaching me the new choreography they changed at their "private" practice right before we were about to go out to minister to another congregation. *For Every Mountain* by Kurt Carr. That was the song we were ministering to. As I performed the choreography taught to me minutes before the performance, I stopped dancing. I mean my body was still moving, but I stopped dancing. I knew I began to minister, but it was because God was ministering to me. Every word of the song began to resonate and take over my body. *For every mountain, you brought me over, for every trial, you see me through. For every blessing, hallelujah. For this I give you praise.* As I waved my flag through the air tears rolled down my face. But these weren't the tears my mom was talking about. These were tears of happiness. I could feel every emotion within me. I didn't really understand the meaning of what was taking place, but I heard every word unlike anything I've ever experienced before.

The next day as we were preparing to minister the dance before the congregation of our church, the youth minister had us all gather in his office. A man walked in, who was there to pray for us, but before he did he looked around and started connecting with everyone he was led to speak to. He caught my eyes as he said, "Stop expecting things from man. Only God can bless you, and He will." A tear rolled down my face. He prayed, and then we performed. It felt like a completion of something, but I wasn't sure exactly what it was. When service ended, I walked into the sanctuary where everyone was congregated, looking for my parents and meeting with a few friends.

A mother of the church called me over to her saying, "Baby, come here."

She'd watched me grow since I was a baby. She shook her head slowly, looked up, took a deep breath, then looked to me.

In a still, powerful tone she said, "Baby you are anointed. You don't think we see it, but I know how you've been treated. You keep your head up because you are blessed. God is about to make a way for you. Just hold on a little while longer and stay strong. He'll work it out."

Strong. I heard everything she said, but that one word sat there in my ears. It was so regular and I was still trying to figure out why. The story God told me He had for me kept coming up. Little by little He was revealing to me He saw me. If I kept looking to Him, He would reveal the meaning of everything.

When my parents put me in ballet at four, I didn't expect at this age I would have endured the level of warfare I did or know God was preparing me for something greater. It seemed like only my parents took talent to the extreme and made sure I was versed in every art category there was. Piano, singing, acting, public speaking, and modeling accompanied my dance background. They had to force piano on me, but I soared in each form. Dance and acting is what I loved the most! From starting out doing speeches in front of the entire congregation of over 2,000 people at the age of five, to getting lead roles in the church and school plays. I knew along with dance, acting was what I wanted to do.

I hated playing the piano. My dad made me practice for an hour and a half every day on top of having private lessons every week. I hated that as much as I hated going to practice. "Do you want to be like everyone else? Basic? Average? Now sit up straight and cuff your hands before I get my wooden spoon." Yes, that was my piano teacher. I would give her a hard time

8

every practice and this is what she would say to me almost every time. She was around seventy-five years old, black, southern, and old school. I didn't see the point in fixing my attitude. I was only going to get home and get another lecture from my father. He would say, "What are you going to do at your first audition when everyone is good at the same part you're going for? What is going to make you stand out? The fact that you can act? So can everyone else. Baby girl you want to be able to raise your hand and say you can dance, act, sing, and play the piano. Now wouldn't that be something!" There he was smiling again every time he knew he said something meaningful. For some reason his energy never transferred to me. I was still mad at the fact I couldn't go to my friend's house. I had to practice. He got up, walked out, and closed the sliding door. Before he would walk off he gave me a wink, which made me even more mad. I would wait until my timing was correct for him to be down the hall then I'd smashed my foot on the pedal while slamming my hands on the keys. To my surprise, as sick as I was of it, I was actually pretty good. I didn't want to admit it to myself. Around the age of fourteen I was trying to figure out why I was so busy practicing and my friends were enjoying their lives as normal kids. It made no sense to me. Everything came back to back. If it wasn't piano practice, it was choir rehearsal. If it wasn't choir rehearsal, it was drama practice. If it wasn't drama practice, it was dance practice. And I still had to deal with the fact I was really a one-man band amongst the dance team. I began to think it was my fault the other dance girls didn't include me. My dad was so focused on me mastering every talent I had and my mom didn't really trust anyone. I didn't understand the foundation they were building. I just knew I wanted to be a normal kid and it wasn't happening.

There was only one mom my mother trusted. If my parents had to work late or went out of town, my mom trusted me with her. She was the mother of one of the dancers on my church dance team. Her daughter wasn't bad either. It seemed like it was only different when everyone was together. Well, true colors finally came to the light. One practice she was fitting everyone for our church's Christmas performance costumes, which was normally her task as a parent. Of course everyone else already had their final measurements. I was the only one with nothing. She walked up to me saying "Can. You. Fit. A. Medium? Try it on!" loud and obnoxiously as if I was slow. My heart began to race. I tried my hardest to hold back my tears from the embarrassment. I felt everyone looking at me. When it was all over I walked to the car. I tried to hold it in, but I could no longer contain it. The moment my mom turned out of the parking lot and got down the street a few yards from the church, I let it all out. She instantly went from two to twenty. She stopped the car in the middle of the street. "What's wrong? What is wrong?! You better tell me what's wrong or I'm turning this car around." I told her. She did it anyways. I didn't want her to go back. I knew what she was capable of. She whipped the car around and parked it right in front of the woman's car. They were all still there. I got out with her. She stormed in and went at it with the other mom. Once again, like Déjà vu, tears are falling down my face. We were back to square one. After my mom said what she had to say, she left all of them standing there with nothing to say. She turned me to the door and we walked out. The lady came walking out a minute after her with an angry look on her face but said nothing. My mom turned around one last time, gave her a look, and got in the car.

The car ride was different this time. She couldn't wait. She called my dad, eyes red, tears falling down her face slamming

10

her hand against the wheel. I knew she was hurting for me. Her physical emotion expressed every way I was feeling inside. I knew there was no way I was going to fit in now. Why was that even on my mind? Despite that question, a big part of me wanted nothing to do with them. But another part of me just wanted answers. In my mind I would ask God, "If you love me so much, why do you put people around me who hate me? Why is it you continue to allow me to go through this crap? Why?" No response. At least that's what I thought.

It was the night of the church Christmas performance. No one said anything to me. They laid my uniform on a table and formed their own little corner. I put my leotard and skirt on, went in the restroom, looked in the mirror, and took a deep breath. As I stood there I repeated, "Be strong, be strong, be strong," and walked out. I was standing down the hall from them waiting to get ready to line up when one of the girls from the group walked up to me with a picture frame in her hand. It was a picture of all the girls except me. I could see it from my side view, but I didn't let her know I could see it. She said, "Look! Isn't it nice? It's for our instructor." I knew she was trying to taunt me. I continued looking forward and said "Yea, that's nice," and walked off.

We didn't have another performance for a while, so I chose to let it go. I wouldn't say I quit. As much as I faced, I for some reason never wanted to leave, but there was a new show in town. The *Chocolate Nutcracker*. I wanted to audition so bad and my parents gave me the choice to do the show or dance for my church. I joined the *Chocolate Nutcracker*. This is what I needed without me truly knowing what I needed. It helped enhance my dance ability and challenged me to be a better dancer. That's when my parents enrolled me back into a dance school to further my technique professionally.

Chapter 2
Everything's Changing Yet Remaining the Same

My new instructor was one of the church dance instructors as well. I'd known her for quite some time and she'd now opened her own studio. I knew I would feel welcomed and so did my parents. I enjoyed the atmosphere it brought and the girls around me. I went from being the outcast to being the person everyone leaned on. She depended on me and I didn't want to let her down. Yet part of me would find myself going off in a complete daze. My mind thought so deep at such a young age. Sometimes I would stare at my instructor. She didn't know how I truly felt at times. She didn't know she played a part in the burden I carried from my previous instructor. She was there. She saw me face the things I did, yet I didn't hear her say anything on my behalf. Not that she was supposed to, but I wanted someone, anyone, to stand up for me and do what I thought was right. She knew I longed for her to break silence. I knew I had to let it go though. Deep inside I knew she didn't want to say anything, but this was her way of apologizing. Can I pause here and say God has a serious sense of humor? He can switch your role in the blink of an eye. You could know, but wouldn't understand. It's amazing how you can see the story because He takes you through it, but you won't truly understand until it is all said and done. That was me. I was always going off in a daze because I didn't understand what He was doing, but I knew it was something. I wanted to do well just because of that. It made me dismiss the despair and embrace the love. I'd snap out of it and hit a perfect triple. She had a way of smiling without smiling. I knew she was proud. I was proud. Not just because of the triple, but I felt as though I was accomplishing this journey God was taking me through. It wasn't just because I was finally being seen because that was short lived.

It was funny to me how I could be seen and accepted in the world, but invisible and an outcast in the church. Just when I thought things were looking up, here comes the church to let me down. I'd been attending the same church since I was born. Everyone knew my parents, and everyone knew me. Big church. Great church. Great Pastor. Plenty of drama. But I could deal with that. What I couldn't deal with was it was the same group of girls who pushed me aside before. I was never the clique type, but why did I want to be friends with them so bad? The way I saw it, they came into my church, my territory, but I wanted to be amongst them as if I was joining their church. It's something about the "mean girl" group; everyone wants in. My situation seemed as though it was different, although it wasn't. For some odd reason individually they were fine with me. But me with the group just didn't fit. I had my own friends, but I was more independent anyways. I believe I began to grow based on the many circumstances I was experiencing. It just seemed as if it was cool to have the big group of friends at times. I didn't see the harm in it, but my mother did. The moment I thought they accepted me, she turned down every chance of me being around them. No movies. No sleepovers. "Those girls are not your friends, but if you want to go, ask your dad." I knew I wasn't going anywhere then. I would get home only to lay there and think, why was this so important to me? It's like that question constantly hit my brain. Why in the moment did it seem so hard to answer? I had to find ways to make myself feel a little better. "Just don't think about it," I told myself. The way I saw it, they had their leader who bossed them around. "Ain't nobody bossing me around" I thought to myself. This was my way of coping.

This went on until it was time for my first year in high school which I spent in a private Christian school. Let's just say I needed to get out of there fast. Don't get me wrong, it helped me in many ways, especially in the acting arena. However, I was still missing something. During my time there, dance was still around, but acting took top priority. I signed up for drama class and had an amazing acting teacher. He gave me my very first monologue. It was a first for me in school. Just about everyone in the class, including him, knew this monologue was supposed to be performed a certain way. It was meant to be funny. But I read it, practiced it, read it, practiced it, and decided I wanted to switch it up. I knew it was supposed to be funny, but I decided to perform it the way I felt it would best suit me. When the day came to perform I was so nervous. I couldn't concentrate on anything except my monologue. Once the bell rang signaling it was finally time for my drama class, I stalled. I walked through the door as soon as the final bell rung. I sat down and began to run my lines in my head.

I couldn't hear a word anyone was saying until the teacher said, "Before I go in order, would anyone like to volunteer to go first?"

What the heck! I need to get this over with.

"I'll go first."

I shouldn't have said that. I regretted it already, but what could I do now? Nothing.

He'd already said, "You have the floor."

I walked to the bench he had as a prop. "God, please do not let me bomb this." I stayed randomly talking to Him. I opened my mouth to start my first line. I started off subtle just as I

14

rehearsed, then began to reach the climax. I dropped to my knees, tears rolling down my face, lines coming out my mouth so smooth. On my last line I made eye contact with everyone in the room, and lastly my teacher. "I'm not just talking to me. I'm talking to you, and to you, and to you!" When I was finished I dropped my head. "Scene." The entire room was speechless. No one uttered a word for the first ten seconds of me sitting there. "Oh Lord, they hated it." Next thing you know everyone was clapping, saying they didn't see how they could go after my performance. My teacher was never the type to go crazy, but I could tell he was pleased. I walked to his desk to retrieve my grading paper.

He looked at me and said, "Stay after class."

No score was on my paper. As everyone was walking out, I walked up to his desk.

"Is something wrong?"

"Actually, the total opposite. Have you ever acted before or trained?"

I told him besides the plays I did for my church and the things I learned from them, I never had real professional lessons.

"Well you have a gift. I want you to audition for our next musical."

This is when I knew for sure I wanted to be an actress. But once they fired my original teacher things changed. I felt like I really didn't want to be there anymore. I mean acting was the one thing keeping me there in the first place. I had my friends and they were great, but I wanted to feel and see some culture. I wanted to look to my left and my right and at least see one person who looked like me.

My parents enrolled me into public school the next year of high school. I was now in my sophomore year. Once I arrived, the roles were once again reversed. I still took a drama class, but dance was now top priority. There was not only a dance class, but a team, and they loved me. I think it was because I had so many other races around me and it was mesmerizing to them to see a girl of my race who could dance the way I did with so much technique and personality. After class one day the dance teacher pulled me aside. "Are you going out for my dance team? You won't even need to audition. I want you." Things were finally looking up. I was instantly put on the team the very next year. I had no real issues with anyone and my boyfriend was one of the top football players of the school. I just felt like my life did a complete one-eighty. I couldn't have asked for a better junior year, but I spoke too soon. It was the last month of my junior year and the first day starting that month. I remember it like it was yesterday. Everything was going so well. Even the bus ride home was good. I could not foresee anything ruining my day. That was until I saw the vision at the end of my driveway through two big glass windows that led straight into my home. It changed everything. I knew something was off because my mom's car was in the driveway. It was about 2:45pm on a Friday. She didn't get off work until 5:30pm and didn't get home until a little after 6:00pm. I began to speed walk up my driveway. My heart started to race. We had a long driveway, but not that long. It seemed like it took forever just to get to the door. Once I made it to the window I was a little scared to go in. I saw my mom laying in my dad's arms crying. I began to think the worst. The last time I saw my mom cry was the incident from dance class, but she never cried. Never. All that was going through my head was sickness. What if she was sick? I had to pull myself together because I was ready to collapse. I couldn't imagine life without my mom and I didn't want to. I walked through the door and once she saw me, she wiped her face, but her eyes were still red and puffy. As soon as our eyes met, I started crying and ran to her.

"Ma, what's wrong?"

"Mommy's ok sweetie."

I got louder.

"No, you're not ma, what is wrong," with tears rolling down my face.

She started crying again. I know I shouldn't have yelled, but I couldn't help it. I was just as concerned as she was upset, if not more. My dad told me to go to my room for a moment. My little sister was already home, but he was waiting for my brother to walk through the door. Once he got home my dad called all of us to the living room. We sat there in silence. I finally stopped crying, but I needed to hear something. The suspense was getting to me. I put my hand over my mouth.

"What's going on?"

Dad finally decided to speak up. "Your momma's job laid off some people today." He continued to stall, pausing between each comment. "They want to keep your momma, praise God, but she will have to relocate to Minnesota, Detroit, or Louisiana. Now me and your momma are thinking Louisiana because me personally, I'm not trying to be where it's cold and I know y'all probably wouldn't want that either."

Were they serious?! All of this for him to basically tell me I'm going to miss my senior year, and everything I've built for myself here, and all he could talk about was the weather?! I broke down in tears. My mom knew it was going to hurt me the most. Me crying made her cry even more. I brought up every possible solution: staying with friends, family, church family, anyone, but I refused to leave. My dad wasn't having any of that. It seemed so unreal at the time. I still had hope they would change their mind and we would end up staying, not realizing making that decision could possibly change all our lives for the worst. All my dad said was that if this was God's plan, we were going to follow it. They decided on Louisiana and we were due to move at the end of the summer.

We went three months without our mom. She moved without us because my parents wanted us to enjoy our last summer with our friends. What a fine time to start caring about what we thought. Regardless of the gesture, it still didn't make much of a difference. We were still leaving. She came back so we could all move to Louisiana together. It was the worst road trip I had ever been on. The fact it was permanent did not help. There was absolutely no strength left in me. I hated it. Every chance I had alone I cried. It seemed like things just got worse each day. I figured the least I could do was continue dancing. So once we found one of the more talked about dance schools in the city, my mom enrolled me. I guess coming into an area where the town is small can be intimidating to others because out of a class of about fifteen girls, maybe two liked me. I can admit I came in with a different type of talent. My skills were a little more advanced, but that was something I couldn't help. I wasn't the type to hold back for others. I knew it wasn't the best fit for me, but I remained because I wanted to continue my training.

School was beginning in a week and I was about to experience my first and last year as a senior in high school. Of course around this time most students are figuring out what college they want to attend or have already figured it out. All I knew was I had my top three schools picked out in Florida because that's where I wanted to be. My parents were trying so hard to convince me to stay in Louisiana for school due to the out of state fees. I wouldn't budge. What possibly was in Louisiana for me? In my mind I had already convinced myself it was too slow for me and there was absolutely nothing I could be interested in that my hometown did not have. Three days before the first day of school I met a girl who was hired for the same job as me. We started to link. We went to the same school, so she invited me to come with her to orientation to meet all the seniors and get to know the school a little before classes started. This was my first opportunity to get cute because first impressions were everything to me. Once we got there I literally felt like I was in a movie as I walked down the hall. Everything appeared to be moving in slow motion as if I was the only one there. The guys were turning their heads and the girls were trying to figure out who I was. I guess since I was a new face. I sat there with the girl I came with as she introduced me to her friends. One by one guys started walking up trying to make conversation and figure out who I was. I was starting to think it wouldn't be too bad being the new girl in town. That same day I found out about the school's dance team and decided to inquire about it. Unfortunately they'd already held tryouts so I couldn't be on the team. However, the dance coach heard about me and invited me to one of their rehearsals the first day of school.

The first day wasn't that bad. I was ready to get to the dancing. That was the only thing that kept my mind off everything weighing me down. I walked through the door and all eyes turned to me. The same girls who stared me down during orientation were watching me now. This was perfect for me because I'll be honest, I was a "subtle mean." I wouldn't say anything with my mouth, so my eyes did all the talking. I made sure I looked every girl in the eye, giving them a slight smirk. I found a spot within their circle and began to stretch. I could feel them trying to watch me as I effortlessly got into my split sitting perfectly on the floor with my toes pointed all the way to the ground. The coach glanced over here and there. I did a little technique and had to leave to get ready for work. As I walked out, the coach followed me. She explained to me she would've loved to have me on the team, but school rules were set in place. I understood and I was okay with that. She then made a statement that would change my life forever.

"I could see you auditioning for a dance team that is under a well-known college here in Louisiana."

"Who?"

At this point I had no clue who or what she was talking about. I had already looked into every local team in the area and this particular school didn't ring a bell because I had never heard of it. She explained they were a very well-known team in a city in Louisiana and the school was very popular in the south. I told her I would look into it. We exchanged a few more words and I left.

As soon as I got home I got dressed for work and sat there on my bed. My first mind was not to look up the team. I really did not see the importance or understand. I laid back, thought about what she said, and typed the name into YouTube. The very first video all I saw was beauty. My eyes were fixed on this gorgeous girl in the front. I was her. She was me. I was sold from that one video and that one girl. I was just in awe at how beautiful all of them were. I now knew where I wanted to go and what I wanted to do. That night I showed my mom and she was just as excited. I think they were more excited at the fact I chose to stay in Louisiana. But nevertheless, their happiness came from me finally displaying happiness they missed since we left Florida. Unfortunately that form of happiness was put on pause. I still had two whole high school semesters to finish before fulfilling this newfound dream and it was going by slow. I met friends, but I wasn't very big on having many. I had one girlfriend and three guy friends who I occupied my time with all throughout my senior year. Life went on as normal, for my form of normal. School, work, up one day, down the next, cry, then smile. It was regular for me. When I took the time to sit down and really think, it actually wasn't turning out to be as bad as what I thought because I was beginning to learn and notice more about myself than I ever had before. The change in me was mainly evident with my school. It wasn't like the average public school I was used to. I guess because the people were different. It was new to me.

I was in one of my moods this particular day. I debated on pretending to be sick so I didn't have to attend school, but I decided to suck it up and drive myself to my misery. My first class on Wednesdays was math class with a teacher whom I didn't have the best relationship with. It was like she tried to get under my skin. I always felt as though she made it her mission to constantly single me out. I sat towards the front of the classroom to the left of her desk. She had given us an assignment to do and as much as I didn't want to do it, I finished and proceeded to do my own thing. I wore a necklace that had a knot at the end of the heart shaped pendant that hung from the bottom. I took it off and begin to occupy my time by getting the knot out. She called out my name. "Have you finished the assignment?" I did finish the assignment but that was not the point. I could only help but wonder why everyone else occupied their time laughing and talking and she chose to call on me. She took the necklace off my desk and laid it on hers. I looked down at my desk to the spot where the necklace was laid and then I looked in her eyes. "Umm, I'm sorry, what are you doing?" I will admit I had a smart mouth at times, but she had no right. I sat waiting until she turned her back, then I snatched the necklace from her desk. She turned around only to raise her voice towards me claiming she was going to take the knot out for me, but since I wanted to do things my way, I could take a trip down to the assistant principal's office.

My teacher made the call down to the office as I walked into the waiting room. The assistant principal was a short, black, older lady, but everyone always talked about how she was not to be played with. I guess I was about to find out. She called my name to come into her office and I sat down.

"Do you know what your place is at this school?"

"Yes."

"Yes what?"

"Umm yes, I do."

She raised her voice. "You have one more time or I will be calling your parents."

"One more time to do what?" I was really confused. I had no clue why she was getting more and more upset, raising her voice, and she even stood up.

"Your parents never taught you to respect authority?"

"When did I disrespect you?" Eventually I realized she was waiting on the word ma'am. It's not that I wasn't accustomed to it, but it wasn't a serious term I was raised on. I was never forced to say it. When she finally made it clear what she wanted I finally added the word. I may have had a smart mouth, but I was always going to be honest and clear about what was going through my head. I knew how to fix most things in my favor. "My parents raised me quite well. I am very clear of the term. However, being forced to use one word just to show I respect you is not a form of respect. It's you basing the respect I should have for you on one word, which only makes me wonder why it was an issue in the first place, with all due respect... ma'am." She tilted her head to the side and smirked.

"Where are you from Ms. Lady?"

As I responded to her question she began laughing and said she had never met anyone like me. "Now go on back to class before you make me regret my decision."

As I walked to the door I turned around, gave a small smirk, and said, "Yes ma'am."

She nodded her head and winked. Believe it or not, why did that feel like the highlight of my senior year looking back on it? Within those few months of being in Louisiana, that was the third time someone told me they had never met someone like me. I knew I would never forget her.

School was coming closer and closer to the end. I had applied to many schools and was receiving acceptance letters, but I was only waiting for one. It came! I finally received my letter of acceptance from my now dream school and I began to imagine my life from that very moment. I dreamed of being the girl I saw when I was first introduced to what felt like my destiny. After months of growing, learning, and life situations, graduation night arrived. My family came in town and I was excited at the fact this felt like a step closer to my dream. I decided I was going to school for law, but not many people knew exactly why I wanted to go to the particular school I chose. I was very reserved when it came to my personal dreams and goals. That's the way I was raised, but I made the mistake of telling the wrong person. It's not so much what people physically do, it's the thoughts they can put in your mind that cause you to second guess who you really are. "You're pretty, but those girls are tall and you're too short. You're not light enough." Because of things like that, I became very particular in who I allowed in my life when it came down to the things I hoped and prayed for. My immediate family and my best friends knew. I could trust them. Other than that, anyone else would think I was going to become this big-time lawyer, and to a certain degree I wanted to, but that was the second plan.

The big day everyone was waiting on finally was here. My best friend came to pick me up from my house to get ready for graduation. Once we got there, two girls parked right behind us and walked up to the car. One was his cousin and the other was her best friend. He introduced them to me, but what was coincidental is they both went to the college I chose to attend. I felt like it was a sign I made the right decision.

"What are you going to school for?"

I hesitated in my answer because of course my first mind wanted to say the dance team, but I stuck to my morals and led with law.

"You're so pretty. You look like you could be one of the band's dance girls."

There it was again! I had to keep my composure. "Don't let it get to your head," I kept telling myself. I played it off.

"Really? I've heard that before, but I'm really focused on becoming a lawyer and I don't know much about the team."

They proceeded to give me more details of what they knew, but it was time to head in for the ceremony. Honestly the moment didn't feel like what everyone talked about when it came to graduation. I felt a few butterflies, but I wasn't sure if my feelings were normal or not. They were getting closer to calling my name. As soon as I made it to the stage they announced the school I would be attending in the fall. Out of everything, that seemed like the best part of the ceremony to me. After it concluded, we took our pictures and everyone came back to my house. My mom laid everything out for everyone. She did her thing as usual. She cooked most of the food and my dad fried the fish. I sat and talked to the girls more about their college. They said they would be my big sisters on campus. Again, I had to act cool, but on the inside, I felt grown! I hadn't even made it there yet and I was already forming acquaintances. I was getting excited, but I was still very guarded. It was just something about seeing that next step and things already working out the way you didn't even expect them to. After everyone finished eating all the "kids," as my parents would say, left the house to head to the parties. I wasn't much of the club type and I couldn't stop thinking about college. So most of the night I held the wall thinking about my future. I came just to look good anyways.

Once we left my best friend and I headed back to my house. We sat outside for a while talking about where our lives were headed. He knew I wanted to be a dance girl for the college I was attending. We were determined to make our dreams come true. We didn't know when it would happen or how, but we knew speaking it into existence was a big step. That night I dreamed and prayed, prayed and dreamed, and put it on repeat until summer was coming to an end and it was finally time to prepare for what would make my dream a reality. During a portion of my senior year and for the summer I worked for a law firm as an intern. It was the last three weeks before it was time for me to leave permanently for college. As I finished up my last evening in the office, the moment I walked out I got a text from my best friend.

"You heard about the team?"

My heart dropped. Ever since I found out about them, everything with dance and the team was all that was on my mind. I sped up my walk to the car and immediately called him.

"What are you talking about? Don't play games with me."

He loved to joke, but I knew he was serious when he started his statement off with my full name. He said they already held auditions and two girls from our school made it. Mind you, these are the same two girls who hated me when I got to the school, so I was furious. One question and one statement went through my head. "How did they make it? They're not even cute!' I didn't know much about teams of that sort, but what I did know was if I auditioned the next year I would have to be under them and I wasn't having that. I knew it was the last thing I should have been thinking about, but if I'm being honest, I was crushed. My dream wasn't working out how I planned. On top of that, I had to watch two girls who I felt didn't deserve it as much as I did, make it. What made me feel like I deserved it and not them? The simple fact was I was only thinking about myself. The fact I thought comparing myself to others was the answer to my problems. But when I got home, the team was still the same, and I was still not on it. I didn't even want to go to the school anymore. Nevertheless, my parents packed up the car and we headed to the school for freshman orientation.

Chapter 3
A Dream Deferred

It was the second longest car ride ever, besides the first one when I moved to Louisiana. This one was different. We were only three hours away and it felt like three days. As we rode I played my music in my headphones as I stared out the window. A tear fell down my face. The main reason I wanted to leave in the first place was not even a factor anymore. I was trying to put myself in a good mood, but all I could think about was someone else living out my dream. We finally made it to the school. It was about 9:00am. We tried to move into my assigned dorm room for the weekend, but the dorm mother was nowhere to be found to hand out keys. I was already starting to see the perks of attending a historically black college. We ended up waiting at the hotel my parents booked for the weekend. First, my hair didn't turn out right, then my phone shut off. The college experience was already stressing me out. I sat on the couch trying to hold back tears, but I could not help it.

The moment my mom said, "What's wrong sweetie," the tears took off. "You didn't come to college to get your way. You came to get your education and be on that team and you'll get there."

Then my dad sat down, put his arm around me, and pulled me close.

"Baby girl, you made it here. God allows things to happen for a reason and if you just hang in there, He's going to work this thing out. Watch."

There he was smiling again. I guess I couldn't help but put a small smile on my face. I touched up my makeup and my hair.

We left to head back to the school in hopes we could get some things done this time. My parents dropped me off at orientation while they handled some other things. As nervous as I was, I didn't let it show. I wasn't looking for friends, guys, or anything. Just the dance team. As I walked to the door the Student Government President and the orientation leaders greeted me. They all commented on how pretty I was. I smiled and decided to be a tad bit social. Then the question came.

"Are you one of the dance girls for the band?"

It was better than the question I was normally asked. She asked me if I WAS one. "Yes!" Lord knows that's what I wanted to say, but I held that in and gave my real answer.

"No, I believe they've already held their auditions." As if I had no clue what it really was.

"Well, there's always next year because you look like you could be one. But you could also tryout for the basketball dance team!"

I was unaware of any other team, but as far as I was concerned, I was not interested unless they danced at the football games. I shrugged my shoulders, said my goodbyes, and walked on. I went through orientation like every other student trying not to think about what could have been that wasn't. It wasn't that I didn't like it, it was just the fact there was nothing I could do about it but go through my freshman year and prepare to tryout the next year. I met so many people. I began to cling to one group of girls whom I thought was cool, but one person stood out to me. We were pretty much the same. She was laid back and chill. She didn't care for the loud partying and doing a lot. I was the same way. We instantly clicked and decided we were going to be roommates for our freshman year.

Time flew by to the official day to move in on campus. I was the first one who made it to the room. My mom, dad, aunt, and uncle came to help me get everything situated. So many emotions were going through my head. A big part of me was excited because I felt grown, but that was just it. It was now more than just a dream. It was reality. I would be there, without my parents, handling a lot of things for myself. It was an overwhelming feeling, but nothing I would portray openly. I was someone who tried my best to take on many situations alone and to the best of my ability. My roommate and her family eventually came and set up her side of the room. When it was time for my parents to head out, my dad called everyone to a circle to pray. He prayed and my mom cried. I knew she was going to do that. I didn't want to, but when I saw her crying, I couldn't help it. I was trying to hold back because my roommate was there. She didn't shed a tear. I let maybe one or two tears fall and that was it for me. I hugged everyone, they departed, and it was just me and my roommate.

The same energy we had for orientation, we kept, and it continued to grow. We had two other roommates whose room was attached to ours. We shared the bathroom. The first day they came in our room and we all laughed and talked like girls do when they get together. It felt good. I hadn't had that for so long. We went to our first few college festivities and it was exactly what I imagined it to be and better. So many people, guys everywhere, and just so much to get into. My roommate was gorgeous! Together we were the perfect set of friends. We walked around to look cute, turn down guys, and go back to our room to chill. We spent a lot of time just talking. I still had not told her the real reason I came to this particular college. I had to feel her out a little more. College for the most part was exactly how I heard it to be; busy hallways, always a turn up, and financial aid lines. If I wasn't alone, I was always with my roommates. We attended some parties, but for the most part, we spent a lot of time in the cafe or in our room talking. I had yet to go to a football game, but I knew I wouldn't be going to watch football of course. I wanted to see the dancers. We decided to go to the next home game. The day of the game came. I got really cute and wore some strap-up sandals that came to my knee. It was bad enough neither of us had a car and had to walk from our dorm all the way to the stadium. Things just didn't seem to be going right. Not only did my hair fall, but my shoes kept coming loose if I didn't tie them tight. When I did tie them tight, they cut off the circulation in my legs. It was just a mess. We finally made it to the game. The student section was right next to the dancers. Sad part is, where we could find a seat, we couldn't see anything. It also didn't help we were both short. I did everything to try to see them. No luck. I don't know why I thought if I saw them that would be my way of knowing it was meant. We decided to leave. All that was on my mind was the team and the two girls from my school who made it. For some reason I still couldn't believe it. I was determined to find out. My roommate still had no clue why I didn't say much the whole walk back to the dorm. I wanted to tell her, but I had no room in me to hear anything aside from what I believed.

The very next day we were sitting in our room going through our normal routine when our two close guy friends came over. It was normal and regular for them to come by for no reason. One of them started talking about the game.

"Y'all seen those dancing girls yet. I want me one." My heart dropped. My eyes opened wide and I looked at him. I acted oblivious.

"What dancing girls?"

My roommate chimed in, "You mean the band dance girls?"

My head snapped to her and my eyebrows caved in. I thought to myself, "You mean the whole time you knew about these girls and didn't say anything to me?" I felt like I was having a heat flash. I knew I was probably over exaggerating, but this was serious to me. I was still trying to hold back my emotions all while wanting to engage in the conversation. He had me pull up a video of them on my laptop. I sat there in amazement. There was me again, or at least me imagining myself gracing the front and looking like perfection. I was partially relieved that I finally got my answer on the girls from my school. My roommate watched my whole aura change, but I knew she purposefully didn't say anything.

"Man, they so bad!"

He just kept going. Shut up already.

"You think you could be one of those girls? I think you could because you look good, but you're too short."

Then the other jumped in, "Yea, and them girls all red, you're too dark."

Boys....that's exactly what they were to me.

I reluctantly just said, "Shut up," rolled my eyes and returned to watching "myself" on the screen.

I knew my roommate could see the shift in my energy because she said, "I think she would be perfect for that team."

I just smiled.

"It's time for y'all to go."

Yes, I was kicking them out because I had no time for the negativity. Although I knew they had no idea they struck a nerve in me, I still needed to protect my mind. I'd already started believing what they said was true. The moment I shut the door, I hopped in my bed and shut the video off as if I wasn't interested anymore. I could feel my roommate just looking.

"You want to be a dance girl, huh?"

Were we finally about to have this moment? This was important to me because I wouldn't have to hide it anymore. From then on, she would see every part of me that cared about it.

"Yea I do, but I'm too 'short and dark'."

In her New Orleans accent she responded, "Girl, they don't know nothing. You have everything you need to be on that team, and when you make it next year, we gon' sit back and laugh because you proved them wrong."

It's like my heart took a deep breath and relaxed. I needed that. I needed her. I needed someone to speak encouragement into me. She was that friend.

I carried on with my days, the same as always. I started getting word of auditions for the basketball dance team I heard about during orientation. Part of me wanted to audition and part of me didn't. I felt like I was letting the band dance girls down if I did, but I knew I wanted to keep dancing. I talked about it with my roommate. She made it very clear that if it was on my mind to just do it. I'd rather do it than have regrets. With that, I decided to go for it. It was a three-day audition. I'm not going to lie, I hadn't prepared for it. I went to the gym a few times, did a few splits in my room, and called it a day. I relied on my natural talent of dance to get across the finish line. To me that was all I needed.

The first day was simply learning all the choreography and rehearsing it. I could feel myself in my groove. It wasn't simple but it wasn't challenging on a level I couldn't handle. The hard part for me was seeing the judges staring into my soul. It felt as though they were only looking at me. I knew they weren't, but it seemed as though I was the only one dancing. I didn't know anyone except for a girl I met during orientation. We kept in touch and I decided to stick around her which made me feel a little more comfortable. But that was the problem. My comfortable nature caused me to become just that, comfortable. I still performed well. At the time no one could tell me anything about my performance. It wasn't until I got back to my room that I knew I could have done better. I wasn't beating myself up, however, I knew deep inside my best didn't come out.

The next day was the audition for the cut down to the top twenty girls. I did my makeup and hair as close to perfect as I could wearing all black from head to toe. I knew I looked good enough to stand out only to get there and see one girl with her entire outfit bedazzled. A part of me felt like I didn't do enough.

34

Another part of me felt like she was doing too much, but I needed to stay focused. I came in, took my headshot, got my number, and sat down in my own area. This time I stayed to myself. The judges were sitting across the stage beaming down on us. It was time to line up for progressions. I watched as the girls went across the floor. Some were amazing, with flawless technique, others, well let's just say hopefully their looks were more of an interest. It was my turn. I took a deep breath and began my technique. From my jazz strut, to my turns and leaps, I knew I had it. My goal was to simply get it done because I was extremely nervous. Next, it was time to perform the choreography. I was ready, but nervous. As I waited outside for my group to be called, I paced back and forth in my little area. "You got this" as I rehearsed the dance repeatedly in my head and openly with my hands. They finally called my number. I walked in with my hands on my hips and stood in my spot. As soon as the music started my body took over. I couldn't hear the music anymore, nor did I have control over myself. I could only hope I performed the dance in its entirety by the end. I got up from the ending pose and stood with my hands on my hips smiling. "Thank you," and with that, they escorted us out. I was so glad it was over. I sat down with everyone else waiting for the director to announce the top twenty finalists. The director's assistant finally walked out. "Good job tonight ladies. If I call your number please return to the auditorium. If your number is not called, please gather your belongings and exit the building." My heart dropped. Number. Number. Number. It was going in slow motion. "thirty-..." my heart started beating fast. I knew she was about to call my number. "four"... never mind. A sharp pain stung my heart. Number. Number. Number. She finally called my number and my heart beat even faster. A huge smile was planted across my face. I grabbed my things and walked through the door. I tried to control my emotions, but I was overjoyed and relieved. They announced to us we were the top twenty finalists, the rules for the very last audition day, and how everything would go. As they prepared us to take a picture with the group, the director walked up to me. "You're the shortest in the bunch. Bring it tomorrow." My heart took off. It was the pressure of feeling like I had to be better just because I was the shortest. When we finished I gathered my things and left. My mind was going crazy. For some reason I wasn't excited anymore. I was just content and ready to get it over with.

The day came. I had my things packed and ready. I caught a ride with some of the other finalists to the performance venue. Once we arrived it seemed like forever until the event started. Every girl found her own corner to do her makeup and hair. I took my time and did everything perfectly once again. We were set to perform two dances. The one we did for the previous audition day and a second dance we learned. This time the audition was open and many people were downstairs ready to see us perform. I was lined up with my group backstage ready to be called. My hands were sweating. I kept rubbing them on my tights to dry them, but it kept coming back. I just wanted to get it over with. They finally called our group and we performed the original dance. I did good. No different than the first time I performed it. It was the second dance I was concerned about. It was a hip-hop routine. I was good at hip-hop. The problem was I was performing with girls who were better and I wasn't afraid to admit that. As soon as my group was called I walked out and stared into the crowd. It was so many people. I was used to crowds, but not college crowds. I didn't know anyone there to even slightly take my mind off the fact I was nervous. The judges were six feet away from us with absolutely no expression on their faces. The dance floor seemed so small. I began to worry about my spacing even though I really did have enough room. I just needed something else to worry about. The music started and my body took over. Once again, I had no control. I couldn't even hear the music anymore. It was over before I knew it. I got up from my ending pose and came back to myself, but it was too late. I walked off with a feeling that I did just okay. I watched from the top balcony while some of the other girls performed. I paced back and forth as the last group finished. After what seemed like an eternity, it was time to announce the final team. They escorted us downstairs, but we stayed backstage. Only the girls whom they called could walk out. One by one they began to call the names of the girls. They made it to nine names and I still hadn't been called. It was down to the last two names. I waited in anticipation. My heart was beating faster and faster. Last name. It wasn't me. I turned around, went and grabbed my things. I didn't cry. I didn't show any emotion. I honestly was thinking about the bowl of noodles I was going to fix as soon as I got back to my dorm room. Once I made it back downstairs the only way out was to walk through the room where the girls who made it were being celebrated. I stopped and looked just thinking that maybe someone would see me and possibly change their mind and put me on the team. No one noticed. I instantly felt the hurt I didn't feel just five minutes ago. It was that very moment I knew for sure it was over. It was that moment it became real. I walked to the car. I got in, not saying one word the entire ride back to the school while the other girls complained about how it wasn't fair and how the judges already knew who they wanted. Maybe they did, maybe they didn't. But as soon as I got out of the car my mind was made up. That was the last time I would be rejected. There was a reason I didn't make this team and I was only anxious to find out why. There was one thing I did know. I played the game not to lose, but my new focus was to win.

I spent some time feeling down about myself. I wanted things to work out my way. It was crazy how you would think you're doing everything right, only for things to go wrong. It wasn't all bad. I spent a lot of time in the gym dancing. Besides regular classes, I joined the debate team to occupy my time. I also participated in a few pageants. I guess you could say things were decent. The fall semester was getting closer to the end. I was really starting to get the hang of this college thing and my own flow. Before I knew it, the fall semester was over and I was one semester away from fulfilling my dream.

Everything was pretty much the same upon making it back to campus for the spring semester. Same routine: classes, gym, hangout with roommates, eat, sleep, repeat. I woke up one morning scrambling, trying to get my presentation together for my freshman seminar class. I didn't have a car so I had to walk all the way to the front of campus in heels. I got to class exhausted and my feet were hurting me. I wasn't fully prepared. Thankfully I was quick on my feet and good with words. So even though I wasn't fully prepared I wasn't worried. Upon coming into class I noticed a very beautiful woman sitting towards the back. Having never seen her before I assumed she was a guest speaker. For some reason she looked very familiar. I found my seat, and within a few short minutes the teacher called my name to present. I set everything up and began my presentation. Everything went exactly as planned, if not better. I engaged my classmates, answered every question punctually, and with that, I was finished. I wasn't nervous because speaking was something I did best. The only thing really on my mind was where I knew the woman in the back from. Class was finally over. As I made my way to the door, she stopped me.

"Very good presentation."

I said thank you and proceeded to leave, but she stopped me again.

"You are so pretty. What is your name?"

As she got out of her seat I told her my name suggesting I knew her, but I didn't know from where. Turns out she was one of the judges from the audition I participated in last semester.

"I remember you from auditions. You did good. It was something about you that stood out."

I was still trying to figure out if there was something about me why wasn't I on the team. Because I was so straight forward I asked her. She was honest as well.

"There's still some things you need to work on, and that's okay. You'll find exactly what is for you here."

As we walked the courtyard we continued to exchange words. I told her besides what I came to school for, I always wanted to pursue an acting career. She shared the same career interest. She'd already accomplished a few things. She told me she knew someone who helped her and would be a good person for me to speak with. We were on a good start so I took her word. We continued walking and began to approach a gentleman. As she introduced us I noticed he looked very familiar. It was the "you're the shortest in the bunch" director from the basketball dance team auditions. He was nice. I talked to him about how I wanted to get involved more but I didn't know where to start.

"I'll be on the lookout for you, but there are so many things you can get involved in here. Your time is coming soon."

As I walked away those words rang in my head. "Your time is coming soon."

It was still the beginning of spring semester and I spent every waking moment in the gym. From class to the gym is how my schedule worked. If I wasn't dancing, I was working out. If I wasn't working out, I was dancing. My roommates came with me at times, but they supported me from the room for the most part. Along the way I met a guy who was a few years older than me. He attended the school a few years back but was now out of school. We dated for most of the semester. Although we didn't make it official, we still functioned as if we were in a relationship. It was different but I liked it because it was new. I was on my own and he was a bit further than me in life. Maybe a lot, but nevertheless he was there. He knew about my dream and he supported it.

School was getting closer to the end. I was just leaving my last class of the day and stopped by the restroom before the long walk back to my dorm. As I took a step into the restroom a familiar looking girl walked out. She was bare faced, her hair pulled into a messy bun, and she was wearing sweat clothes. I instantly realized who it could possibly be. It was the woman I saw from the first video I ever watched of the girls I aspired to be. I called her name in hesitation out of fear I was wrong. I was hoping I wasn't. She slightly turned her head. It was her. I walked up and introduced myself. She had to know how much she inspired me and how from one video I aspired to one day be in her shoes. She felt honored. And with that, she wished me all the best. She said we'd possibly speak with one another again. I walked away with so much joy. I adored the simple fact they were so inaccessible. I'd been looking for the chance to walk past one of the football dance girls all school year, and this was the first. It made them even more interesting. I knew I had to be a part.

Weeks started to get closer and closer to auditions. I was heavy in the gym. Nothing was stopping me from achieving the goal I set out to conquer. Everything seemed to be working just right. One of the current members posted a flyer regarding a training class she was hosting for girls preparing for the audition. She was hosting the class in the same city my family moved to, but I was still in school and didn't have a form of transportation home. I didn't want to take it as a sign, but I was leaning towards it. My mom encouraged me to reach out to her just to see, so I did. I asked if we could still work but possibly at the school. She immediately responded and worked out plans to have a private session. I felt like this was almost like an audition. If she liked me maybe she would tell the director about me. Of course I eventually learned it didn't work that way, but at the time that's what kept me motivated. As I walked in the room to meet her I was mesmerized. She was gorgeous. I'm sure she didn't know what all went through my head and I planned to keep it that way. We started talking and getting to know one another. She was excited at the fact we both came from the same place. She blessed me to work with her consistently up until tryouts. It was only God. She critiqued every little thing which is exactly what I needed. She was sweet, but tough. I needed someone like her to stay on me so I could stay on myself.

Weeks turned to days before auditions. School finally let out for the summer and everyone was moving off campus. It was now one day before auditions. The girl from the team met with me to prepare me with everything I'd need. She even invited another dance girl to watch and critique me. They both helped me in every way; from my walk, to my technique, to my

41

choreography. Everything was touched on. With every critique my confidence rose higher and higher. I slowly, but surely, gained everything I needed. Even the drum major came in giving his critique from the male perspective, "You gotta give more woman - think grown." When they left, I stayed to practice. I wanted to make sure every part of me was prepared. I wasn't leaving that gym until I was satisfied with myself. As I practiced, a girl walked in. It was one of the dancers who made it the last season. She was preparing for auditions as well. She was short just like me and could dance! I told her I was auditioning and she let me practice with her. She even gave me a few pointers on things they would possibly do for auditions. After I left from working with her I finished my day by working with some other girls who were auditioning as well. We went across the floor repeatedly, performing the same move until we saw improvement. I stood close to the mirror and just looked at myself. I figured maybe if I was satisfied with what I saw the judges would be too. As I packed my things up a somewhat tall, beautiful bright skinned woman walked through the door. Everyone walked up to her speaking and hugging. Out of curiosity I walked up but was still unsure of who she was. I whispered to the girl standing next to me, "who is this?" She told me she was a former member of the team we were auditioning for. I immediately felt as though I needed to introduce myself. I walked up and smiled.

Before I could get a word out of my mouth she looked at me and asked, "You're auditioning?"

I said, "Yes", with much excitement and proceeded to ask questions on what I needed to work on and what was expected for auditions.

She answered me by saying, "Well they already have a short girl on the team, and they don't need two, so you're probably not going to make it."

I looked away but quickly turned my head back to face hers. Despite what she said I knew I had a decision to make. Was I going to let her opinion defeat me or build me? With a slight smirk I responded, "Well I guess we'll find that out from the judges tomorrow, huh?"

She dropped her head and raised her eyebrows. I walked off with a slight smile on my face, but my heart was pounding. I didn't know what to think. I thought so highly of these young ladies and who was she to tell me what my future held?

The night before auditions one of the dancers who came in to help me earlier that day did my hair at her apartment. She talked to me a little about what the team was like and what the judges expected at auditions. Once I got back to my dorm I laid on my mattress with nothing but a blanket and one pillow. Everything was packed up. I stared at the blank white wall in front of me thinking about everything that happened to me leading up to this point. I finally made it. I had to think and reflect now because I knew I would be completely focused the day of auditions. No one knew I was auditioning except for a few people. My immediate family, my roommates, the people who trained me, and the guy I had been talking to. I kind of backed away from him for the sake of getting my mind right for auditions, but he never missed a moment with me. In the middle of me reminiscing there was a knock on my door. I hesitated to open it because everyone had pretty much already left campus. The other girls I knew who were auditioning as well were sleep. "Who is it?" It was him. I opened the door to him standing there with flowers and a large cookie cake that read: Good Luck, You Got This. Even though I wasn't looking forward to any visitors it put me in good spirits. He knew, as well as I, that I needed that right before auditions. After we spoke briefly he left. I called my best friend to make sure everything was set for him to pick me up after auditions. He had no idea I was auditioning. I didn't plan on telling him until it was over. I hoped for the best and prepared for whatever.

The day finally came. I woke up early to do my makeup and make sure everything was done perfectly. "Not too much, but just enough," is what the former team member I worked with told me. I packed my bag and headed downstairs to meet some of the other girls who were auditioning so we could ride together. As soon as we made it to the band hall there was already a line. My heart was beating fast. I thought about the first team I auditioned for last semester. "You got this. Tunnel vision." I kept talking to myself. This was the only way I was going to stay focused and motivated. I walked in, gave them my I.D., and found a room to prepare myself. There were so many girls around and for the most part many of them were beautiful. I scoped the room to see what I was up against. "Umm she's cute...cute...tall...flexible....umm, definitely not. Okay, stop looking and focus on you." I began to stretch, not knowing I was in the room with a girl who was previously on the team in years past. A few minutes later, the girl who did my hair walked in. I got excited because I thought she came for me, but she was there for the girl who was on the team before. She did see me and helped fix my hair. I'm not going to lie, I felt special. I was already getting noticed by someone who was already on the team! "Ladies, please leave all of your belongings and make your way to the band room." It was time. My palms were sweating and my hands were shaking. "Hair, check. Outfit, check.

Number, check. SMILE." As I spoke to myself I walked in with the biggest smile on my face. "Tone it down." Okay, maybe it was a little too big, so I got it together and lined up with the rest of the girls. As we stretched I began to scope the room again. I wasn't very familiar with who was on the team currently. I just looked for who could possibly make the team with me strictly based on looks because I had yet to see anyone dance. Before I could make my decision we were directed to line up for technique across the floor. "We're going to start off with the strut." Oh Lord, this was my biggest critique. I knew the concept and I had the attitude, but I still looked like a kid, and had no way of looking any older. It was so many girls. I knew I couldn't watch everyone, but as we started I could immediately tell who was already on the team. I tried not to pay too much attention. I knew if I watched I would try to do the same and I needed to stick to what I learned. It was my turn. The space was so long. I knew it was going to feel like forever before I made it to the other side. As the sponsor called "5, 6, 7, 8!" I took my first step, kept control over my body and was very conscious of what I was doing. "Just imagine being one of them." I knew I wasn't doing it like the girls on the team, but I had the attitude and confidence. I was young, but I felt grown. I knew I owned it. This was exactly how I needed to start to get me through the rest of the audition. Technique continued. I nailed everything how I practiced, if not better. Besides the current team, there was one girl who stood out to me. She was gorgeous. I prayed she would make the team with me. I already knew I had it. Something was just telling me so. In my mind all I could think about was how I had yet to find someone who looked better than me. Of course there were girls whose technique was flawless, and mine probably wasn't all the way on that level, but I figured the team was about looks first, then dance. I just kept checking off my list. Besides me hyping myself up, I had to keep steering my mind back to remaining humble. The first part was finally over. They escorted us out of the band room. All the girls migrated back to their respective rooms. It was time for the first cut. I never stopped praying from the moment I walked in the door. I had a feeling I was going to make the next round, but there's always a little something in you that says, "No you can't," or "This isn't for you." I tried my hardest to keep those words out of my mind.

An hour went by. The slowest hour ever, and might I say the quietest. Everyone was on pins and needles as we waited for what was next. "Ladies, if everyone could meet me at the band room door." I quickly got up but took the slowest walk. My heart fell to the middle of my stomach and it was beating so hard it felt as though it was going to come through my body. The space was small and we packed in tightly. "If I call your number, please return to the band room. If I do not call your number, please gather your things and try again next year." It was almost Déjà vu, but this felt so much more serious. As she called each number tears began to form in my eyes. The anticipation was real. She finally called my number. I walked in as calm as ever, but the inside of me took a lap around the hall a few times in excitement. They eliminated half of the girls and my nerves were beginning to get the best of me. I was almost halfway to making the team. It was now the choreography portion. As I was learning it, all I could think about was my choreography and how it would blend with theirs. What they taught seemed easy, but it wasn't about the dance, it was about the performance. Every word the dance girl whom I worked with told me filled my mind. "Yes, you can dance, but when you perform, that's when you catch their attention." We had twenty minutes to learn the choreography. We were then escorted out to practice on our own until my assigned group was called. I began to practice on the dance. My focus was how to transition from their choreography into my solo. Once I got that down, I focused on my memorization and performance. I wasn't paying attention to how much time had gone by. My mind was on one track until they called my number. There were three other girls. All I could think about was how I was going to stand out. We lined up and turned to the back. I was right in the middle. It seemed like forever until the music started but that was okay with me because I didn't know what was about to happen. "Your music is on ladies." The moment the song started something took over me. I didn't feel like the same girl. It was like Beyoncé turning into Sasha Fierce. I turned around and snapped! Landing every move, making eye contact, smiling, everything. It was time for my solo. I went straight into my piece from their choreography beginning with a double turn into a leap. I used the entire area around me and honestly forgot there were girls next to me. As my finish, I jumped in the air to go down into a middle split. I knew I killed it and I made sure they knew I knew they knew. I gave a look like "that's how you do that," and went right back into their choreography until it was finished. Once it was over I stood at attention waiting to see what came next. The sponsor stopped the music. "Thank you, ladies," and with that we walked out.

I felt good about it. I had given it my all and literally had nothing left in me.

I returned to my spot only to find a message on my phone from my best friend that read, "Are you at that audition?"

I knew he was waiting at my dorm to pick me up, but how did he find out? I called him and before I could get a word out him and his friends were all talking at once.

"My boy said you at that audition."

"You know you bout to make it right."

"Dude, you really bout to be one of those fine girls in front of the band."

As good as it made me feel, I couldn't get distracted. I laughed it off and hung up. Two hours went by. We had yet to hear anything. All the participants performed and we were now waiting on the next announcement. Every moment seemed like forever, but it was the suspense. I knew everyone started to get restless because I was and so were the girls around me. "Ladies, please come by the band room door." Finally. This was it. This was going to put me halfway where I needed to be. I put my head down, because honestly, I didn't know what was about to happen. "When I call your number please make your way into the band room." This time I didn't wait that long. My number was called and I was relieved. I displayed my excitement on the last round. This time I walked in like I'd been there before, which I had, but I was ready to win. It was about twenty girls left. We all lined up in front of the judges. I stood there, at attention with a smile on my face. My hair had fallen out of its curls and my lipstick was faded, but I stood as poised as I possibly could, as if everything was perfect. One by one each girl stepped forward to introduce themselves. It was now my turn. I stepped forward and gave them my name. "I will be an upcoming sophomore majoring in English under Pre-law and I want to be a dance girl because I want to be the girl younger girls look up to and aspire to be. I want to be an inspiration." I nodded my head and stepped back. My heart was beating fast. I was just thankful I didn't stumble over any words. Once everyone spoke, they directed us back to our designated rooms where we would get dressed in our business attire to have our individual interviews.

I was a good speaker, but I was still nervous. I didn't know who I would be speaking to and I didn't know what they wanted. "Be yourself." I kept repeating in my head. I found a spot to myself and prayed in my spirit. No one else mattered. I was right there towards the finish line and I needed God to take my hand and get me across. Depending on myself wasn't an option. Once I finished taking time to myself I waited amongst the other girls. I got excited on the inside because I saw the one girl who I thought was gorgeous. She was still there and had the possibility of making the team with me. It was almost 9:00pm and we were still sitting there waiting. This time was the longest time we had to wait out of the entire day. I sat with my legs crossed, looking around one moment, then staring forward the next. I watched the girls slowly, one by one, come from the interview room. I tried to study their faces to see what kind of vibe I picked up. Nothing. I overheard some of the girls ask, "What did they ask you?" I didn't know anyone so I didn't feel comfortable to walk up and listen in. They were speaking too low for me to eaves drop. I stayed where I was and tuned everything out. They called my name. I stayed still for a moment. My eyes opened wide. I got up and walked to the room. It seemed like everything was moving in slow motion. It took me a good five minutes just to get around the corner. I opened the door and sitting there was the band director and the sponsor. One faint light was shining through the window of the room. Other than that, there was no light. I sat down and crossed my feet at the ankles. Slightly smiling, I looked both in their eyes and we began the interview. They asked me to tell them a little bit about myself and what my first year of school was like. I was answering every question with no problem. Speaking clearly and articulating, which is something that always came easy to me. Then the real questions came pertaining to the team. Two questions.

First question. "Why should you be on this team?"

I sat and processed the question for a moment, made eye contact with them, and spoke. "You need me on this team because I can contribute more than just dance. I have a passion for motivating others to be the best they can be. In this case I'm motivating young girls and even women to be confident in who they are and showing them how to carry themselves in the process."

They both started to smile but I didn't let them know I was concerned with the expressions they were giving me.

Last question. "What can you bring to the team that is different from everyone else?"

I thought for a moment and then said, "My spirit." As I began to explain tears started rolling down my face. I couldn't control my emotions at this point. The band director grabbed some tissues, handing them to me while the sponsor rubbed my shoulders. "I don't know much about the team or even being on the team, but I do know there is a light about me that you or anyone else won't forget. Although I'm still trying to figure it out myself, I want to be able to figure it out on this team."

They looked at each other and smiled. The sponsor turned to me and said thank you. "Thank you."

I left feeling good. I took a deep breath before I walked out in front of the others and tried to wipe my face as much as possible, but the tears in my eyes were still visible.

All eyes were on me when I walked out. I walked straight to the restroom. "What's wrong...what's wrong?" One by one girls followed me into the restroom. They tried to comfort me, but I figured they just wanted to know what happened. "I'm fine." Of course I wasn't going to say anything. This was serious to me and I didn't want to share my feelings with anyone right then. I walked back out to wait with the others as they winded down the interviews. It came down to the last girl. We were all waiting in anticipation. Everything was still and silent. The door cracked and everyone looked up in anxiousness. "Ladies, if you could please meet me by the band room door." I didn't know what the next step was. I didn't know whether there was another interview or if they were going to speak to us again. I looked around. The current team from last year stood lined up together on one side, while everyone else stood to the other side. They began to call numbers. They called every single girl who was currently on the team first. I didn't know how many people were going to be on the team, but I did know there wasn't room for many spots. Because they picked all the former girls, there were only a few spots left. She paused...then she called my number. I didn't know exactly what to think. I walked in the room. It was just me, the former team members, the judges, and the band directors. The band director walked towards me. I looked him in his eyes as more tears formed.

"What does this mean?"

"Congratulations, you are an official team member!"

51

I screamed and fell to my knees!

He hugged me and said, "You earned it."

I didn't know what to do. I stood up to run to the former team members, but they didn't look very happy. So I looked for the girls who made it with me. It was only four of us, including me. Out of 107 girls who auditioned, I was one of the ones. I had two new sisters who made it for the first time with me and one was the girl I prayed for. We hugged each other and cried. I ran to the sponsor and gave her the biggest hug I had given anyone in that room. She whispered in my ear, "You sold us in your interview. You earned this," and hugged me again. I was still crying. Even the director of the first team I auditioned for was there. He walked up to me hugged me saying, "I told you there was something for you." I couldn't believe it. This moment I prayed and waited for finally happened and my dream came true. As we stood there they went through some rules to prepare us a little for what was about to take place. We were no longer "normal girls." I was listening but my insides were still running around the room. Then they announced the captain. It just seemed like everything that had been happening to me was adding up. This was the same girl who helped work with me, did my hair, and gave me advice the night before auditions. After we took our group picture I walked up to her and she hugged me. "See, I knew you could do it. Welcome to the team." I couldn't stop smiling. I walked in the room to grab my things and meet the team in their actual dance room. As I walked to find the room, the fourth girl who had been on the team in the past, making it back again, was walking in front of me. I had no clue where the room was.

"Excuse me, can you help me find the dance room please?"

52

She looked back to me. "You don't know who I am?"

"Umm, no." I really had no clue who she was. For all I knew she was new and would be one of my sisters, but I didn't know much about anything. This was a new world to me. She never responded to me so I just followed her until she walked into a room. I watched her walk up to the one who would be my captain as she whispered something to her. They both looked at me.

I stood next to my new sisters. I really didn't get to bask in the moment because everything was moving so fast. Our captain came up to us.

"Delete every picture except for one off your social media and put your pages on private when you leave."

I had no idea what to think. I had a smile on my face, but my mind was confused. I was scared to move and really didn't know what to say. I looked at my phone as it kept going off. How did the news get out so fast? Everyone was texting and calling me. People who talked to me and people who stopped talking to me were texting and calling me. I was just ready to tell my parents. It was a little after 10:00pm and we were finally dismissed. My best friends were waiting outside for me. I quickly got in the car. I was ready to call my family. I went to my social media account to delete all my pictures except for one, only to find over 200 friend requests. This was unreal. In the midst of my best friends going crazy in the car, I tried to act calm but the moment I called my aunt and told her I made the team, she sent my adrenaline through the roof because she screamed so loud. As soon as we got to the back where the dorms were I went in to drop off my key. While I waited I called my parents. I knew they were waiting by the phone in anticipation because the moment they picked up I could hear it all in my mom's voice.

"Sweetie....what happened?"

I left them in suspense. Then excitement took over me. I took off running down the hallway screaming. "I made the team!"

The moment my mom screamed the tears started flowing again. My dad came to the phone. "I'm proud of you baby girl. I knew you could do it."

I had so much to say but I didn't know how. "I can't believe He answered me. He really gave me what I asked for." I looked up, blew him a kiss, and whispered, "I love you." My heart decided my destination. God's one desire was for me to believe in Him. I did, and I finally got to see that I accomplished what He had planned for me from the very beginning.

PART II

Be Smart

Proverbs 15:21 The empty-headed treat life as a plaything; the perceptive grasp its meaning and make a go of it,

Chapter 4
Good Times, Bad Times

Every moment from there on felt unreal. Thoughts filled my head with the imagination of what the experience was really going to be like. From the moment I made it my crab sisters and I spoke almost every day. These were the girls who made the team for the first time with me. I instantly loved them. I felt like I knew them already. One I prayed for. She was gorgeous. The other I encountered in the past and she was like a regal black barbie. I was excited to start my process with them. My family was more than happy for me. My mom couldn't stop hugging me and my dad couldn't stop smiling.

I hadn't spoken to any members on the team since the night before, not even my captain. I didn't know if this was a good thing or a bad thing. I honestly did not know how to feel. I heard many rumors about what it could possibly be like, but I was so caught up in the bliss of the moment that that was the furthest thing from my mind. I had just made it home and I was drained. I didn't even think about unpacking any of my things. I dropped everything in the corner of my room and fell on my bed. I was exhausted but still too enlivened to sleep. Out of nowhere I received a text message from the sponsor. "Good Morning beautiful. I just realized why you seemed so familiar after auditions." I sat up. I braced myself. I didn't know what she was going to say. She explained her godmom and my mom were sorors. She went on to say her godmother told her about a girl she wanted her to speak to who was looking to audition. She agreed to do it but never got around to it. The sponsor explained to me how she had intentions on finding out who I was but was so busy and lost track of some things. She did not know my name or what I looked like. She only knew I was a young lady looking to audition. I was sort of glad she didn't know who I was beforehand because it made the moment even more special. I instantly loved her. She ended the conversation by letting me know I was her little baby now and if I ever needed anything she would always be there. I could only smile and think on how amazing everything was going to be. After only one encounter and one conversation, I already felt close to her.

Summer was just beginning. Within the first few days following auditions things were already taking a turn. I wouldn't say for the best or for the worst, things just began to change. I was heading to pick up my little sister from school when one of my crab sisters started sending message after message in the group chat. We talked consistently but this time was different. Apparently we were going to get a new sister. How did she already find out this information? I had no clue. Nevertheless I was kind of worried. Who was this new girl? Was she going to come in and ruin what my sisters and I were already creating? I got home only to receive a text message in the group from the captain.

"Call me four way."

My sisters and I went back and forth trying to figure out how it could work.

"Okay you call me and then I'll call her, and then she'll call her."

"No, I'll call you then she'll call me and then I'll call you." We always seemed to make things complicated.

Once we were introduced to our new team member, or crab sister, things began to take off. We weren't practicing in person just yet, but the pressure was beginning to be applied. I gave myself a daily routine. Daily I would wake up around 9:00am, eat breakfast, work out, dance, run errands, and repeat. Not this day. It was 7:00am in the morning. This was the first official day I was getting some good sleep without being up half the night thinking about everything occupying my mind. My sisters and I received a message from our captain. She asked for us to learn some dance moves and have them recorded and sent to her by 2:00pm. One might think this was a lot of time but judging by the fact I was completely new to all of this and did not know what to do, this wasn't as easy for me. I scrambled out of bed, rushed to find my laptop in all my things yet to be unpacked, and headed to the guest house to start learning the dance routines. I spent almost four hours learning from what I could find on the internet. I went to the very first video I watched of them in the beginning when I was first introduced. In my mind I was more so living the fantasy than learning. I was so caught up in who I wanted to be and looking more like them, only to learn just about every move in the opposite direction. It was about time to record my video. I sat in front of the camera, pushed my hair behind my ear, and smiled. I stood back in attention, gave the camera a wink, then I began. I just knew I was doing so well.

My sisters and I all sent our videos in the group. Two of my sisters were really good at it, to say they were new to the style, and my other sister and I, well it was newer to us. Everyone was on their own level of good. We encouraged one another and sent our videos off. I waited in anticipation for a response. This is what I struggled with - the suspense. I thought I did good, but not getting an answer when I wanted made me a little insecure in what I did. I left it alone for a while. I went to my room to watch some videos and I received a call from my new sister. This was the first time we talked one on one. I really liked her, and we instantly clicked. This method of practicing continued for a while until it was time to start practicing in person. It was still the middle of summer. While most college students were probably vacationing, taking classes, or working a part time job I was practicing non-stop. From sending in videos every day to preparing to drive to school for in person practices with my freshman sisters and our captain. I liked this routine because I knew I would get the chance to spend time with my sisters and really get to know them.

It was the night before our first practice with our captain. We all laid out on the couch eating our pasta and talking, nervous about what our first practice was going to be like. My captain gave me mixed feelings. This would be my first time seeing her again from auditions and the only recent memory I had of her were the messages from her telling us what to do to prepare. It wasn't that bad, but it still was the suspense of not knowing what was next. The day came. I was on pins and needles. I wasn't talking much because I didn't know how to feel. As I sat there on the couch waiting for my sister to get out the shower, I tuned out all the noise of my other sister in the kitchen making breakfast and thought on what was about to take place. I was somewhat trying to prepare myself while growing an understanding that some things you just have to deal with when it happens. This was something I realized I didn't know the preparation tactics for. I had to always be ready to conform and adjust. I folded the covers next to me and prepared my bag. We were all stuffed in the kitchen sliding and pushing past one another in a hurry to get our breakfast, pack some snacks, and make it out to the car in time.

Once we made it to practice we walked in to find her sitting there. "Hi little babies." We responded in small voices. I laid my stuff down and occupied the corner until further directed. We began to work on our strut. I was in awe of her. My captain. She glided across the floor so smooth. You could see her hips effortlessly sway side to side. Everything she did was so perfect. It was my turn. I tried my hardest to channel what she did, but my body couldn't move like hers. At least not yet. With each step I pushed my arms out. With every step I thought about it, stepped again. And with every step she corrected me. I was stiff as ever, but it was worth a try. It's not like I had much of a choice anyways. We stood by the door waiting for our turns to come up as she critiqued us one by one. I stood with my back against the door waiting when suddenly there was a knock followed by the visitor proceeding to come in. My heart dropped. It was the same woman who told me before auditions they already had a short girl on the team. I wanted to make sure she caught my eye just so she could know I did exactly what she told me I couldn't do. I was still nervous, but my attitude kicked in a little. I felt like I had to be on guard with this one. Our captain looked over to us.

"Do you know who this is?"

I knew. I was not going to forget the first dance girl who brought discouragement to me. I said her full name. My sisters looked at me in relief.

"I know you."

She caught my eye. I can admit I lifted my head a little and smirked.

"You're the girl I said was too short, well you still are."

My captain laughed.

I looked over at her as my heart slowly dropped to my feet with a steady pounding feeling hitting every inch of my body. I thought she was supposed to protect me and have my back. I tried not to give it much thought in the moment because I was just ready for it to end. As our captain made us dance the woman sat there with the ugliest look on her face as if we disgusted her. It was my turn to lead. I tried my hardest to tune her out, but all I could see out of the corner of my eye was her whispering to my captain and laughing. "Why is she so stiff?" she said out loud. I clinched my teeth together. I had no clue what to say or do. Was this a joke? I was beginning to wonder what I signed up for. I came here to practice and work on my craft and every moment I was being belittled. Once again, I hid my true feelings behind a smile. "Have they kicked yet?" the woman asked. I wasn't familiar with what she was talking about, so we stood there just looking. Our captain laughed, got up, and showed us how to do them. "Give me 30." As we began, the woman got up and started to do them with us. "My kicks shouldn't be higher than yours crabs." I was over her and ready for it to be over.

We packed up our things in relief that we were done only to be told to follow her to another dance class for a continued practice. As we walked to the car no one said a word, but when we got in we let loose.

"Who does that girl think she is?"

"It's okay, you did good leading."

64

"Let's just get this over with y'all."

We encouraged each other on the ride to the next practice. I didn't want to tell them how I was really feeling. I stared out the window. I knew I had the choice to let this make me or break me. I spoke light into myself. I had to. "You've faced worse. Shake this off and do what you were called to do. You got this." As we walked in for the next practice we sat to the side while the other dancers just looked at us. As we began, other dance girls from the current team and some from the past squad walked in the door including the one I was not too fond of. "Wassup crabs?" As we lined up to strut they all jumped in front of us. One looked very familiar. It was the other girl who made it with us who was on the team before. She walked up to me, "Who are you?" As I opened my mouth to say my name, she flung her hand in the air, "I really don't care," and walked to stand in front of me. I instantly remembered this was the dancer from auditions who I didn't know. I knew she was being petty. She knew exactly who I was. I tilted my head up and smiled as she whispered to the others about me and took her turn across the floor. It was rather intimidating to see them do it so well while we were just getting in the groove of understanding how to execute the moves. As we danced for them they snickered, whispered, and laughed. It was one of the most humiliating feelings I had felt in a very long time.

My sisters and I occupied the car ride home with a discussion of every little detail taking place that day. It was the attitude we all voiced but as everyone spoke I analyzed eyes and facial expressions. Theirs weren't too different from mine. I wasn't as comfortable sharing my deepest inner most feelings, so I said what I felt on the surface, but kept the rest to myself. As soon as we made it back to where we were staying I stepped out to call my mom. I really stepped out to let out everything I was feeling. Once I walked around the corner I looked back to make sure no one was around. I slid down the wall, sat, and stared out into the window that filled the dusted yellow walls surrounding me. Tears began to form in my eyes. God was the only one I could talk to at this point. "Why me? No one else got humiliated like I did. I did all of this praying, dreaming, and believing, all for you to put me in a position of humiliation?" I slammed my fist into the ground and my cry got heavier and heavier. I was looking for an answer. He wasn't saying anything. I looked around the corner again to make sure no one was listening. I held my hands over my face and took a deep breath. I let my tears continue to roll down my face until there was no more. I laid my head back against the wall and looked into the sky. "I'm going to stick to this because I'm trusting You." With that I slid my hand down my face, took a deep breath, and called my mom.

"Hey sweetie, how is everything going?"

I didn't want to tell her what was really going on out of fear she would react, so I kept it simple. "It's going okay. Just a lot of work and really tiring."

"I know it is. Just try to make the best of everything."

We talked for a little while longer. I then made my way back to our room.

Being with my sisters made me feel much better. When it was just us we could forget about all the horrible things said or how hard our day was and just be ourselves. We were all crazy. To pass time we pushed the table and the couches over, stepped through all our bags and clothes laying on the floor, and set up our cameras. We stood in formation as if we were in the stands, blasted a band song, and one by one we took turns leading. Just watching them I admired how we all had our different strengths. My gorgeous sister who I prayed for had long limbs and moved effortlessly. My beautiful regal sister moved so big and flawlessly, and my sister who I felt the closest to, danced with so much power. I took from every one of them because I knew I needed to. I wanted to. I wanted to be like the team and the women I looked up to, but my sisters were enough for me.

We continued the routine of alternating weeks for practice with just our captain. At the same time my sisters and I bonded. It was our last week for rehearsals. My sisters and I planned a day at the water park to celebrate the draining but successful practices. It was also a time just to be amongst one another. This particular morning we took our time waking up since we knew there was no practice. One by one we sat up and reached for our phones, still half sleep. One of my sisters grabbed her phone first. We knew something was up when she said "y'all" in the most depressing voice I ever heard from her. She read a message out loud from our captain basically telling us we needed to come to the school. She seemed upset but we really didn't know what was going on. It was our last day and we were supposed to be at a water park, not practicing. We looked around at one another trying to figure out what it could be.

The ride to the school was quiet. For the most part I knew we hadn't had any real problems during practice, so why the urgency? As we pulled up at the school we parked and stayed in the car. It was drizzling and we didn't see our captain anywhere. A few minutes later she pulled up next to us. She stayed in her car. We looked through her window waiting for her instructions. She sat there looking into her mirror visor above her head. Anticipation grew inside of me. She looked over to the window and backed her car out. Was she leaving? We were so confused. She flicked her lights and we assumed it was an indication to follow her. We drove for what seemed like an hour. This was time which cut into our water park plans. I was aggravated but more so anxious. What could we possibly be doing? After about thirty minutes we pulled into a nice townhouse complex. I forgot about what I was feeling because the place was so beautiful. We parked beside her and got out of the car as directed. In slow hesitation we walked toward her. "Hi my babies!" She was all smiles. As I inched the corner of my mouth to the side resembling a somewhat confused smirk she reached for a hug. Her attitude was perky and upbeat so I calmed my heart just a little. I kept it slightly on guard out of preparation for anything. As we walked up to the house a beautiful brown skinned girl opened the door. They were excited to see one another. She didn't really speak to us, just walked in and sat on the couch. As we laid our things on the floor we proceeded to sit on the stools in the kitchen. "No, you can stand. This won't take long," in her same peppy upbeat tone. We stood there leaning on one another with blank expressions on our faces. I knew my sisters felt just like me - confused. "Come stand at attention. Smile." Both her and her sister's expressions changed. My sisters and I were all clothed in bathing suits, cover ups, and flip flops. I assumed we were about to dance because I only knew to be at attention for practice. We lined up in front of them with our hands on our hips and smiles on our face. Before she could say anything one more person skipped through the door. It was the girl who I 'didn't know' at auditions. My hands began to shake. She walked over to us.

She walked down the line and spoke to all of my sisters and soon as she got to me, "I don't know your name," and turned away.

I proceeded to let her know "It's-...."

She snapped her head back at me and my captain jumped in.

"She didn't ask you to respond."

At this point my whole body was shaking. "Smile." As I smiled my lip began to quiver.

"Get on your toes."

I stood in the best relevé I could, but it was kind of hard with flip flops. I gripped the base of my shoes with my toes and held that position for dear life.

"Who do y'all think y'all are?"

Her and her sisters began to smirk and laugh. I was the smart mouth in the group. I knew I wasn't going to let no one come for any of us. I opened my mouth to respond not knowing I was only getting us into more trouble.

"What do you mean who-"

She raised her voice louder than the last time. "DON'T RESPOND."

Her sisters looked over at me, dropped their heads, and raised their eyebrows. I was used to getting that look. As I went back to smiling I clinched my teeth together and took a deep breath loud enough for everyone to hear. "Problem?" I looked at her like "Can I respond to that," but I didn't say anything. I was only trying to think of my sisters and how whatever I did affected all of us. As she continued to speak and complain about the things we didn't do, did do, and the things she heard, five minutes slowly turned into fifteen minutes which quickly turned into twenty-five minutes. She got up from the couch and stood in front of us. "Get in attention!" I knew I had fallen a little from my relevé due to my shoes not having enough grip and trying to keep steady on the sweat forming under my feet. She went down the line one by one with a problem about each of us. She spent about ten minutes with each of my sisters. I stood at the end of the line. She positioned herself in front of me, dropped her hip to the side, clinched her hands in front of her, and slightly cocked her head back.

"You had the audacity to come onto my team and not know who my sister is? How would you feel if nobody knew who you were? Ooppps....they don't." She looked back at her sisters. "Do y'all know who this is?" One of them just laughed and grinned. The one I didn't like, she fumbled through my name a few times then proceeded to say, "It's really not memorable." My captain looked back to me. "Looks like you're not memorable then." She continued but I tuned her out the rest of the time. I was praying in my spirit to keep my composure. I could feel the energy from my sisters standing next to me. The only thing going through my mind was, "keep it together for them." I looked straight through her as she continued to talk.

"What's my sisters' names and crab names?"

I knew their names, but I wasn't as familiar with crab names. I slowly turned my head to my sisters and turned back as an indication I needed some help. They didn't hesitate. One of my sisters gave one name, but we didn't know the other.

"How come only one of you knew that?"

At this point I didn't know what a real question was and what I could answer to. We'd been standing there for so long we lost track of time. She talked some more then finally dismissed us. As I walked to pick up my things I looked down at the inside of my palms watching the sweat slide down my fingertips. My feet slid to the front of my sandal every time I took a step because they were sweating so bad. We all turned around and said bye as if none of us were affected by what took place. A big part of me was starting to form this 'I don't care' compartment in my soul. I was over the non-sense. It had finally stopped raining and I just wanted to get to the water park. The moment we got in the car we all looked at our phones and realized we had been there for over an hour. My crab sister looked over to me. "You are crazy, but we got each other's back."

As we all talked about what we would do if anyone messed with any of us our bond grew. At that moment we made up in our minds we were always going to be solid to one another and would have each other's back no matter what.

Chapter 5
Facing Big Reality with Little Understanding

The summer was winding down. We had close to a month remaining before school began. We all returned to our respective homes and as tiring as practices were, I still wanted to be amongst my sisters. I thought I would get home and just lay out from exhaustion, but I spent the majority of my time practicing and thinking about every little detail of my experience thus far. Our sponsor sent out a message about a retreat taking place at the end of the month before band camp began. This would be my first time being amongst the entire team so I was thrilled. I spent a lot of time speaking with my sisters but spent more time talking to my sister who was new to the group. We were catching up on the phone about everything, as girls do, and she asked if I wanted to stay with her before the retreat. I knew my parents were going to say no. I basically would be living with her for a whole month. They were strict on things such as that. Even though I was older, they still saw it as I lived in their house, I follow their rules. I still decided to ask.

I presented the idea to my mom because that was the best way it worked in my house. You tell mom, she tells dad, she gets a better answer. One afternoon I was in my room watching videos. My dad calls my name. I yelled back, "Yes?" No response. My dad purposefully did that to show there was no option in just a response. When your name was called your answer was to show up. I walked to where they were seated in the sunroom at the dining table. I already knew it was about to be a discussion of something I would believe to be small only to be made big. My dad sat at the head of the table and my mom sat next to him. I took a seat. I tried my hardest to read facial expressions, but my dad kept the same slight smile on his face so

I never knew what that meant. And my mom sat relaxed with one leg in the chair. She took one look at me, looked down, then over to my dad.

"Your mom tells me you want to stay with your dance friend before the retreat."

My eyes opened wide and I looked over to my mom. I slowly said, "Yes", and then looked to my dad.

"Well, what do you think about them?"

I knew my response would determine a lot so I didn't respond too quickly. I thought about it and then responded. "Well, we have been staying with her brother for the practices and her parents always made sure we had everything we needed. And this gives me some time to learn how to make some decisions on my own and be responsible in a place I'm unfamiliar with."
It was silent. My heart started pounding. I was waiting for my dad to say, "Baby girl, I just don't think that's a good idea right now," so we could get it over with.

He opened his mouth and I looked up. "Well I think it would be a good idea for you to get to know one of your sisters. You're growing up baby girl and I trust you will make sound decisions so I don't mind."

This time was strange. My dad was okay with it, but my mom was still on the fence about it. Nevertheless I didn't complain. I grinned ear to ear, got up, hugged my dad and headed to call my crab sister. Within a week we met up with one another. Our mothers sat and talked for a while, but we were okay with it since we were able to be amongst each other.

I was still somewhat nervous to be away from my family. It wasn't that I wasn't used to being on my own because I had done it for a year in college. It was the fact I knew me. I really didn't know her yet. Yes she was my crab sister, but that was just the term we were told to use for the team. But as far as someone I knew, I was still trying to figure it out. She loved to talk and play. Although we were a lot alike in that area, I had my times where I was more reserved- just observing the scene. She hadn't picked that up about me yet, but I didn't blame her. She was still in the process of getting to know me. As her dad helped me get all my things out of the car and into the house, I thought, this will really be my home for the rest of the month. They had a nice house. I had my own room, which was a good thing I guess. Normal sleepovers I was used to everyone stuffing in the same bed or making a pallet on the floor, but I liked having my own space. I walked in the room, laid all my things against the wall, and sat on the bed. Her mom walked up to the doorway.

"We'll give you a minute to get yourself settled. If you need anything don't hesitate to ask me."

I smiled and nodded. "I will."

I looked over to my things sitting in the corner. I didn't unpack because in my mind I was still trying to process how much time I would be spending with my new sister.

We didn't waste any time getting in girlfriend mode. We spent our days throwing counts in front of the TV or dancing for her mom. On our relaxed time we all worked out together or cooked whatever was in the kitchen. It was like having a sister my age around consistently. I enjoyed it until it started to become almost like a complete sister thing. We got so use to being up under each other for the first few weeks. We began to learn each other's moods. Me a little more than her, but nevertheless I respected her boundaries and she tried to respect mine. One night we planned to spend the next day getting our nails done so we could get ready for the retreat the next week. I still had the majority of my things packed from my big suitcase to my shoe bag and my makeup bag. We both woke up early to eat breakfast and then proceeded to getting dressed. We were a lot alike in this area. Like me, she found the smallest reasons to get cute and put on makeup. That was perfectly okay with me. Throughout my time living with her we explored other ways of doing our makeup. I learned a few tips from her and vice versa. So this day I took a little longer. It was mid- afternoon and I was still working on my makeup. She finished and was on her way downstairs to make lunch, but not before she did her everyday "come see what my sister is doing right now" routine. The door was shut to the bathroom in the room for which I occupied. I left my makeup bag in the bedroom and only brought the products which I needed. As I lined the bottom of my eyebrow she knocked on the door.

"Budddd, what you doing?"

"My makeup bud." She continued to knock. This time continuously. She repeated her question and this time I didn't respond. I locked the door.

"Hey! We don't lock doors in this house!" She immediately began to jiggle at the handle as she repeated her statements. I slammed my eyebrow pencil down on the sink and opened the door.

75

She stepped back, smiled with innocence, and with a kidlike voice said, "Are you ready?"

"No bud, I'll be ready in a minute."

I went back into the bathroom and started back on my makeup. A few minutes went by and I was glad to just have this moment in silence to concentrate. I was just about to begin the highlight process and the nonsense began again.

"Buddddd, what you doing? Hurry up!"

She began kicking on the door non-stop. I sat looking in the mirror turning the structure of my mouth into a straight line and rolling my eyes upward. This time I let her carry on. I chose not to respond. I kept doing my make-up, tuning everything out. Instantly the noise stopped. I didn't think much of it other than "finally some peace and quiet," so I continued. As I was coming closer to the end I paused. I was happy all the commotion stopped but something seemed weird. I laid my brush down, unlocked the door and opened it. As I looked forward my eyes opened big and I clinched my jaw together. All of my suitcases were dumped all over the floor, including my makeup. I was boiling on the inside. I stood there in awe trying to figure out how to handle the situation. I could do one or two things; fight about it or let it go. As I processed in my mind the best way to deal with my anger she stepped in the doorway.

"You ready?"

It somewhat scared me at the fact she did all of this and was so calm. I looked at her with a confused expression on my face.

"Why would you do this? How could you be so childish?"

"You wouldn't hurry up."

I left her standing there. I walked back in the bathroom, locked the door, and sat on the toilet seat to gather all of my thoughts. I honestly did not know how to deal with this. I already grew a strong care for her so I didn't want to stop being her friend. I had no choice but to be with her for the rest of the school year, but who does things like this to the people they care about? I continued to gather my thoughts as I came out of the bathroom to pack up my things and put my clothes on. I grabbed my purse, walked downstairs, and proceeded to fix my lunch in silence. She started calling my name. I continued what I was doing as if I did not hear anything. I took a seat and began eating my food. She stood in front of me and continued to call my name.

"Are you mad at me? Why won't you talk to me? Say something."

She put her hand on the side of my plate with plans to pull it away. I snapped my head to meet her eyes and clinched my mouth together. She let the plate go. The car ride to the nail salon was quiet. Although we didn't go far, I had plans to continue my silent treatment for the rest of the day. I sat two chairs away from her as I prepared to get my nails done. I could feel her looking my way. When she knew I could tell, she walked over and sat next to me.

"Bud, I'm sorry. I didn't mean to do that to you. Now can you talk to me please."

Surprisingly, this was when I knew she would probably end up being my best friend. I didn't know what it was, but I wanted to forgive her. And as angry as I wanted to be, it was kind of funny to me, and in a strange way the reason why I loved her. Of course I was still mad at the fact she would do something of that sort, and a little concerned, but I couldn't help but forgive her. We continued the day as normal, preparing for our retreat.

The day we were waiting on finally came. Our bags were packed, sitting by the door, and we were finishing the last touches of our makeup. My sister and I talked about what we were going to wear. The way I saw it I was not going to be caught slipping when it came down to standing next to the current team. I had it on my mind to look extremely cute. My two other sisters left with the team. They were going to pick us up from our location. As we waited at a local restaurant for the team to arrive, I tuned everything out and prepared my mind for the unknown. I was excited about being amongst everyone, but as I thought on the things that had taken place with me before, a sense of worry came over me. Nevertheless I hid it within in hopes of everyone being together now, things would be different. As the van pulled to the side of the car everyone got out. I walked up to my other two sisters who were dressed up similar to us with their make up on. As I looked over to the team they all stood together no makeup, dressed in sweat clothes and hair not done. This was the second time I saw them presented the total opposite of the original image I was used to. My only thoughts were to keep up with them, but I didn't know if I was behind or doing too much. As we said our goodbyes to my sister's mother I walked up to all the girls. I put on a slight smile and hesitantly said, "Hey." They all looked back at me. Some responded, some continued to make their way onto the bus. The sponsor on the other hand was who I looked forward to speaking to. She was so upbeat, full of life, and she made me want to be a part.

Once we made it to the hotel we were given some time to relax and settle down before the activities started later that night. My sisters and I didn't get much down time because we were doing things for the upperclassman. I didn't have time to really sit and think because my mind was working as I moved. It was the first day and I wanted everything to go how I thought it was supposed to go. I learned quick that all things don't work how I want them to. That night we all gathered in the sponsor's room for a girl's night. I was prepared for this moment. My mom bought me a nice night set and I was ready to show them I could fit in. I just knew they were going to have the cutest outfits with their hair done and flawless faces with no makeup. My sisters and I walked in the room, squished together on one bed, and waited for the team to come in. As they walked through the door, once again I was in complete shock. They had on baggy clothes, mix match outfits, and bonnets. Even though they were cute they still didn't look how I imagined them to. I could've came normal if I knew they were going to pull this. I was still in awe because it was just the thought of them being the actual girls I aspired to become. That made them beautiful to me. I felt like a child around them though. Despite them not looking the way I thought, they still gave this grown woman vibe I so desperately wanted. We began the activities. Everyone was laughing, talking, bonding, just having a genuinely good time. This is exactly what I thought they would be like. At least for this moment.

Once we wrapped up the night we headed back to our rooms around 10:00pm. My sisters and I immediately got into bed. Within five minutes all our phones went off at the same time. I took a deep breath and picked up my phone to a text

message, "Come and knock on my door sixteen times at 10:16."
We all sat up in aggravation. I posed the suggestion that maybe if
we didn't respond she would think we were sleep. We pondered
on it, but we all knew that was not the best idea. "Let's just go
y'all." I was not the one to come to that conclusion because I
was still satisfied with my idea of pretending to be sleep. I kicked
the covers off me, slipped into my shoes, and we walked to her
door. The door was slightly cracked. We could hear all of them
sitting in the room giggling and talking. My hands were sweating.
I was just ready to turn around and go back to the room.

"You knock."

"No you knock."

"Okay we'll all knock."

"NO, just one person knock."

This was us whispering outside of the door amongst each other.
We stood there, waiting in anticipation for the time to land on
10:16. 10:16 hit. As we knocked we were so nervous we lost
track of our count. We pressed our ears against the door. No
comment. Seconds went by. All of our phones rang. Even
though I knew we all got the same message I still looked at mine.
The message read, "Nope, try again. Come back at 10:21." We
returned to the room. I was over it. I got in the bed waiting for
the time to get closer for us to go back. As we made our way to
the door, 10:21 hit and this time we slowed down our knocks to
make sure we hit the right number. We waited. "Come back at
10:27." I stomped my way back to the room. "She got one more
time and I'm staying in this bed." I had to make this known even
though I knew it probably wasn't all the way true. It's exactly

80

how I was feeling. When we made it to the door for the third time it was still cracked. After we knocked we were summoned in and stood in front of them. We lined up timidly as they laid comfortably in the bed watching us in humiliation. "Get at attention." Here we were again. This time I took on a sarcastic attitude I had no intentions of allowing to come over me. "Smile." As we stood there I tried to think about anything else besides this moment. Time passed by as she gave us our rules and mottos for being a part of the team. I tried to process each word as her and the girls wasted no time flowing through the motto with ease. "Now say it back to us." My sisters and I looked at one another no clue of most of the words that came out of their mouths. I stood there full of embarrassment. "Who do y'all think y'all are? Are those nails on your fingers?" I just knew she wasn't about to come for my freshly manicured nails. The next thing I knew she pulled out a bottle of nail polish remover. I only smiled bigger because little did she know I was wearing the long-lasting polish that couldn't come off with just regular nail polish remover. I didn't say anything because I figured if we just sat there rubbing on our nails time would pass by. Two of us had no luck, one of us succeeded, and the other stood on the end trying to snap her nails off with her teeth. Eventually they got tired of watching us and our captain gave us until band camp to have our nails off and fingers bare. We all stood there as perplexed and humiliated as anyone could possibly feel. As she began to ask random questions I smirked and let out a slight snicker. My sisters kept their heads forward, but I could feel their energy.

"What is so funny?"

Every girl looked at me with much disgust. I shook my head and remained with a sarcastic smile on my face.

"Pull your bonnet over your face."

I looked at my captain as I thought in my mind why would she tell me to do such a ridiculous thing.

"Pull your bonnet over your face because you think you're cute and we don't want to look at you."

As I pulled my bonnet down I contemplated walking out, but I had to realize it wasn't just me. All of us were being humiliated. I just felt like it couldn't get any worse for me. As they all laughed she continued to play on the gesture.

"Doesn't she look like a ninja turtle? Act like a ninja turtle!"

As I hesitated into a karate stance I yelled, "NINJA TURTLE TO THE RESCUE!"

I had no clue where it came from because my mind was still trying to comprehend what was really going on. Hours were spent occupied with nonsense. Whether it was us sitting in splits or sitting on the wall while she dumped large items in our hands. We were spread across the room eyeing each other from different sides encouraging one another to hang in there. Before we walked out she made it very clear we needed to have her favorite drink and candy by tomorrow. As we walked back to our room, sweating and eyes red, I clutched my fist and dragged my feet on the floor. I went into the bathroom, sat on the toilet seat, and dropped my head in my hands. I didn't shut the door because I was pretty sure my sisters felt along the same lines as me. As I took off my night clothes, wiped off my body and changed, I laid on the edge of the bed in disbelief of the time. It was past 1:00am and we were due to be downstairs and ready for

8:00am. As much as I knew I needed to get some sleep, I stayed up for another hour thinking about everything that was said and done to me. To think I was confident, head strong, and far from ugly, why did I begin to second guess who I knew I was?

It was easy for us to sleep in a little longer and make it downstairs in time since we weren't allowed to wear makeup anymore. I watched as they passed by me with their faces flawlessly done only to know I looked like I still belonged in bed. Everything felt so different since it seemed as though we couldn't do anything. We sat in the back of the bus in silence while the other members talked and listened to their music. I was so sure this trip was going to be filled with fun, but that happiness was taken from me within one day. We pulled up at a restaurant for breakfast. We waited towards the back as the team pushed past my sisters and I to order first. While we sat and ate I watched as they all enjoyed their food. How I wished I could wash my chicken biscuit down with an ice-cold orange juice, but all we could drink was water now. I picked at my food waiting for my other sisters to finish ordering and take their place next to me. As we ate, my last sister came walking up, oblivious to why I dropped my chicken biscuit and gave her a stare. She sat her coffee down and looked at us. My sisters and I looked at her drink and then back at her. I looked over at the team. They were smirking and shaking their heads. I looked over at my captain as she acted as if she didn't see but held a big smile on her face. I looked back at my sister as she realized what she did. She shyly pushed the coffee back and ate her food with uncertainty. At this point, I just wanted an orange juice since we were already in trouble anyways.

The day was long and filled with dread. Although I was amongst the team and things were supposed to be fun all I could think about was the night before. I didn't know how long it would last, or when it would end, and I was honestly just ready for it to be over. Yes, I had already experienced some good moments, but the bad was outweighing the good and I didn't remember signing up for this part. This was our last night on our trip. My sisters and I were sitting in the back seat going back and forth about what excuses meant. As we whispered between one another, counting the minutes until we would make it back to the hotel, the van stopped. We pulled in front of a small gas station. We all turned our heads to one another because the same thought of soda and candy came to our mind. "Y'all maybe we should get out and see if they have what she wants." I just wasn't feeling that idea. I figured that as freshmen we would get in trouble for just getting out to get "snacks." All three of my sisters wanted to go in, but I insisted that we didn't. All I could think about was how I was going to explain myself if I was wrong. I was battling two different decisions not realizing that either way we could be wrong. I decided to stick with my gut. As much as they disagreed, none of us moved. I watched as my captain whispered to the sponsor and then got out of the van and went into the store. Some of the team cut their eyes towards us as if they knew something we didn't. Still, my sisters and I stayed put.

As we pulled up to the hotel I began to prepare my mind for one more night that I, of course, was not looking forward to. Same routine, but this time I experienced a different reality check. We stood in front of her and she asked,

"Where are my snacks?"

I knew my sisters were probably looking for me to answer since it was my decision to not go into the store. I made sure I exuded a sense of confidence in my response because whether I was right or not, I stood on what I believed.

"We just didn't have a moment to get what you asked for."

As confused as I was in my head, that was the best answer I had.

"So, you mean to tell me that a store doesn't have snacks? What are excuses?"

As we recited the definition the decision I made began to reveal a different meaning to me.

We prepared to leave the next morning. The night played in my mind, but this time for different reasons. I was becoming more and more observant through every situation because I was slowly making up in my mind I was going to master whatever it was they were putting me through. I knew that either way certain problems could go, it could always lead to something right, or wrong. I just hadn't figured out how to choose what was best.

The week of band camp finally came. My parents and I packed all of my things up for what would be the beginning of my sophomore year. I was set to live on campus with my sister I spent a whole month with. I guess we couldn't get away from each other. She was actually becoming my best friend. Like any typical HBCU(Historically Black Colleges and Universities) campus, things never happen on your time. Our apartment was not ready for move in and the team was assigned to stay in the dorm rooms until further notice. As a freshman I knew I needed to make it before the scheduled time to have my things ready before the upperclassman. My sisters and I made our way into the building to pick our rooms. They weren't the best of dorms, but we picked one of the better rooms. This particular room had plugs by the bed and an air conditioner. As my mom, dad, and I unloaded the last few items of my things into our room, the upperclassman started to drive up one by one. I walked to greet my captain and assisted her with any help she needed as well as speak to the other team members. We walked inside and I could tell they weren't too pleased at where we were staying. I didn't like it either, but I knew my opinion didn't matter. I had one of the better rooms so I didn't worry too much about it. As we helped our captain move her things in she walked into our room. Without any deep thought I knew exactly what was about to happen next.

"Y'all got plugs and air conditioners? Ummmm, who y'all think y'all is?"

Amid her admiration, I walked out. I knew if she was going to say and do what I thought she was about to do I didn't want to be there for it. A few minutes later, my roommate walked out and whispered something to me in passing.

"She wants our room. She said switch with her."

I was heated, but I was more so worried about my parents' response. I didn't know if she didn't know they were there or knew and just didn't care. I walked outside, and from a distance I watched as my parents stood outside of the truck carrying on a conversation. I took my time getting to them because I knew I had to be very strategic about how I approached the situation. My mom pledged when she was younger, so she understood certain things. My dad, all he would see is someone messing with his baby girl. As I explained to them what was taking place my mom turned to my dad.

"Baby, just get in the car, we'll move the stuff."

I looked at my dad, "Dad, please don't say anything, I'm fine. It doesn't bother me."

I was lying. It did bother me, but I knew I didn't want to make the situation bigger than what it was. My mom walked back in with me. As we moved our things she pulled me and my sisters together.

"You girls stay strong and stick together. I know it's hard but we're going to be praying for you all every step of the way."

My mom and I walked out the door to meet my dad. The first thing we see is him talking to my captain. My heart dropped. I looked over to my mom. As we walked over to where they stood, she walked away. Surprisingly she had a smile on her face, but with everything going on I couldn't tell if it was real or fake. My mom spoke up before anything could come out of my mouth.

"Daddy, what did you say to that girl?"

I knew it was nothing bad. My dad wasn't that type, but I knew he was the type to get a situation in line before it got out of hand.

"I just asked her what the reasoning was for having my baby girl move. Don't worry about the conversation. It went well."

Everything in me knew I was going to hear about this later.

We waited in our room for instructions. Everyone was moving around trying to get settled. I laid down in my bed hoping I could get a slight shut eye, but the experience having already started and continued kept me awake most of the time. My mind was always filled with what was going to happen next or how, and would I be able to get through. I know I had come to the realization that I just had to go through it, but it was this small word called curiosity that played a big role in my everyday thought. Hours went by and we were called to the dance room for a meeting. As my sisters and I walked through the door I looked around just to admire the moment again. This was my second time being in the room amongst the team, but the moment still felt brand new. The team was sitting along the wall.

"Stand at attention in front of us."

I knew I needed to start getting used to not being treated like one of the team members because I was seeing this was going to be a regular routine. Sitting down in the presence of them was not an option. I stood on my toes, hands to my hips, with a smile on my face. I waited for her to begin her what seemed to be a "daily rant." But to my surprise she addressed me first. It wasn't a surprised that she addressed me, but what she said.

"Who do you think you are having your dad address me?"

I opened my mouth to respond, but before I could get anything out, I was stopped.

"I didn't ask you to respond."

She laughed continuing to speak as I clinched my teeth.

"I'll have my daddy run into your daddy. Try that shit again."

They all knew by the look on my face I was more than heated, but what could I do? I raised my eyebrows and stared her down. My smile slowly dropped.

"Don't look at me!"

I slowly drew my eyes to the wall. Every second I reminded myself this was my dream and I had three sisters standing next to me who were going through it too. I couldn't give up, but everything in me wanted to. She gave us our rules for our band camp. I knew this would be the longest two weeks of my life. My sisters and I walked out in silence and honestly did not say one word until we got into our room.

"Girl, I can't stand her."

"She do the most for no reason."

"And who her daddy gonna run into, she don't know 'bout me or my family."

We went on and on until there was nothing left to say. We prepared our things to wake up in the morning to start our first official day training for the team.

It was six o'clock in the morning when my alarm went off. I turned over to find my roommate already up. She was good with waking up and feeling peppy around this time. I knew it was a good thing she would be my official roommate for the school year because I could sleep straight through an alarm.

"Bud, time to get up."

I slowly sat up and stared at my feet sitting on the ground for a good five minutes. I then lifted my head to look at my all black attire we had to wear for the remaining time of being on the team. This was all new to me. I watched my sister as she got ready and fixed her breakfast. I wasn't much of an early eater so I ate as much as I could of a banana, drank a few sips of water, and called it a meal. I stood in the mirror, dreading my all black outfit and the ugly black hat I had to wear with it. I looked like a child. The time was getting close to 6:30a.m. and my two other sisters met us in our room. We looked around at each other, not that there was much of a difference between us to look at other than the shades of our skin. We were all dressed in black with the same sad hats on. We gathered our things and made sure we had everything we needed for the day. As we drove to the hump in front of campus my stomach started to turn. I took another small sip of my water and dropped my head back onto the seat. I knew the majority of what I was feeling was nerves, but I also knew I had to shake them off. The time hit 6:45a.m and we sat in the car waiting for the team to come for 7:00a.m. We leaned on one another trying to get a few more minutes of sleep. Once the team arrived, we got out and met in front of the hump. The sun hadn't completely come out yet, but it was slowly rising. We began running back and forth across this long hump. Looking from afar, you wouldn't think it was that long, but judging by how I felt once I made it to the other side, I stood corrected. This was something I wasn't used to. I ran track in high school but this wasn't that. We motivated one another as we switched positions and continued to run back and forth. My roommate

90

held us down in the front. My other sister kept things moving from behind. As we took turns leading the line we stopped for a moment where we began. I dropped my head and crouched my body with my hands on my knees.

"Stand up! And put your hands over your head!" My captain yelled. I, along with my sisters, looked around as the team drank their Gatorades and water. My sisters and I had one bottle amongst all four of us.

We stood close to one another away from the team and whispered, "Should we ask can we drink our water?"

"Y'all I need something or I'm going to pass out."

"Maybe we should ask one of the other girls."

I got tired of standing there. I knew we needed something. I walked up and tapped my captain on the shoulder.

"Can we get some of our water please?"

"Oh y'all are thirsty? Go get your water."

I went back to my sisters and grabbed the water bottle, but before we could pass it around to drink, she called after us.

"Only a cap full."

The other team members dropped their heads and walked close to each other. My sisters and I looked at each other with frustration in our eyes.

"We got this y'all," my roommate said with slight hesitation in her tone.

But we still needed that and it felt good to hear. My sister grabbed the bottle and one by one we poured water into the cap to drink. I savored every bit that slid down my throat. We did our best to sneak another cap, and we did, until she caught us. "LET'S GO," and we took off running again up the hump. The sun was now completely out. I was gesturing to my sisters that my head was starting to pound. They did their best to encourage me to keep going. Everyone took turns jogging halfway up the hump and sprinting down. It was my turn. I was praying in my spirit I could make it. My roommate was waiting at the halfway point for me. As I began to jog I felt myself doing well. I started off with a good pace and it seemed like my endurance level was up. The moment I hit the top, I stopped. I looked at my roommate as my head started to dip back. I couldn't catch a breath and started to gasp for air. "I can't see, I can't see." My vision started to become black as my body fell forward. My breath became shorter until I couldn't push for one anymore. I grabbed onto the railing, losing control of myself, going in and out of consciousness. I could faintly hear my roommate yell for the team as I fell into her arms. My vision shifted in and out and I could see tears falling down her face. Once I saw her tears, my vision went black and I dropped my head in her arm. As I drifted in and out they took me to the car and put me in my captain's hands. I looked into her eyes and started to cry.

"What is going on?!"

She responded in a gentle sweet tone. "You're okay, you're okay."

Everyone crowded around as I laid in her arms. I looked over to my sisters and saw tears rolling down their faces. A police car pulled up and a female cop got out of the car.

"What is going on? Is everything okay?"

My captain immediately answered, "Oh nothing, we're fine. She just needed something to drink." As she smiled and pepped her voice up the officer walked back to her car but didn't move. My captain looked down at me. Through her smile she said, "I need you to get it together." I took a deep breath and at a leisurely pace I sat up. We all watched as the officer drove off. Suddenly my captain's whole entire mood changed. "Okay, we're done here. Meet back in the dance room in ten minutes."

My sisters and I walked into an empty room. We sat our things down and stood at attention in the corner waiting for the team to come through the door. My head was still throbbing, but I knew I needed to pull it together. They all walked in together and sat down. My captain called us to the middle of the dance floor. She dropped her head, looked up, and stared at me. I looked back into her eyes. I was waiting on her to be sympathetic, make sure I was okay. Little did I know, I would experience the exact opposite. She yelled.

"How dare you?! I am so angry with you. Don't ever do no shit like that ever again! You could've gotten me and the entire team in so much trouble! And for what? All because you want to do the most?"

My heart began to pound. Tears sat in the bed of my eyes, but I didn't let them drop. I was angry. How could she make this about her? Wasn't she supposed to comfort me, show me she cared? Instead, it was all a game to her. The sympathy, the smiles, it was all lies. Was that what a captain was supposed to be like? I didn't know but I didn't like what I was experiencing. I continued to look her in her eyes.

"Don't look at me!"

I kept my eyes on her.

"Kick."

We turned around, faced the mirror, and began kicking until she said stop. I looked over to the other team members. They seemed to not be as in tune as I would think most team members would be, but I still didn't know much about them. Our kicks dropped. I could barely pick my legs off the ground.

"Stop."

We were dismissed for break.

My sisters and I drove back to our rooms for our break and the first thing I could think to do was call my mother.

"Hey sweetie how's it going....sweetie?"

She called my name. She could hear me breaking down in tears.

"Calm down. What is going on?"

As I sniffled through the words, I answered her. "Mom, I almost died."

I explained to her everything that took place, even my own captain making it my fault. My tears came stronger and stronger and I raised my voice.

"I don't trust her. How is she supposed to be my captain and I don't trust her, nor do I even want to be around her?"

"Sweetie, what have your dad and I always told you? Let God fight your battles. If she was acting ugly God will handle it. You just pray for you to get yourself together. You can't expect Him to handle it if you don't let it go and believe. You hear me?"

"Yes ma."

"You would not be there if you couldn't endure. Until someone puts their hands on you, stand your ground with integrity. And you need to eat in the morning because that's all that was! You didn't see that oatmeal in the box? Don't act like you don't know how to take care of yourself." And then she prayed with me. "I love you sweetie. Hang in there."

I knew I didn't really want to quit, but it was what I felt. I wasn't a quitter, but I also wasn't going to let anyone get away with treating me any kind of way. The way she treated us became a routine that was noticeable for the first week of camp, especially the way she treated me. I can admit, my attitude wasn't the best towards her. I listened and did what I was supposed to for the sake of my sisters. What one does, we all do. If one acts wrong, we all get the consequence. I did my best to control my attitude, but it was evident to me when unnecessary things were done. I hadn't experienced much yet, but I knew when things were being taken too far.

It was the end of the first week. We headed to lunch after hours of strenuous practicing. As the team sat down with their food my sisters got up to get ours. Before we could walk away our captain stopped us.

"Before y'all come back, fill one cup with every drink at the fountain."

As weird as it was to me it instantly went over my head. I had so much more on my mind. My eating habits started to change. I was contemplating what to do because I knew I needed to eat. I went from always wanting to eat, to barely being hungry during the day. I settled for a pizza, salad, and fruit. We all stood in front of the fountain machine.

"What y'all think we about to do?"

"You think she's going to make us drink it?"

"Come on y'all, they lookin."

My sister grabbed a cup and filled it slightly with one fountain drink at a time. Every single drink from the tea to the soda and even the juices. We sat down at the table. I was reluctantly sitting in front of her. I didn't even look her in the eye. As I took small bites of my food, I could feel something getting ready to happen. My roommate tapped my leg with her foot. I did it back. Our captain looked at my sister on the end.

"Go get another slice of pizza."

I still had no clue what was about to happen. As soon as she sat down with the pizza, my captain wasted no time.

"Now dip the pizza in the drink and take a bite."

My sister looked at us and we all looked back. I tilted my head and raised my eyebrows indicating, "You can do what she wants, but I'm not doing that nasty shit." She hesitated biting into the pizza after she dipped it into the drink and slowly chewed.

"Now pass it to your sister."

As it came down the line, my roommate took a bite and passed it to me. I took the pizza from her hand and laid it on my plate. My captain stared into my eyes.

"Eat the pizza!"

"No."

My roommate put her hand on my thigh. I looked at her. She looked at me with a look that read, "Please just do it."

Our captain's sister jumped in.

"O girl eat the pizza! It's not that serious."

Maybe it wasn't that serious, but I still wasn't doing it. My captain was still staring at me.

"Do you want to be here? Because we can easily find someone else to replace you."

I sat back in my seat, clinched my teeth, dropped my head, and stared her in the eye.

"Either you eat the pizza or you leave. And since you want to be difficult, you can finish it."

I stood up, pushed my plate forward, pushed my seat back, walked out of the cafe and into the bathroom. I stood in the stall with tears rolling down my face. And the first person I dialed was my mom.

"Mom I'm about to punch this girl in her face! I have had it up to here with her!" I explained the situation that took place. For a moment it was silent. She didn't say anything. "Mom?"

"Sweetie, you have to stop letting this girl get under your skin like that. If you're going to be strong and stand your ground, you say what you have to say and let it be that. Let her say what she wants because that's all it is, words. You need to go back out there with your sisters. And don't call me no more crying."

"Mom, I don't cry in front of anyone but you. I let how I feel out to you."

"I know you don't sweetie, but you're stronger than that. Say what you say, mean it, and let it be that. Now dry your face and don't let another tear fall. I got to go back to work. Bye."

I laid my back against the stall door, took a deep breath and looked up to the ceiling. "God, what are you doing? I don't even want to know, just hold my hand through this please. Make me stronger emotionally and show me how to handle my strength." I wiped my tears. As soon as I grabbed the door handle, my sisters pulled on the door.

"Girl you okay?"

I looked in their eyes.

"I'm sorry y'all."

"Don't trip bud."

"Yea, we got your back."

As we walked off, the team went through the door before us. We knew we needed to be back to the room before them so we rushed past, jumped in the car, and booked it back to the dance room.

We walked in the room just in time to clean up anything or hang up our posters she assigned us to make as decoration. A few of them had fallen so we used the last few minutes to hang them up. Once we finished we lined up in our corner and stood at attention right when they walked in. They shut the door behind them. Our captain's sister stood in front of the door. Our captain aggressively walked toward us and started ripping our decorations off the wall, tearing them in half.

She charged up to me, an inch away from my face and yelled, "Who do you think you are??! You feeling froggy? Jump then bitch!" I pressed my hands on my hips and moved my eyes towards my sisters.

I saw my sister on the end clinch her teeth together. My roommate standing next to me put her elbow on mine. She continued to yell as I tuned everything out and listened to the words my mother spoke to me play in my head. I looked at the other team members. Because I really hadn't gotten the chance to get to know them yet, I identified them as simply my dance sisters. No one did anything, but I read on their faces they were uncomfortable with what was going on. The whole room felt uncomfortable. Practice was continued just as that - uncomfortable. She didn't look at us the rest of practice and I was okay with it. It had finally come to the end. We prayed, gathered our things, and left. I knew my sisters felt just like me. We couldn't wait to leave just to talk.

"Girl, I was waiting for her to touch you."

"Yea, one fight we all fighting."

"She was this close to your face!"

"Just as long as she didn't touch me."

"We got each other no matter what."

I was simply just glad I survived the first week of what would change my life forever.

It was the beginning of the second week. Besides learning the basics of being part of the team, we engaged in other activities I would say didn't go with dance. We were kicking for eternity and at this point there was nothing else to pull from. She left the room to meet with someone and the upperclassman were in charge. I liked most of the upperclassman. There were the girls who were freshman the year prior. They pretty much minded their business. There was one who made it two years before, and she was my big sister. She was my favorite. Then there was my captain's sister. I didn't even care to look her way. My big sister spoke up majority of the time whenever my captain stepped out, making sure we did what we were supposed to do, but she talked to us better. My sisters and I lined up in our corner standing at attention as our captain walked in. "We're about to break for lunch and a guest will be joining us." She looked over towards us. "Y'all can go."

We gathered our things in a hurry and headed to the cafe to get the table and chairs set up for the team. We sat down, waiting for them to come in and get their food first. Once we all settled, the guest walked in and sat in the chair right in front of me. She was a previous dance girl from the 90s. She crabbed under one of the most legendary captains within the organization and the team made sure we knew exactly who she was. The lady sitting in front of me was beautiful. Although I was excited to meet her, my demeanor was still on guard. She looked at me and smiled. Then she looked at my captain.

"So, this is the one you were talking about huh?"

My captain nodded her head and gave a slight smirk, like she knew this woman was going to let me have it. She looked back at me. I sat up in my seat, slightly lifted my head, and raised my eyebrows to let her know I was ready for whatever she was about to throw at me. She caught my demeanor and took on the same stance, but with grace.

"No need to take on that gesture with me. I can already get a sense of who you are just by looking in your eyes. Who you are is going to make you captain of this team one day. You just need to learn how to control it. But there is something great about you. You will eventually find out."

I looked around the table. All that was going through my mind was the word captain. I was a freshman. How was she even able to gather that? I looked over to my captain. She didn't even look me in my eye. I looked back to the woman, nodded my head, and continued to eat.

The last week was winding down and things for the most part were the same. The same as in still learning, but still dealing with unnecessary situations and still a captain who I felt cared more about herself than the team around her. Who was I though? I mean that's how I felt coming from the team, but I knew who I was. It was just taking the right situation for me to understand the whole truth.

The first week when every student comes to campus had officially begun. My roommate and I moved into our apartment. This was the first week my sisters and I were preparing for our first performance. Practice was every day, all day, and there was no time to participate in the festivities going on around campus. It didn't bother me much though because I got the chance to experience that type of fun my first year of college. So did my sisters since we were all sophomores. Although this wasn't a game, a performance in general was nerve wrecking. She assigned spots in the stands. I occupied the ace spot. This was the position behind the captain in the strut line and the first person in the stands. It was not much of a big deal to me only because I felt I belonged there due to my height. I was the shortest person on the team. I figured it would look weird to put me anywhere else.

It was two days before it was time to leave for our first performance and we were scheduled to practice outside with the band. This would be my first time strutting in front of the band with the entire team to the field I would soon call my happy place. As we strutted into the gate an adrenaline hit my entire body. No one had to yell at me to smile, flick my feet, or even look happy to be there. It came naturally. As we stood on the sideline getting ready to perform the dance for the first time on the field, my roommate hit my elbow and I knew exactly what that meant.

I planted the biggest smile on my face and through my teeth I whispered, "We're really here."

"Yea girl, we made it this far."

A tear planted itself in the bed of my eye. As I felt the field for the first time, I let it fall.

Chapter 6
Speaking Loud in the Midst of Silence

We were due to perform in Charlotte, making it an almost 13-hour trip. This was a big day for me: First bus ride, first away performance, and first performance in general. As we packed up our things in the dance room, my sisters and I waited behind to make sure we had everything we were assigned to bring for the team. "Kit...got it...chips...on the bus...drinks...got that." We rummaged through the kit to make sure we had everything we needed, and to our knowledge, we did. As soon as the bus took off, we all went to sleep. I sat next to the window with my roommate. My other two sisters sat in front of us. As we made it closer to our destination everyone slowly started to wake up. We all began to get dressed and ready for the performance. I took my time getting dressed to make sure my hair and makeup were just right. I wasn't the best at curling my hair in pin curls like the rest of the girls so I didn't waste much time on my hair. As long as I was cute, it didn't matter much to me, my makeup was my main priority.

While my sisters and I helped get one another together, the team began to speak nonstop.

"Are there wipes in the kit?"

"Can you get me the scissors?"

"Where's the deodorant?"

Each girl had a request and they expected my sisters and I to respond immediately with the answer they were looking for and whatever item they needed. My captain didn't say much to us.

She sat in the front and made sure her hair and makeup were together. As much as I still had my reservations about her, she always had the best curls. Although I didn't think the Shirley temple look was for me, they always looked good on her. We finally pulled up to our destination. I immediately saw everyone's mood change. It was humid and wet outside. No matter how much hairspray filled the air, it wouldn't stop everyone's hair from falling. Our sponsor looked around to make sure everyone looked decent and nothing was out of place. The band director was ready, and it was time.

"Okay ladies, let's get ready to get off the bus." Our sponsor said.

My sisters and I looked at one another, grabbed each other's hands, and smiled. As we got off the bus we lined up waiting for the rest of the team to get in formation. Our captain walked up and hugged each one of my sisters. This was a surprise to me. She really wasn't the type to display much affection, at least not what I had experienced so far. The humidity wasted no time doing its job on us. Within minutes I watched as everyone's hair fell quickly. The entrance wasn't much of the real thing because it was still drizzling and everything was very crowded. We moved into the stands and packed in the small space we were provided. As the band began to play, I watched as my captain threw the counts back to back. I didn't pay attention to how well I was doing the count, I just had to make sure I was catching them. I prayed every time I stood up that I didn't miss anything. As exciting as it was to finally be doing what I dreamed, I was ready for it to be over. Not because I didn't like it, because I knew I wasn't where I wanted to be and it wasn't good enough for me.

It was finally time to leave the stands and get ready for the field show. We all gathered in the bathroom to wipe the sweat from our faces and touch up anything that seemed to be out of place. Everyone took off their gloves as we all played in our hair trying to make it look better than what it did. My sister and I stood off in the corner while the team stepped in front of us to get to the mirrors. As we stood to the side one of the team members walked up to us.

"Do y'all have extra gloves in the kit?"

We looked at each other. We knew we didn't have a pair, but we also didn't know we needed it either. I could feel an attitude kicking in so I made sure to keep my mouth shut and observe. I saw my captain watching from afar. I knew it wouldn't be too long before she made her way over to add her input. We began to look through the kit as if we knew we were going to find some gloves knowing we didn't have any. I watched as her eyes observed each one of our gloves. For the most part our gloves were close to white, with a small smidge of makeup, but still somewhat brand new. My captain walked over and immediately intervened due to the fact she witnessed the situation from a distance.

"Give her one of your gloves."

We all looked down at each other and before we could choose who would do it, the team member picked for us. We all looked at each other and then looked at our captain as she looked back at us, rolled her eyes and walked away. We sat alone on a bench while the team gathered together in another area laughing and talking. I didn't expect them to be as tight with us, but I did expect our captain to communicate with us here and there.

Maybe a few words of encouragement would've helped, but no. She would glance over from time to time to make sure we were where we were supposed to be and continue to carry on without us, as if we weren't even there. As we sat with miserable looks on our faces our sponsor walked up.

"Well hello beautiful ladies."

We all put smiles on our faces. I knew my smile was genuine because I had no intentions on cracking a smile the rest of the night other than for the performance, but when she came, it made everything okay.

"How are you feeling about your first performance?"

We all spoke at once, laughing and just being happy. She told us about how she was on her first performance.

"Don't let your nerves get to you. I know that it's easier said than done, but just have fun."

As she talked to us I glanced over to my captain. I caught her eyes watching us as she cut them away, turning her back. I didn't let it bother me because our sponsor made the mood better. Even though I didn't know much about her yet, I knew she was someone we needed.

As we lined up on the sideline for our first field show, I couldn't even put myself in a place of emotional happiness because I was completely nervous. I replayed the dance in my mind repeatedly until I watched out of the corner of my eye my captain's hands slide up her body and listened as she yelled '5, 6, 7, 8!' As I strutted out, nothing else mattered. I felt no negativity, no hatred, but genuine happiness for the love of the team and for the love of dance. When we made it back onto the bus I was ready to sleep but I also wanted and needed to get to my phone. Sadly, the first thing on my mind was how I looked and what people thought about me. I watched as the team pulled out their phones watching everything already making it to the internet, while me and my sisters sat, phoneless, waiting to make it back in the place of our own comfort.

That next night I laid in my bed as I scrolled through the many social sites we were on, reading every comment. There were some good comments but the majority of them, let's just say I would have preferred not to see. I wasn't everyone's biggest fan like I thought I would be. I read comments like:

"She's just another pretty face."

"Why does she move like that?"

"She's not bad, but she's not blending."

The list went on and on. As I laid there trying not to think much about it, I yearned for some type of validation. I turned on my back looking to the ceiling thinking about who could possibly stroke what ego I had left. I decided to message the guy I dated my freshman year. I hadn't completely cut him off, but because the team occupied all my days, I didn't really have the energy or time to be with anyone. It was late and I hesitated, thinking maybe he wouldn't respond, but he did.

"Hey, wassup?"

"Just getting some rest after our performance yesterday."

"Ohh yea I saw that."

My heart started to pound. That's all he could say? Him, out of all people knew how important this was to me and that was all he could respond with? "Okayyy so what did you think?"

"You did pretty good."

"Just pretty good?"

I was not prepared to hear anything I didn't want, but the conversation had already hit the climax for me and my heart was too invested.

"I mean, you just started. You ain't do bad, but you just need to loosen up. You don't look like a grown woman right now."

As I read his message my heart started to sting. I dropped the phone and left him right where he sent his last comment. I made up in my mind he was officially cut off. But I sat up and contemplated what I was really upset about. Was it the fact he had the nerve to say that to me, or the fact he was possibly right? At the time I didn't see it that way. My feelings were hurt. I let my tears roll down my cheek and continued to repeat every comment in my head. And that was my problem. Who was I becoming? I was internalizing the things that made me less of a person. I put my phone on the dresser face down. I looked up and out loud I spoke, "Take these thoughts out of my head. Remind me I'm better than this." Then I turned over and went to sleep.

The first week of classes began and I was just glad to have something else to occupy my day other than practice. Don't

109

get me wrong, I loved dancing, but practices I dreaded. Our rule was to be five minutes early to class and sit to the very front of the classroom. Thankfully I was already a front row type of student but seeing as though I was always exhausted from late practices, being to class earlier was not my forte because I needed that extra five minutes in bed.

I spent almost every day eating lunch with my sister. Besides me and my roommate being close, I started to spend a lot of one on one time with the sister I prayed for at auditions. It became a normal routine to meet for lunch. We shared the same love for food and just good conversation. As we walked up to the cafe we began to talk about some of our crab brothers, the band members who made the band when we made the team. Because we were not allowed to communicate or hang out with any guys other than our crab brothers, we had to choose to crush amongst them. I hadn't seen anyone I was interested in so I didn't have much to say, but my sister spotted one. We met the majority of them during our band camp, but we still weren't familiar with many names. As we sat down to eat, a few of them came and joined us. We laughed, talked, and began gaining a relationship with the people who would share in our journey.

It seemed like the days went by extremely fast up until it was time for practice. My sisters would meet at my roommate and I's apartment, talk about how much we weren't ready for practice, shove a few pizza rolls in our mouth, and be out the door. Thirty minutes before the team would start to walk in we would scramble around wiping mirrors, sweeping the floor, and putting our history on the wall. As the time hit, almost minutes before the designated practice time, we would quickly get to our spots in the corner, standing at attention with smiles on our faces, talking through our teeth. "Bayou Classis this weekend y'all." That was our thing. Bayou classic was the end goal. As soon as that game was over, and the clock hit 0:00 we would no longer be considered bottom of the barrel. We would officially be the dance girls we dreamed of being. As we finished our out loud daydreaming, the team walked in one by one and practice began. We were preparing for our first away game. It was a little more personal for me as it was in the city I moved to for my senior year. That was something to me. The place that started the change of my life was the same place I would perform my first game. Practice was normal. The antics became common. I knew what to prepare for and how. At least I thought I did. One moment our captain looked at us like we disgusted her and the next minute she talked to us like we were her best friends. As we stood in the middle of the floor kicking for dear life our captain spoke.

"Do y'all know your big sisters?"

Of course we knew their names so that is how we responded.

"What is her favorite color?"

No one answered.

"That was a question!"

We cut our eyes at one another and one of us spoke up.

"Blue."

The team member laughed. Our captain looked over to her. "Is that right?"

She shook her head as she looked back down at her phone.

"It was wrong, try again."

No one answered.

"Plank!"

As I crouched my body down to the floor, I looked into the mirror.

"Don't look in the mirror, you're not cute!" My captain's sister yelled.

As much as I wanted to respond, I could feel myself slowly realizing it didn't do me any good. We would sit in our plank as she asked us question after question. I could feel myself falling as I clinched my abs. I looked over to the side to see how my sisters were doing. We all took turns watching one another but still focusing on staying in it. Time finally made it to the end of practice, but only for everyone else.

"Crabs y'all stay."

Everyone left out of the room except for our captain. I didn't know what to expect. We stood by our bags in the corner waiting to see what was going on. She laughed.

"Y'all can relax. Practice is over. I'm just going to work with y'all."

I still didn't know how to feel, but it was honestly good to get one on one help without the pressure of feeling scrutinized.

112

Times like this made me want to trust her. I would hear the way the team talked about their captains and I wanted to feel the same way.

As she wrapped up the critiques she had us sit down.

"So, how do y'all feel?"

This was probably the most relaxed I felt around her, yet I was still on pins and needles. We all answered. I was happy she was just trying to talk to us, genuinely about us. But after that one question, it changed.

"Has the team talked to y'all?"

I was confused. I didn't know what our answer was supposed to be. She began to tell us to be careful and to watch how we got involved with them. I didn't think much of it because I didn't really understand what we were supposed to watch. I hadn't heard anything from the team let alone spent two seconds with just them. We still listened and let her do all the talking. This was the best friend attitude that would come immediately after her acting like she couldn't stand us. We were released and headed to the car. As my sisters and I got into the car we discussed what she asked. We weren't stupid, but we still didn't know the capacity to whatever problem it was we would eventually find out.

The day came for the first game. I sat in my assigned seat looking forward as the band girls and the team laughed and danced to the music playing. I wanted to turn around so bad, just to see what was so funny, but if our captain didn't see anything else, she always saw when we did wrong, so I kept my eyes forward. We finally pulled up to the school. The first person I saw standing to the side was my dad. My palms became sweaty and I prayed no one asked me for anything or to do anything because my mind was solely focused on everything that would take place the moment we got in line. It was time to get off the bus. I got into my position. My dad stood right next to me and I looked over to him. "Work 'em out baby girl!" He smiled, gave me a wink and proceeded to record every step I took until we made it to the entrance. It was the best and worst feeling ever. It was the hype and the excitement that made it such an amazing moment. For the same reason of it being a blessing, also made it a curse.

The hype: everyone wants it, but many cannot handle it. That's where my nerves came from. The thought of fans liking me and not liking me. Although I felt more relaxed this performance, I still thought about every moment, every motion, every little thing having to do with being on the team. It was time for the field show. As we walked to the sideline the sponsor stopped us to pray. We formed a circle and I bowed my head. She spoke up, looked at me, and said, "I want you to pray." I looked up to her. I hesitated for a brief second. I thought that was something only the captain and the sponsor did. I looked around the circle as the girls watched me and then bowed their heads. I said a prayer and we were ready to take the field.

As the game came to an end and we marched out, it was hard for me to enjoy the last few seconds because I was busy thinking about how many times I messed up in the stands. I knew I wouldn't be able to live it down come practice time. I couldn't wait to get home to see what the fans thought. As we strutted back to the bus my family stood nearby waiting. I was so happy to see them. For the moment I could forget about all the madness and the judgement and be okay with the fact my family was okay with me. As we took pictures, our sponsor walked up.

"Are these your parents?"

I loved when she came around. She was always happy and seemed to make moments better. While my parents introduced themselves and they went back and forth I watched, and smiled.

"Your daughter is truly a blessing to this team and something special."

Of course, my dad was the first to respond.

"Praise God. That's my baby girl. And thank you for being a blessing to her."

We were now preparing for game two and the week was going by rather fast, but slow at the same time. Class, cafe with my sister, and my room to sleep before practice, started to become the daily routine. Practices seemed to get worse as the days and weeks progressed. As we strutted across the floor one by one I always imagined myself as the first girl I watched who introduced me to my love for the team. She always gave a face that could make anyone move. I strutted across the floor in my own world. "Fix your face crab! Smile." There was my captain's sister again, budging into what was none of her business. Maybe it was her business, but she always felt the need to say something to me, and our captain used any reason for us to turn around and do it over again or to punish us. She turned the music down while we stood to the side. The team took their seats and pulled out their phones. They laughed and talked amongst each other while we stood there, standing on our toes with our hands on our hips, awkwardly smiling.

"We want to laugh.... skit."

We immediately huddled into a circle. We whispered about everything we could possibly think of.

"What is taking you so long? Let's go."

We walked to the middle of the room. She stopped us before we could get started.

"Do your introduction first."

My sister stepped up.

"A oneee and a twoooo and ah," then we all started shaking like wet dogs. My big sister slightly laughed, but she just about laughed at anything. We then started to run around the room like we were airplanes, making airplane noises with our mouths. "Errhhhhhhhhhhhhhhhh." I looked out the corner of my eye as they all laughed. But I knew they weren't laughing because it was funny. They were laughing out of confusion because we didn't even know what we were doing. We then pretended to crash into one another. And once we finished, we lined up in the middle of the floor and faced the team. "Scene." They all just stared at us, as we stood there embarrassed for ourselves. Our captain tilted her head to the side and let out a small chuckle. "What was that.... that was not funny...kick." I wasn't surprised. I knew it was bad, but did that really matter? We rehearsed the dance over and over, kicked some more, and practice was finally over.

It was now time for our second game. This time my crab
sisters and I made sure we had everything plus more in our kit.
As we pulled up to the game everyone scrammed to get dressed.
It was wet and muggy outside so the majority of the team did
loose curls, except for my captain. When it was time to get ready,
she didn't mind us too much, unless she needed something for
herself. It was about five minutes before it was time to line up.
"One of y'all pass me the hair spray." We were all occupied with
something so my sister quickly went into the kit and gave her the
spray bottle. What she didn't see is that she gave her oil sheen
instead of hair spray. As my captain sprayed and sprayed all over
her head everyone finished their last-minute touches. Our
captain's entire mood changed. Her eyes began to water and she
walked up to the sponsor. We all looked around and in passing
our sister told us what happened. I let out a small laugh because
I thought it was rather funny, but that was before I knew the
effects of putting oil sheen on hair. The moment we stepped off
the bus, our captain's hair began to fall slowly. It was definitely
not what she started with. I started to feel bad a little because I
could only imagine what she felt like. As we marched in it began
to rain. We immediately went to stand under a pavilion. My
sisters and I stood off to the side as the team gathered on the
other side. I knew she was telling them what happened. A big
part of me knew she thought it happened purposely. While we
stood in silence, our sponsor called me over to where she was
standing with her boyfriend. She introduced me as the girl who
knew her godmother. "I guess that would make you my
godbaby" and she hugged me. Before I could walk away my
captain walked up, looked at me, dropped her smile, and
squinted her eyes. I walked back over to my sisters. As we spoke
to each other out of the corner of our mouths she walked up.
"Stop talking." We finally made it into the stands to perform and

117

everyone's hair had completely fallen. Despite my hair I felt I was doing much better in the stands and my spirits for the game were high. That didn't last long. It was time to head to the locker room to get ready to perform the field show. Everyone filled the restroom reaching into the kit to find anything to make them up again. I saw the brush sitting on the sink and picked it up to brush out my hair. My captain's sister walked up behind me.

"I need to brush my hair."

"Okay, I'm almost finished."

She dropped her head and raised her eyebrow. I continued to brush my hair and proceeded to hand it to my crab sister, but my captain's sister snatched it out of my hand. We continued to situate ourselves in the mirror. Our captain called.

"Crabs!"

I knew it was about to be something.

"You think we're supposed to cater to y'all? Y'all have been messing up all day. Kick."

My sisters and I looked at one another.

"Now."

We began kicking while she talked.

"When an upperclassman asks for something to be done, you do it right then. There is no hesitation."

I started to drop my legs, trying to preserve my energy for the field show.

"KICK...don't even look in the mirror no more. From here on out you do what we say and you stand where you're supposed to until I say otherwise. Last twenty-five and kick your face."

I tried my hardest to push through but at the same time she got the bare minimum out of me. All I could think about was how this made sense right before a performance. I looked over to our sponsor who sat to the side. It was hard to tell if she was shying away from watching us or didn't think much of it. We were down to the last five and as I dropped my legs and arms I placed my hands on my hips trying to catch my breath. I clinched my teeth and rolled my eyes as she called for us to form a circle for prayer. She looked over to me.

"Is there a problem?"

I shook my head looking down and closed my eyes. I knew she was still looking at me.

"You can pray."

As I gasped for air, with each word coming out faintly, I said a prayer and we walked out of the locker room as if nothing happened. I had lost all happiness for the rest of the game. I knew I mentally wasn't there anymore. I made pointless errors and could hardly keep a smile on my face. I felt as though maybe if I understood why she did most of the things she did to us maybe it would be better. But I knew she wasn't looking for it to be better.

It was the beginning of the next week. I was just glad the weekend was over. Games were starting not to be fun and instead of being happy for games to come, I was ready for them to be over before even getting started. It was time for another practice. My sisters and I walked in the room early to clean, only to walk into our captain on the phone complaining about the past weekend's game.

"Yes, she messed up my viral video. She was the only one who messed up." She laughed. "I can't even believe it. Just pathetic."

My sisters and I looked at each other. They whispered to me it was okay. I knew she was speaking about me. I knew exactly what video she was talking about. All I could think was that she was the cause for the problem she had with me. As practice started I tried to dismiss everything out of my head, but she didn't make it easy.

"Go to the bathroom." she said.

My sisters and I quickly walked out of the room and into the bathroom.

"What y'all think about to happen?"

"Don't worry about her girl, she's pathetic."

"Bayou Classic tomorrow y'all."

After we went back and forth we sat in silence. I laid my back against the bathroom stall, as my heart pounded, wondering what was going to happen next. An upperclassman came to the door.

"Y'all can come back."

We walked into the room and went back into attention in our corner. She looked over to us.

"Beat us outside to the stadium."

We took off running. As we waited for them while standing in the stadium they all walked in together. We stood on the track at attention. She came up to us and walked down the line.

"Run."

We took off running around the track. She yelled "kick" amid us running. We hesitated, looked around and began to kick.

"Run....Kick...Run...Kick."

I knew it was a joke to her. Once we made it all the way around she wasted no time.

"Kick."

My body was tired. I could barely get a kick out of me.

"Stop."

She directed us into the stands and told us to run up and down each step. While we ran, her and her sister yelled,

"RUN! Y'all so weak. Can't do nothin'," as they laughed while watching us.

The other team members just watched in silence. I looked down at them yelling and stopped running all together. They called my name. "Run." I started to walk. I was fed up at that point. I knew there was nothing else they could do to me and I wanted someone to try and touch me, so I walked. They kept yelling as I watched my sisters tire out. I refused to engage any longer. She called us to the stands into our position. I stood there at attention along with my sisters and the team. She walked onto the track and looked up to me.

"Move to the back and switch with your sister."

My heart dropped. As I stepped to the back everyone watched me. She walked back in the stands with a smile on her face and laughed.

"This is much better."

Tears filled my eyes, but I refused to let her feel like she had won. I took a deep breath, said a small prayer, put a smile on my face, and hid every emotion I felt inside of me. Practice continued as if nothing took place. No one said anything to me. Not the team, not my sister, and of course not even my captain. I kept a look on my face that I hope portrayed the idea that I wasn't bothered, but it took everything to mask what I truly felt.

I wasn't expecting things to be easy on me, but I consistently asked myself why it was so hard. Why did it seem like it wouldn't get any better for me? That night I sat up and I couldn't help but cry. I decided to call the first dance girl who worked with me and helped me prepare for auditions. She answered immediately. She listened to me cry as I explained what took place. My biggest problem was I was ashamed and embarrassed for what people were going to think. That's what I was worried about. How others would feel about my situation. She let me vent and get out every tear and then she spoke.

"Let me remind you of the girl I met before you made the team. She was strong! She believed she could and she did. Find that girl. That is who you are. I know it is tough. A lot of things are going on I might not agree with, but this isn't my situation, it's yours and you must be strong and endure. Don't worry about the comments, stop reading them. They're going to say what they want. It's okay to cry, but you cry and then you get back up and do what you have to do, because that's what the legacy is about."

This coming from a two year co-captain. I had only the upmost respect for her and everything she told me. A part of me felt a little better but I still didn't feel I was ready to go back into that room and face dealing with anyone, not even my sisters.

On the way to class the next morning I called the sponsor. I called with the hopes that maybe since I felt she liked me so much she would tell my captain to switch me back. As I told her the situation she paused. I waited in anticipation for her answer. "You know I was in the back. And during my time I thought many people didn't notice me. And then I was moved to the front. All the way to the front... you're a star miss lady. Do you know that? You are going to shine wherever you stand because that's just who you are. You dance in that spot, and you better do it like no one has done it before. I guarantee, if you do that, you won't have to worry about anyone noticing you, it's just going to happen and it's all going to work in your favor." She didn't know it, but she sealed the deal for me. Whether my captain told her what she did or didn't tell her, I immediately made it my mission to get better each game. She was right. I was a star and the sooner I started to believe it, the sooner I would see the benefits of being one.

Every game from there on out was about growth to me. I stayed away from the comments and worked on getting back to who I was. I knew it was something that wasn't going to happen overnight, but just like life, the moment you begin to work to get yourself in order, things come in to try and stunt your growth and move you from where you planned to go. Practices got worse. There was more of what I believed as pointless when it came to behavior or tactics. They seemed to last longer and longer for reasons I was very unsure about. It was a late night and the time was vastly approaching 11:00pm. After just doing over 1,000 kicks and planking, I stood in the corner trying to control my breathing with sweat sliding down my face, thinking about how late I would be up trying to get my school work done, glittering shoes with my sisters, and memorizing history. She called us to the middle of the floor.

"We will pray out, when two of you tongue kiss."

I looked over towards my sisters. We all looked at each other. My captain looked at me.

"You can be the boy. So whoever is next to you has to tongue kiss you. And we're not leaving until you do it."

We all stood there still facing forward. She raised her voice.

"Turn to her."

I turned to the side to face my roommate. We both looked at each other and shook our heads. I knew she wasn't doing it, and neither was I, so I guess we were going to be in there all night.

"Do it!"

She kept insisting and we just stood there. Our captain's sister came and sat in front of us.

"Just do it so we can go!"

I mumbled through my teeth, "Hell no."

I was still facing my sister, but I could see her out the corner of my eye as she snapped her head up.

"What did you just say? Did you just say hell no?"

I took my direction away from my sister and looked down at her on the floor as an answer to her that yes, I said it and I meant it. Our captain spoke up.

"Turn to the other side."

I turned around and shook my head to my sister as she continued to stand there looking back at me. We stood there for another five minutes until our captain realized it wasn't happening. She continued to push. She told my last sister on the end to come stand next to me. My sister looked at me and nodded, opening her eyes real big indicating to just do it so we could get it over with. I still shook my head and stood there. I could feel everyone in the room getting restless, but I didn't care.

We continued to stand there looking at one another. Our captain spoke again.

"I'm going to give y'all a minute to talk amongst yourselves and figure out what you're going to do, but we don't have all night."

My sisters and I formed a tight circle. I spoke up.

"I won't be doing this y'all. Eventually they'll get tired and let us go so it's fine with me if we just stand here."

"Well, I'm with you because I don't believe in that."

My sister, who she moved next to me spoke.

"Well, we have to do something. What if we just tap our tongues together?"

I looked around the circle and decided it would possibly be the only way for us to get out of it.

"Time's up, let's go."

We turned back to face the team. She instructed for me and my sister to face each other. As I slowly turned to look at her, she gestured for me to come on. I clinched my jaw and took a deep breath. I stuck my tongue out and shut my eyes. It took less than a second before the tip of her tongue touched mine and we backed away from each other. The entire team began to speak at once.

"Ewwwwwwwww," and they laughed.

Our captain stood up.

"You were supposed to put the tongues of your shoes together, idiots."

I looked at my sisters. My jaw was still clinched and I rolled my eyes.

The car ride home was silent. We were all mad, at least I know I was. Judging by the looks on my sisters' faces, they didn't seem too far from how I felt. We walked in our apartment and let loose.

"I'm done y'all. She crossed the line."

"We need to do something about this."

"She can't keep getting away with treating us like this. It's just not right."

We stayed up half the night going back and forth about how much we disliked our captain and what we were going to do about it. I woke up the next morning and contemplated who to call. I knew if I called my dad he would shut everything down. I called my mom hoping she would understand.

"Hey sweetie, what is going on?"

I hesitated to get the words out. I didn't know how she would react. I tried to anticipate her response. I finally came out with everything that took place. She went silent. I waited for her response.

"Okay, I'm calling up there because I'm sick of this!"

"Mom please don't. This is my situation let me handle it."

I listened as she went on her own rant. At the end she told me what she thought was best. That night my sisters and I met at our apartment. We decided we were going to talk to the sponsor about everything going on. She listened as we all took turns telling her what took place during practices for a while. She didn't tell us exactly what she was going to do, but she listened. Thinking this would be a step in the right direction, things got worse, but this time between the people I always thought would stick together no matter what - my sisters.

Days began to pass by quicker and quicker and besides not knowing how any practice would go, my schedule stayed the same throughout the day. I would go to class, meet my sister at the café to grab our food to go because of how stressful practice had become, and go back to my room to eat and sleep before practice. We woke up about two hours before practice. My door to my room was open and my roommate had just walked in from class and sat down at the mirror to wipe her makeup off. As my sister and I sat up in the bed talking with my roommate, our crab brother called my sister. She answered the phone and I grabbed it to talk to him. As I held the phone up, looking at myself in the corner of the screen, my sister got out of the bed to get herself situated for practice as well. Before I could hang up a message notification from our other sister popped on the screen. The message was open to read. It was about my roommate. I looked up to see that my roommate could see my face from the bathroom mirror and turned to look at me. I mouthed to her I needed to tell her something. My sister left to head back to her room to finish getting dressed informing us she would meet us back at the apartment before practice. That was fine with me. I needed to tell my roommate what was going on. The moment I locked the door behind my sister my roommate looked at me.

"Girl, what is going on?"

"Girl, why are they talking about you?"

I told her they were expressing their concern about how she would tell her mother everything that took place with us and the team and how they didn't like the fact that her and her mother took matters in their own hands behind the groups back. She looked down and shrugged her shoulders. I stood next to her.

"I'm going to say something because if they're talking about you, then I'm not too far behind and that's not cool. We don't need this."

She got up and started to walk to her room.

"I'm not even going to worry about it. Don't say anything."

I sat down in the seat once she got up. Because she was my best friend I cared about how she felt. As I sat I thought about if she really didn't want me to say anything or if she was just being modest. I tried to look at the situation from a different standpoint, but I couldn't get past how I discovered there was a problem.

Our captain's mood started to change for maybe a week, but it didn't last too much longer. To me it seemed as though conversations only aroused when she wanted to know if the team had said anything about her or if they said anything to us in general. "They just don't mean y'all no good." It didn't seem that way at the time to me. They worked with us and broke down many things I couldn't seem to get from the one person who I was supposed to learn from. I had respect for my teammates, but I held a lot of respect for my big sister. She always seemed to hold things together and make the mood a little less intense when problems arose in the room. One night my big sister texted my sisters and I. She asked if we could meet in her room. When we got there the entire team was sitting on the couch minus our captain. My sisters and I sat against the wall. I tucked my legs and held on to my knees. I moved my eyes to look at my sisters, but I didn't turn my head. Then I looked over to the team. My big sister started to speak.

"We just wanted to talk to y'all because we haven't really gotten the chance to just get to know y'all with everything going on."

Although I believed her, I still questioned the moment. My sisters and I said nothing. We just listened. Some of the other team members began to speak.

"We just don't want you all to think we don't care about y'all, we do."

"We just don't agree with your captain and a lot of the things she does so we don't say anything."

"That doesn't mean we can't have a relationship with y'all, we would just rather have our own separate relationship."

Judging by the way they were speaking I knew they were fishing to see if our captain was talking to us about them. My sisters and

I looked at one another. I spoke up. I explained we wanted a relationship with them, but we were honestly confused on what we could and could not do with them due to the things we would hear from our captain.

"What does she say about us?"

We looked at one another. My sister answered.

"She just tells us we should be careful and watch our back."

My sisters and I agreed with her as we went back and forth with our teammates. We were always going to be honest because there was no reason to lie. The way she treated us was evident along with how she felt about our teammates. I didn't care much for my captain, nor did I know what the meaning of everything was about, but what was very clear after the moment was that our teammates didn't rock with her and she didn't rock with the team. As my sisters and I walked back to our apartment I couldn't wait to get back to hear what everyone had to say. We were all pretty much on the same page, but in the back of my mind, all I could think about was how the team was at odds, but what position did me and my sisters stand in?

I was well past the stage of not caring when it came down to our captain. It was the week of one of the biggest games against our rival school. I heard besides the Bayou Classic this would be one of the most stressful weeks. Practice had just started and no time was wasted. Our captain told my sisters and I to run to the practice field pumping our hands in the air, one at a time, without dropping them. As we stood in a line waiting for the team to come outside we continued to pump our hands in the air. There were still quite a few students outside, making it to their cars. We failed to see initially that our band director was amongst a group on his bike. He was my first band director. I didn't speak much with him, but what I did pick up was he was a no-nonsense type of guy. He was fun, but cared about how we looked and presented ourselves every moment. We whispered amongst each other trying to be sure if it was him. When we were fully aware, we didn't hesitate to stand high on our toes and pump our arms in the air with all the strength we had left. I watched out of the corner of my eye as I noticed him spotting us and then I continued to look forward. He rode his bike up behind us as we all continued doing what we were told. I could feel him standing there staring at us.

"What are y'all doing?"

We all continued and hesitated to answer.

"Stop. What are y'all doing?"

As we turned around to respond to him, I watched as the team walked around the corner. The moment they saw him they turned around. He could see our eyes focused in that direction and he looked. He called them over and looked at us.

"I see y'all doing this again and y'all are going to be in trouble with me."

We all nodded and responded with a yes sir as he directed his attention to the team. He looked over to our captain.

"You all can see me in my office when you get back. Don't ever let me see this foolishness again."

He rode off on his bike. No one said anything to us. All the girls looked at us rolling their eyes and shaking their heads as they walked past us. After we rehearsed the field show a few times, getting formations in order, we immediately headed back to the dance room. As we gathered back with the team in the room we stood in front of them. This time our captain didn't speak. It was my big sister. "Y'all have to be smart. Were y'all trying to get the team in trouble? If we go who are y'all going to have?" She was right. The rule was, we went through our process in private regardless of what it was or how bad it was, but in public we were to present ourselves as if we were official members on the team. I could see she was disappointed. I didn't like seeing her that way, but in my mind it was our Captain's fault. She told us to go outside and do it. Our intentions weren't to get the entire team in trouble, but I saw in that moment when we tried to take matters in our own hands, it backfired.

Practices remained stressful and every moment we received a visitor. My sisters and I decided to get to the dance room early this day only to walk in on the previous captain from the last year's team. All I could do was think back to the day when I ran into her from leaving class. This time she was dressed up, but I still felt the same about her. Her presence and aura were breathtaking. She planted the biggest smile on her face and gave each one of us a hug. We stood in the corner as she went back to what she was doing. I couldn't help but keep a smile on my face because I was genuinely happy for her to be there. She looked in the mirror at us.

"You guys can relax! Don't worry about me, just getting some work done... have you all eaten?"

We looked at each other and slowly shook our heads as she laughed and responded.

"It's okay! I'm only here to help. But it's important that you eat before every practice."

She pulled a chocolate bar out of her purse. She walked over to us, breaking the chocolate piece by piece as she went down the line handing one to each of us. We held on to the chocolate and stood there smiling.

"It's okay you're not going to get in trouble, you can eat it. I won't say anything."

I looked at her, smiled, and bit into the chocolate. I'd never tasted candy that was so nasty, but what was I supposed to do, spit it out in front of her? As she turned her back to finish her work I looked over to my sister who I could see was letting the chocolate sit in the side of her mouth. I looked at her, then looked down at the trash can. It was sitting next to her. She mouthed the trash was empty. I knew if we took the risk of spitting out the chocolate, she would hear. We took the risk anyways. Each time we spit into the trash can, one of us would cough. All you could hear was a loud thud hit the bottom of the can, followed by an exaggerated cough. She looked up from her work. "Good?" We all nodded our heads and smiled pretending to chew.

The team walked in and all filled with joy when they saw her. Her crabs ran to her with big smiles on their faces just like we did and we didn't even know her like they did. As I watched them interact with her I thought about how I wanted nothing more than to feel that way about my captain. But every time I tried to give my heart a chance to feel that way, she interfered. She called us to the middle of the floor as their captain sat amongst them. I looked at her and I looked at my captain. As she made us kick, nothing but harsh words began to flow from her mouth. I tried to tune it out, but with each word my legs dropped. I could tell she was angry, but I didn't care. As we continued to kick, with no number assigned to us, I looked over to their captain through the mirror. Her smile had faded, and she just looked.

"You all can do it! Give me a good twenty! Push through!"

The moment she counted us off, we all began to kick our face. As we got to the last one we stopped and stood there with smiles on our faces. It felt good to hear a sweet voice be so stern yet, easy going. Our captain's mood went from bad to worse.

"Did I tell y'all to stop? Who is your captain?"

We all just stood there. She stood up.

"Break for dinner. Be back in an hour," and she walked out.

The room stayed silent for a moment as my sisters and I walked to our practice bag. Their captain walked over to us.

"I'm very proud of you girls. Continue to work hard. If there is anything you all need I am always here."

As she hugged us and walked off, I followed her and tapped her on the shoulder.

"Can I speak to you please?"

She grabbed my hand and we walked into the restroom. She looked me in the eyes.

"What's going on?"

As I looked back at her I could read exactly who she was. She was honest and gentle. She could see my eyes began to water. She took me into the stall and hugged me as I cried. She grabbed a tissue and wiped my eyes.

"How do I continue to be strong for me and my sisters?"

As she wiped each tear she spoke.

"You continue to understand your purpose. You are here for a reason and I can tell you are so strong. Just do what you have to do so nobody can tell you nothing. Look at me, water off a duck's back."

She hugged me, helped me clean my face, and we walked back into the room. She stayed for most of the practice. The mood felt refreshing, and different; what we needed.

The middle of the season was coming to an end and the end of the season was vastly approaching. I continued my lunch dates with my sister, but I began to be a little more observant. We sat next to each other, but slowly our conversations became less and less. Our crab brothers would sit with us to eat. While laughing with them I would notice my sister watching me then messaging on her phone under the table. I tried not to give it much thought, but as days went on, we seemed to get even more distant. One night we all went back to my apartment from a late practice. She came over to study with my roommate and my other sister took my phone to make a phone call. She gave me her phone while she used mine. I sat on the couch eating my food as I proceeded to text my crab brother whom I had been talking to from her phone. As I got ready to form a new message I couldn't help but see my sister's name. It's almost like it lit up amongst the other names. I sat the phone face down on the couch. My mind went back and forth, "don't open the message, don't open the message." I continued to eat my food in hopes it would be a distraction from what I really wanted to do. I took a deep breath and looked up. "God forgive me for what I am about to do." I picked up the phone and clicked on my sister's name. I scrolled through the messages only to find they had been carrying on a conversation about me.

"Who does she think she is?"

"She walks around in her sports bra trying to look cute like she can't put clothes on."

I scrolled up to a date where I knew I was with her for lunch. My heart dropped as I read the messages.

"Girl, she is annoying me."

I sat and thought how I was going to approach the situation. I called my roommate in the living room and whispered to her what I saw. She put her hand over her mouth as she opened it and started to laugh.

"What are you going to do?"

"I'm going to confront the situation!"

She shrugged her shoulders.

"Well, you gotta do what you gotta do."

She walked back into the room. I got up and immediately walked outside to find my sister.

"Can I talk to you?"

She knew something was wrong by the look on my face and immediately hung up the phone.

"Wassup sis?"

As we walked I took a deep breath.

"I want to start off by saying I apologize. I went through you and our crab sister's messages."

As I spoke I didn't take my eyes away from her face. I wanted to catch every response. She scrunched her eyebrows together, looked down, and looked back at me.

"Oh."

"I'm not upset with you per say for saying anything because you didn't say anything about me, but you didn't stop her either. And if there was a problem you should have come to me."

She responded that she agreed and asked what I was going to do about the situation.

"I'm about to say something. I just wanted to apologize to you first but still address it because it was your phone."

She followed me into the apartment as I walked into my roommate's room.

"Can y'all pause with that really quickly?"

My sister started the conversation by letting her know I saw the messages in her phone and saw what she said. She looked over to me. I looked back to her.

"Why would you do that? It's been me and you for a while and this whole time you've been feeling a way."

No one spoke as she began to justify her actions. I kept my eyes on her and hardly blinked. As I looked at her she began to cry. My roommate started to console her. She apologized for what took place. I looked around the room and back to her.

"I can't rock with you like that right now. I'll make nice for the team, but I have nothing else to say to you."

She looked up.

"I respect that."

I walked into my room, shut the door, and began to analyze everything from thus far. Who was I able to trust? I didn't want to be mad, but I knew in my mind the one thing we had was each other, and that was slowly drifting away. The next morning I woke up to a long message from my sister apologizing again for everything. I laid there and read it twice. I forgave her, thinking that a little time of silence between us would resolve the issue and everything could go back to normal. Instead of me and my sister using the silence to help mend our relationship, it only made it worse. We argued about everything and could never find a common ground.

This day practice was looking to get out earlier than normal. Our captain told us we needed to present a skit to the team before we were dismissed. As my sisters and I huddled in a circle, we went back and forth about ideas. When I came up with an idea, my sister would turn it down. She came up with an idea and I wanted to make changes. She didn't like that. I was surprised the team didn't hear us arguing. My roommate laughed as we went back and forth. "Okay y'all, chill out." Surprisingly the skit turned out to be rather funny to the team despite me and my sister arguing for half the time it took us to get an idea together. After practice we road back to our apartment in silence. We all sat in the living room while my roommate fixed her food in the kitchen. I decided to say something. "What is the problem?" As my crab sister explained how she felt, I responded and laughed in a sarcastic tone. My roommate chimed in and laughed with me, making a joke of the situation. My sister got up and left out of the apartment. My roommate shrugged her shoulders and continued to make her food. Our other sister sat on the couch with her head down looking at her phone. While she waited for her ride I sat across from her.

"What is really going on?"

She looked up at me.

"Y'all know she's sensitive and y'all think it's funny. It's not."

I looked at my roommate who was still laughing silently behind my sister with a smirk on her face as she ate her food. I looked back to my sister and decided to try and feel where she was coming from as she continued to talk.

"I know y'all aren't on the best of terms but this ain't cool."

I responded out of defense.

"I try, but everything I do she has a problem with it."

"Well try harder. You obviously are more forward than she is, so just try to understand things from her position."

She got up and walked out. I sat down and looked toward the ground.

"Should I apologize?"

My roommate laughed. "For what, they'll get over it." shrugged her shoulders, and walked into her room.

A few days went by and the situation stayed on my mind. I knew what I needed to do. I messaged my sister apologizing for how things went down. I told her I should have responded to her better. I didn't want to cause her to storm out, but I had to grow an understanding for myself. She immediately responded that she forgave me. We decided to meet up later that day. I asked her how she truly felt. As we talked I listened and I was glad I did. "I just feel as though everyone else cares more than you. That night everyone checked on me but you." As she continued to talk my mind could only focus on that part. I knew I cared so much. I couldn't get it out of my mind. But what instantly concerned me was that my roommate, the one I called my best friend led me to feel like it wasn't a big deal but made a decision that same night to reach out and didn't say anything to me.

Chapter 7
Beyond What Can Be Controlled

We were close to three weeks until the end of the season and my relationship with my sisters was not the same, but it had gotten to a better place. As we sat in the apartment we discussed what we were going to do about our captain. She had been continuously calling us out of our names and it needed to stop. I knew that a person would go as far as you allowed them, and we had had enough. We decided to come up with a plan that would end her thinking that it was okay. The next day we prepared for practice. We never knew how it was going to go, all we knew is to expect the unexpected. As practice time pushed later and later we wrapped up dancing and stood in the corner. We knew what was next. We kicked. We planked. I sat in my plank, sliding in my sweat as it hit the floor. She yelled kick. We got up and began to kick again. As the number rose, our legs got lower from exhaustion. She yelled.

"What number?"

My sister responded. "1,416."

My legs came maybe six inches from the floor as I clapped my hands under my legs. Sweat dropped from my face and my hands. She walked in front of us.

"Get your kicks up!"

All of our kicks stayed the same. She walked up to me.

"Get them up."

I continued to kick the same. She stepped to the side of me as I kicked and she looked in my face.

"Bitch!"

I stopped kicking, got off my toes, and stood there. I looked at my sisters in the mirror and they stopped kicking as well. I looked as the team looked down into their phones. Our captain stepped back.

"Kick!"

None of us moved.

"Why did y'all stop?"

No one answered. She yelled again.

"That was a question!"

I continued to look forward as I answered, "Because you got our names wrong."

"Excuse me?"

This time I looked her in her eyes.

"Our names aren't bitch."

She tilted her head down and raised her eyebrows.

"I know that and I don't care."

I looked at her and walked out. That part wasn't the plan, but I knew I needed to step out because I could feel myself heading toward something I would regret. I walked outside to gather myself. My big sister and her little sister came outside behind me.

"We're not mad at you for what you did, but you have to calm down and go back in there."

I didn't care if anyone was mad at me or not, I didn't need anyone's approval to make the decision I did. But I listened because they were my big sisters and I felt they meant well.

"She's still your captain. Regardless of how you feel, you still have to respect her."

I looked at them both.

"You have to give respect to get it."

They didn't say anything.

As we walked back inside I stood with my sisters who hadn't moved. My captain sat down and refused to look at us but still spoke. "Go stand in your corner. I'm done with y'all...and don't bother standing on your toes because you're not my crabs anymore." We walked to our corner and continued to stand on our toes with smiles on our faces. The room grew silent. During the silence our drum major walked in. We were close to him because he always made sure we were okay. He always seemed to help make our punishments lighter with his mood, but this time he was late. As he walked over to us, he laughed and smiled.

"What up my crabby patties!"

Our captain looked up.

"Don't speak to them."

He looked back to us and as soon as we all gave him that look, he knew. He snuck a low five from all of us and tip toed out of the room. She got up to dismiss the practice when her bracelet popped. Beads flew everywhere. No one moved as she walked around the room picking up beads one by one. We watched her as she walked around the room looking sad. My sister reached for the broom to help sweep them up, but I had no intentions on moving. I decided to help anyways. She looked back towards us and said, "don't help me!" She didn't have to tell me twice. As we lined back up in the corner she called for prayer. As they formed the circle she spoke but looked away from us. "Y'all can pray over there." My sisters and I grabbed hands, prayed amongst ourselves, grabbed our things, and left.

The next day all I could think about was how practice was going to be from that moment on. We had stopped kicking before, but I knew this time was different. Although Bayou Classic was a few weeks away she made it feel like we had an eternity to go. As I walked back to my apartment from class a message notification popped on my screen from our captain. It read to meet her in the dance room an hour before practice started. We all met in our apartment. We agreed no matter what happened we would continue to stick together. As we walked in the room she sat in a chair by the door. We began to walk to our corner to stand at attention and she called for us to sit in front of her. She looked at us.

"What is the problem?"

My sisters and I looked at each other. We were all on the same page. I spoke up.

"It's just the way you speak to us."

She continued to justify with an attitude as she responded.

"This is the way it is, every captain does it!"

"Yes, but you don't have to do that" I responded as I watched her attitude calm. I continued to speak.

"We want to have a good relationship with you and have your back, but how can we do that if we feel like you genuinely don't care about us."

I could see her eyes begin to water as my sisters chimed in. Everyone spoke from their heart and said what was concerning them. As each person spoke up, I could feel her demeanor get softer and softer. Once she listened to us she wiped her eyes.

"I promise y'all I will work on it if y'all promise me you will give me a chance."

We all looked at each other, looked at her, and smiled. We got up and rushed to give her a hug. It felt good. It felt like a breakthrough. We could only hope things would really get better.

It had only been a few days and our relationship with her had improved. Practices were better and she even made it a part of her plans to be there for us outside of practice. The day came for her pageant competition. She allowed us to go so we could support her. We walked in and sat with the team. Each time she walked on stage my sisters and I went crazy. I didn't know about my sisters, but I was honestly happy to start growing a better relationship with her. As we watched her walk across the stage we admired her beauty and her body. She looked amazing. It was time for her solo. She was performing a dance piece. We just knew she was going to kill it. As she started to move across the stage it was breathtaking. She was hitting every move and executing her technique flawlessly. As the climax rose in her music she kicked her leg and fell to the floor. I didn't move. I was under the impression she was performing until we all heard her scream. The music stopped. It seemed as though the whole room went numb. My sisters and I wasted no time. We jumped over chairs and ran through the crowd. My roommate took one big leap and hopped on stage. My other sisters and I ran up the stairs to her. Her boyfriend had already made it to her and was carrying her down. As we all walked outside he laid her on the back of his truck as she cried. I looked down to see her knee sitting to the side of her leg. My sisters and I stood in front of her with tears running down our faces. She looked over to us. "I'm going to be okay. Y'all hold it down." Once the ambulance came to pick her up my sisters and I took off to the car to follow her. My big sister messaged us letting us know what hospital she would be taken to. As we drove to the hospital we all talked at once.

"We were just getting close to her."

"How could this happen?"

"What does this mean for the team?"

As we pulled up to the hospital we got out in hopes to find her and sit with her, only to be informed she was already discharged.

Things were winding down and my big sister had taken over practice to a certain degree. She was leading the dances, but my captain was still present for the majority of the practices making sure we were still receiving our process. At any other time I would've loved this, but I felt the complete opposite. After all she did I kept wondering why I wanted her to be okay. I started to understand I wanted these last few weeks with her to feel like we could make up for the time we lost. It just seemed as though things went from bad to just not knowing anymore. Things continued to go as normal amongst my sisters and I outside of practice. For a while, instead of being with my sister, I began to grow stronger relationships with my crab brothers. They spent so much time at our apartment. My sisters and I formed a great bond with them.

I had two brothers whom I was very close with. One was the guy I started talking to in the beginning and the other was the guy my sister told me she had a crush on in the beginning. We talked all the time. He didn't really talk much about my sister to me, but I knew they spoke. We were preparing for the last home game before Bayou Classic. The majority of our crab brothers came over to help us to finish glittering the shoes. I finished my pair and decided to go to my room. As I laid in my bed half asleep my crab brother walked in the room. I wasn't fully aware of the time, but I knew it was late. He came over to the bed and started to tickle me.

"Wake up! Everybody asking where you are."

"Leave me alone! I'm tired."

He stood in front of me as I turned over. As he walked to the door, he turned back around.

"You cool with me staying over? I don't feel like walking back to my room."

I lifted my head.

"What's wrong with your legs?"

He laughed and asked again.

"Fine, I don't care."

He closed the door and walked back to join everyone else in the living room. He always came over so we could watch movies and sleep before practice, but he had never stayed the night. Some time went by. I knew he was walking in when the light from the bathroom came through the door. I looked up, threw him a pillow, and closed my eyes. He crawled over next to me and we laid back-to-back. Hours went by. I tossed and turned. I turned to the other side facing his back. A few minutes later, he turned around. As I laid there with my eyes closed I could feel his lips touch mine. It lasted no more than a few seconds before I turned over and we laid back-to-back for the rest of the night. Once I woke up I turned over to find him already gone. I sat on the edge of my bed and looked towards the door to see if the light from the bathroom was shining through. I knew my roommate was getting ready for class. I opened the door and stared at her. She turned around.

"Girl, what?"

I hesitated.

"I think my crab brother and I kissed."

I was fully aware of what took place that night. I only said think because I was on the fence for a while on who I could really trust. She dropped her mouth, gasped, and began to laugh. I watched her.

"Should I tell my sister?"

That was the first thing on my mind. I knew she liked him. Because we already had our differences, I just knew she wasn't going to see the situation for what it really was. My roommate shrugged her shoulders and continued her makeup as she responded.

"Why would you tell her? They're not together."

I looked at her. Everything in me wanted to tell my sister. As I walked back in my room, shut my door, and sat on my bed, I replayed the moment in my mind. I spent minutes trying to justify what took place. "It was just a kiss, it was just a kiss," but all I could feel was that I betrayed my sister. I began to regret telling my roommate. I was starting to feel like I made a mistake in who I trusted. I knew my other sister had grown close with her, but why did I feel like I would have gotten a better answer from her?

It was now the week of Bayou Classic. The week I was waiting for finally came. I knew the goal was to get a crab name. I was told there would be an official night experience before receiving it, but I didn't know what that moment would consist of. Friday finally came. My sisters and I ran back and forth from the bus to the room making sure we left nothing we would need for the weekend. Once we made it, everything started to move fast. As we pulled up to the hotel we had very little time to put our things down in our room and make it back downstairs to practice. This was the day of the battle of the bands. As we wrapped up practicing the field show performance, we quickly headed back on the bus in hopes we would have enough time to get dressed and make sure the team had everything they needed. As we rode back to the hotel I looked out the window to the streets of New Orleans seeing all the people dressed in our school colors. The buses rode by and the people waved and cheered. I felt so important and special. Not only did I belong to the greatest HBCU, but I was also a part of the best band in the land.

I started to think about everything, starting with the first moment I heard about the school. It made me proud to be a part. With everything moving so quickly and having to always be aware as a crab, I had very little capacity for emotional moments. The small drift away never lasted long. As my sisters and I rushed in the room I quickly picked up my makeup bag and sat down in the chair in front of the mirror. As I began to sort through my bag, organizing my makeup to begin, my sister stepped beside me.

"I already had my stuff here."

I continued to do my makeup not paying her much mind.

I responded, "Okay, you can still stand here."

As she began to tell me to move, I could feel her energy. I knew everyone's emotions were high, but my intentions for the day was not to argue over a spot. As she began to pull out her things she proceeded to push the chair over and stand in front of me. I could feel my defense kicking in. I placed my foot on the floor to hold the chair steady. I looked up at her.

"Don't play with me."

She continued to rummage through her things as she responded, "Don't play with me."

My roommate and my other sister stood in the bathroom doing their makeup looking at us through the mirror. My roommate stuck her head out, egging on the situation as she laughed. "Bet you won't do nothin'." As she continued to yell out words that influenced the moment I could feel both of our adrenalines rising. My other sister watched in silence. She never really said much unless she felt she had to. But surprisingly for the first time, she wasn't the one I was into it with. As I continued my makeup my sister inched closer and closer to me pushing her body in front of mine. Because my emotions were rising I was waiting for just one reason to retaliate. I continued to look in the mirror as I addressed her.

"If you touch me," followed by a small sarcastic snicker.

She responded as her elbow inched in front of my face.

"Okay, and then what?"

I stopped what I was doing but kept the same position. As she moved closer in front of me, her elbow pushed past my shoulder. I pushed the seat back as I jumped up and pushed the palm of my hand through her chest. Everything began to move in slow motion in my mind. I could see her reaching trying to get a hit in but she fell backwards into her suitcase and her back hit the wall. She quickly got up and charged towards me. I hadn't moved. As I watched her hand move towards me, I grabbed it. Before we could continue my roommate and sister came running over pulling us away and stepping in between. As I grabbed my things and walked in the restroom with my roommate I thought, this is not what I expected my weekend to be like. This was our last few moments as crabs together and because of what just took place, I knew it would be a memory, but I didn't want it to be the last moment.

The time came closer to the performance so we gathered our things and sat down on our beds. My sister spoke up as she mediated the conversation. "Look, y'all need to talk. We can't go out there like this." Despite our differences I appreciated her for stepping in to help resolve the issue. I looked at my sister. We were both strong-willed, straight forward, and aggressive if we needed to be, but I knew I didn't want our relationship to end over something like this. "I'm sorry for how I went about handling the situation. I could have gone about it another way. These are our last few moments together and I want them to be good." As I spoke she looked up at me. I could tell she was still upset, but we both knew the things we had to do were more important than what we were going through at the time. She apologized, said her piece, and we gathered our things to head out for our performance.

We lined up in the holding area waiting to march in. My sisters and I huddled together in silence. All that went through my mind was the hope of not messing up. As the band director yelled for everyone to get in line, I looked over to my captain as she stood to the side on her crutches, nodding her head and smiling. The base from the drums hit and as the drum major sounded off. I could feel every vibration down my body. I looked to my sister and smiled. I didn't care about anything but that moment. As we strutted in, all I could see was lights in a dark room. The announcer introduced us as we marched in and the roars of the crowd took over. I had never been the spotlight in a room filled with that many people. With each song playing I could feel myself giving it my all. I felt like a completely different dancer. I felt stronger, more passionate, and beautiful as ever. As the battle started to end, the band played a song and we danced around each other, away from our assigned spots. My sisters and I formed a small circle amongst ourselves hugging and laughing. Nothing else mattered. As we lined up to march out, a lady walked up to me. She introduced herself as a former dancer from the 90s. "I just needed to tell you that you are fierce lil' mama. I couldn't take my eyes off you and the other short girl." I knew she was talking about my teammate who so happened to be one of my big sisters as well. It felt good to know that despite being next to some amazing dancers, someone noticed me. It made it easier to understand what my sponsor had told me.

Once we made it back to the hotel my sisters and I didn't have much time to celebrate. Our captain messaged us telling us to be ready at a certain time. We knew something was about to happen, but did not know what. We decided to come up with a plan. We called our crab brothers to the room and told them to knock on our door and ask for something a few minutes after our captain walked in. As we sat on our bed in anticipation, she knocked on the door. We said a quick prayer and let her in. One by one her crab sisters walked in behind her, barely looking us in the eye. All four of them sat on our beds as she instructed us to stand at attention. I stood there smiling and shaking. About ten minutes went by and there was a knock at the door. I laughed silently through my teeth. Our captain got up to answer it. She cracked it slightly, enough where I could lean back and see which crab brother it was. I listened closely as he spoke to her. "Uhhh, I just came to get some lotion." She informed him we were busy and shut the door in his face. I knew she knew something was going on because as she passed us, she squinted her eyes and watched us suspiciously. As she sat on the bed her and her sisters began to carry on a conversation amongst themselves. "Make us laugh," she said during her girl talk.

My sisters and I huddled together as we came up with our skit. We were two minutes in and no one laughed yet. They sat staring and I only hoped we could get another knock. The moment I thought it, it happened. She rolled her eyes, got up, and answered the door.

As she opened the door she aggressively said, "What?"

I could see my crab brother out the corner of my eye while I listened to him as he stammered.

"Uhh, is my crab sisters in there?"

I clinched my teeth and held my breath so I wouldn't laugh.

She shut the door and looked over to us, "Get in your splits."

As I slowly crouched down to slide in my split our crab brothers wasted no time and there was another knock at the door. Our captain's sisters began to laugh.

"What is going on?" As they looked at one another and then us sarcastically. This time our captain didn't move.

I could feel her speaking to my soul as she said, "Tell them if they come to this door one more time y'all will be here all night."

I watched as my sister opened the door to our crab brother. Before he could get out a word she opened her eyes real big and we all looked over and shook our heads quickly. As we each sat in our split longer and longer, our captain and her sisters continued to talk as if we weren't there. Then the room went silent. My body filled with anxiety as I waited for her to speak. "Y'all can get up." As I pulled on each limb to move as I wanted it to, I finally stood there after being stuck for some time. Once she finished taking us through a few more things we needed to do we stood there, eyes filled with tears as she told us to walk into the restroom, close the door and turn the water all the way to hot. We were so tired we didn't even speak. Not to mention the steam from the water making the small restroom we were packed in extremely hot. Minutes went by and our phones went off. She messaged us to come out. As we slowly walked out of the restroom the room was empty. We looked around and looked at each other. I had no clue what had happened. I was too tired to find out. I prepared my things for the next day and went to bed.

It appears the night went by so quickly. We marched in the parade that morning and before I knew it, it was time to prepare for the moment I had been waiting for, Bayou Classic. As we got off the bus and walked into the stadium for practice, my eyes watered. I knew I had been in this same place the night before, but I hadn't seen it in light; in its rare form. It was so big

157

and beautiful. I knew we were there to rehearse, but all I could do was admire the moment my journey brought me to. I looked over to the scoreboard, only imagining it reading the time 0:00. Then I would officially be one of them.

It was finally time for the game to begin. As we made it to the stands, I sat up and smiled. Everything about the moment was perfect. After performing our field show I was relieved it went so well, but also that the hardest part was finally over. We danced on the sideline and I looked over to my captain on her crutches yelling and cheering for us with a smile on her face. I could only try to imagine how she really felt so I wanted to make her proud. It was the last few minutes of the game. Our team wasn't winning but I didn't care. I continued to look towards the clock as tears filled my eyes. "5, 4, 3, 2,1." The moment I saw the three numbers I'd been waiting for, my tears began to fall: 0:00. I waited for my captain to look over as my sisters and I rushed down the steps to give her a hug. But what mattered to me most was my sisters. As we hugged and cried in our circle, nothing mattered - not the flaws, the arguments, the bad days, nothing. All that mattered is that we did it. I did it. I finally got to experience a glimpse of what God was doing for me.

Chapter 8
Evidently Understood, Silently Misunderstood

The spring of 2017 finally came. My process was over and I was officially a dance girl. I honestly felt like a new woman. I could feel the change in me. As far as the things I did and the relationships, some things changed, and other things remained the same or slowly dwindled away. My captain and I began to form a stronger relationship. I wouldn't say we were close, but it seemed as though we unconsciously were working towards it. My sisters and I still communicated, but did our own thing. The team was under the direction of my big sister for the few performances we did have. Despite coming to an understanding that the team didn't care much for my captain, I began to figure her out for myself. I wanted to use the time I had to make up for time we lost during the season. I longed to feel just an ounce of what it felt like to have so much love for your own captain. Despite how they felt about her, I wanted it to be understood I needed my own judgement. It never dawned on me I would grow close to her seeing everything taking place in the past, but it was evident she gravitated to me and I had no plans of pushing her away.

The spring semester began and besides for practices, I spent a lot of time in the gym with my captain and my roommate. I wish I could say I was close with the team, but I wasn't. I wanted to be. I had a very good relationship with my big sister until things began to take a turn. It was a Saturday. My roommate left for the weekend leaving me the apartment to myself. I spent so much time focused on the team during the last semester, I didn't make much time for male companionship, however I wanted it. It wasn't something that stayed on my mind, but if it presented itself I wouldn't turn it away. While I was preparing my breakfast I received a message from my captain of a screenshot from a friend of hers who confided in her about being interested in me. I wasn't new to dating, but I knew I wasn't going to accept just anyone. I was interested but my response to her was, "Do men even care to approach women to their face anymore?" She laughed but I knew she was growing to understand who I was and I wouldn't settle for anything less.

A few days went by and I was getting ready to leave my last class of the day. As I gathered my things my phone started to ring. It was my captain.

"Hey, can you meet me out front? There is someone I want you to meet."

I already had a feeling of who it was. As I walked outside, I was right. She was gone, but I approached a guy sitting on his car waiting for me to walk out. He was handsome, and as much as I wanted to smile, I kept my face straight. I walked up to him.

"So, you set this up huh?"

He laughed and smiled as he reached for a handshake and introduced himself. As we exchanged words he came with the question I expected.

"So, can I have your number?"

"That depends. I'm going to ask you three questions. You can have my number depending on your answers."

He stood up smiling, walked a little closer, looked down to me, and said, "Okay, go."

As I asked each question, I listened to his answers, but paid attention more to how he responded to each question.

"Okay then, last question. What is your relationship with God?"

He paused, looked down, then back at me. "I do believe in God, but to be honest, my relationship with Him could be a lot better."

We stood there, looking one another in the eyes, and when he smiled, I smiled.

I continued to look into his eyes as I said, "So are you going to take my number down or no?"

He laughed pulling his phone out as we talked a little more. From there on we talked every day and went on dates. I really began to like him. Despite small college problems or drama, he was the perfect gentleman to me. I had no real problems and I could feel myself falling, but I tried to hide it.

The weekend came. Saturdays were my day. I never knew exactly what it would bring, but I prepared myself every time the day was present. My crab sisters and I decided we would go to the club that night, so they all met at our apartment to get ready. As we walked through the crowd to be let in, I spotted the guy I'd been talking to. Even though we talked all day every day, I didn't know we would be at the same location. I walked up to him, gave him a hug, exchanged small conversation, and walked back with my sisters. As we entered the party, we congregated with the other dancers who stood in their reserved section in the club. I was the type who normally held the wall to simply look cute and remain cute, but surprisingly I made my way to the dance floor with my sisters. After dancing for a while I walked back to where the other dancers stood. The guy I'd been seeing met up with me and we stood by the bar talking. Out of the corner of my eye I could see my big sister and her sisters watching me, but I didn't think anything of it. As we continued our conversation, my drum major walked up and stood in front of my guy. "Crabby patty! You look good!" We talked, he looked my guy up and down, and walked off. Minutes later, one of my big sister's crab sisters walked up. She looked towards my guy. "How dare you? You really gon' do that?" Rolling her neck, as she stared him down. He laughed. I looked at them with suspicion trying to read into what was really going on. She looked at me and walked away. I looked to him, smiling trying not to make anything much of an issue.

"What was that about?"

"Oh nothing, she just used to talk to my homeboy, but we have an understanding."

I tried not to think so much about it and as I directed to change the conversation, in the middle of my sentence, another sister walked up, wrapped her arm around my neck, and proceeded to direct me to their circle.

"Don't talk to him. He's no good."

I looked around the circle. Yes, they were my dance sisters, but simply by association. I had no personal relationship with them, nor did I know them personally. Besides being a part of the same organization, the only one I had a true relationship with was my big sister and what I did know was he wasn't her man.

"What did he say to you?"

"He said you talked to his homeboy."

They all began to laugh.

"See, he's already lying to you. He used to talk to our sister. Now he is in her face talking to you knowing we're all dance sisters."

I didn't say much because I was trying to process what the real issue was. I looked over to my big sister as she looked at me.

"Don't do it."

As they kept trying to convince me of why I was better off without him, I walked away. I needed to find the root of the problem. Him. I walked back to the bar where he stood. I tilted my head to the side, and squinched my eyes.

"Did you lie to me?"

He looked at me, directing we go find a spot where there were less people. As we sat I looked him in his eye again.

"Did. You lie to me?"

As he began to explain himself, I tuned everything out, the music, the noise, even him. I looked into his eyes and tried to convince myself to leave him alone, but also convincing myself of why I should stay. Dismissing the fact that bottom line he lied when he didn't have to, I still tried to justify the situation based on it being small and maybe he did it to protect my feelings. I knew what was right, but I leaned more towards making the decision based on how I felt, and the truth was, I liked him. A lot. In the midst of him talking, I got up and walked away. He continued to call after me but I ignored it to find my sisters.

I was silent the whole ride home. Once we made it everyone got out the car except me. I sat there, staring into the front window as it began to fog up. Moments later he pulled up and parked behind me. As he walked up my sister turned around to look at him. "If you mess with her, we will have a problem." Despite the way I was feeling, hearing her say that made me smile on the inside, especially because we were at odds for quite some time so I wasn't sure if she cared about me like that. He got in the car and looked at me. "Talk to me please." I felt one tear fall down my face and I hated myself for it. I was just an emotional person, but I knew he would take it as something different. Despite it being exactly what I believed he was thinking, I wasn't ready for him to know. He reached his hand over, laid it on my knee and said, "I care about you so much. I promise I won't lie to you again."

The next day after we had breakfast together, my big sister asked if she could come by. I figured she wanted to talk about the night before, but to my surprise that wasn't her concern. We sat in the living room and she began to speak. "I don't know if you all are aware, but a few things are going on right now. The band director is looking into the team for something your captain said to him. You and your sisters aren't in trouble, but because you know what happened and you're the more vocal one, I just wanted to make sure you all were on the same page with us." I knew she was referring to an incident that took place in the stands at a home game last season when no one got up to dance except for my captain. But my concern was from the night before so I chose to bring it up. I let her know I decided to continue talking to him. I went on to explain it wasn't to hurt her sister but I didn't know her sister like that. If my relationship with him wasn't meant, I would find out on my own. She agreed that was my decision and she could only respect it. She walked out and that's when I knew our relationship would begin to change.

School still continued to move as normal and I kept a regular routine for myself. I hadn't been talking to the other team members or my big sister. If I wasn't with my roommate, I was with my boyfriend or my captain. I spent the majority of my time in my room, doing school work of course or just enjoying time to myself. I had just made it back to my room after a long day of classes and engaging a little on the school yard so all I was looking forward to doing was laying in my bed, popping some popcorn, cutting a few slices of cheese, and watching a good movie. As I began to get myself situated I received a call from my roommate's mom. Although her daughter and I were close, this was the first time I received a personal call from her. Nevertheless, I saw her as a second mom, so I didn't mind.

"Hey mom, what's going on?"

"I was just calling to talk to you and check in."

I stood up.

"Did you want to speak to your daughter too?"

As I proceeded to walk to my roommate's room I stopped as her mother began to speak again.

"I just wanted to talk to you and tell you how proud I am of you and the young lady you are. I'm so glad you and my daughter are friends because she needs someone like you around and I can see a difference in her. I just want you to know we are grateful for you."

It made me feel good for the moment, but although it felt good to hear those words, my roommate seemed the same to me. I chose not to give it much thought and simply responded out of love for them being like a second family.

Throughout the time I spent alone, I thought a lot about my first season as a dancer, everything that took place and everything I learned. I began to confide in two alumni dancers who I encountered my first year on the team; one who approached me during the beginning of the season about my attitude, and the other who approached me at the end of my season about how fierce she thought I was. They were my mentors and I believed I could trust them. I spent a lot of time talking to them because they were honest with me and they had a lot of knowledge when it came down to being a dancer and just being a part of an organization in general. They did a lot of the talking. I did a lot of both listening and talking. Every moment we spoke they would always remind me that one day I would lead the team. I would always brush the notion off. In my mind I knew I had the potential, but it was far from my time. We were brought up by our captain and the team to understand seniority and so that's what I went by. They would constantly remind me that when its meant, it's meant. Senior or not, a true leader is always ready and there is no set time. I tried not to focus so much on the position, but rather the things I could do to become a better member on the team. I knew my big sister was next in line to become captain and I planned to learn as much as I could from her. I could sense that from time to time my mentors would hold back some of their true feelings about a lot of things they wanted to say. I learned at a young age that sometimes adults don't tell you everything because they know when the right time is and when it isn't so I didn't push it. I was slowly growing a close relationship with them and I wanted it to work out how it was meant. So I listened and gathered the knowledge and wisdom I could.

Along with my mentors I would call my sponsor for everything. I loved to pick her brain on things based on life issues and things I needed advice on. We started to get closer and closer and she asked me if I wanted to stay with her for the weekend of a special event she was hosting. I was excited because I loved being around her. Her spirit was always great and I felt like I could trust her. As we drove a few hours to her home I mainly talked about my boyfriend, getting her advice on relationships, and managing school in general. As the conversation died down she began to ask me about the team. "How did you feel about your first year overall?" I expressed to her some of my experiences outside of the room, as well as my concern with some things in the room, along with things I learned. She listened and then asked, "Who do you think would make a good captain?" I sat back in my seat and with no hesitation, my big sister was my answer. I explained to her why and when I finished everything was silent. I looked over to her from the side of my eye trying to catch her facial expressions, but she always wore a smile on her face so it was hard to tell what she was thinking. I looked out the window, still waiting on her response. I decided to initiate an answer.

"What do you think?"

"I think that the biggest thing I want you to learn if you make the team again, is paying attention to everyone, and not just what people show you on the surface. You have so much potential and you need to be able to understand who everyone is that you encounter, and make sound decisions. Don't speak on anyone, just learn how to sit back and truly observe. And when I say observe, I don't mean just watch physically. Analyze responses and behavior."

Still trying to process everything as far as truly understanding everything she meant, I looked over to her and smiled, "I can do that."

The weekend with her was perfect. No dance, no boys, just girl time and I enjoyed every moment.

It was the morning I was due to leave. I woke up feeling refreshed and happy overall that I took the trip. As I packed my things I said my goodbyes and I got on the road. As much as I enjoyed myself and being amongst her company, I was ready to get back to my own space. I was about two hours out and I received a phone call from my big sister.

"Hey, you busy? My crab sister needs you to call her at 9:13."

I formed a small relationship with her crab sister due to my closeness to my big sister. She also played a big role in the sorority I planned on joining one day so I was anxious about this phone call. Being under the impression it had everything to do with the sorority, I asked my big sister if there was anything I needed to know or do.

"You're going to be just fine, just make sure you call her on time."

As I hung up the phone all I could think about was what was going to happen. I thought about calling my mom since she was a part of the same organization, but I pondered between the thought of what type of call this was. Would I have to do something? Know anything? Be at a certain place? So many questions filled my mind. It was about an hour away from the time to call her. I sped up in hopes I would make it home in time enough to review history on this particular organization. As I pulled in front of my apartment I sat outside briefly, imagining every possible situation that could take place. Because I had just finished going through a process, I didn't look past anything because I had grown to realize a lot was possible. Once I made it to my room I quickly put my things down, took out my laptop, and pulled up all the information I could find about the sorority. Five minutes before the time hit, my big sister called me again.

"You good? Just reminding you to call for 9:13. You'll be just fine."

I stood in the middle of my room staring at the time on my phone. The minute the time changed I called. My heart was beating fast, but the moment I heard her voice, it beat even faster.

"Hey, you busy? I just want to talk to you for a minute."

I pulled my laptop closer to me, preparing myself to spit out every ounce of information I saw.

"Do you have a relationship with your captain?"

"Yes, I do."

"What is the relationship?"

I paused, trying to think ahead to where the conversation was going.

"It's good. We're not close like that, but I guess we're growing into it." Hesitating through my answer out of fear I was going to say the wrong thing.

"Well, I know how she treated you all during the season and that wasn't a good look. I also know you want to be a part of this organization. She is not your friend. She is not someone you want to be around."

I stopped responding at this point and just listened. When she finished I hung up and sat down on the bed. A few minutes later my big sister called me.

"How did it go?"

"It went fine. I guess. She told me I shouldn't communicate with my captain."

"Well, then it's probably for the best, but you decide."

The moment I hung up I laid back in my bed. I battled whether I should call my captain or listen to what they told me. Part of me felt as though yes, my captain did do hurtful things to me, but she had the chance to make them right and she was striving to do it. The other part of me thought about my want for being a part of this new organization. I mainly questioned why it was done the way it was. A few weeks went by and I hadn't heard from my big sister or her sister. I also chose to isolate myself from my captain, partially because I did allow what they told me to take over how I truly felt.

It was now a few weeks left 'til school was over. My mentor gave me a call asking if I wanted to judge an audition for a high school with her. I was always excited to judge because it made me feel important when it came to dance. As I walked into the building I saw the girl who I made the call to and the rest of her crab sisters minus my big sister. They simply looked at me as I waved. I turned the corner and saw my captain standing by the judges table looking at her phone. I smiled and walked to sit on the bleachers, not saying anything. She walked up to me and briefly spoke, but I left the conversation very light. Inside, I knew I was wrong. I knew she respected me as a person who was honest, but the way I saw it, I was caught between telling her as a friend and telling her as a snitch. Moments later my mentor walked in, hugged both of us as we sat down at the judges table with her sitting between my captain and I. I knew she noticed we weren't speaking but she didn't say anything. As we judged, the girls whom were auditioning took a break. Out of the corner of my eye I could see my big sister walking in. We caught eyes and I called out her name motioning for her to come over. She looked over to me, simply waved and proceeded to greet her sisters, never coming over to where we were. My mentor turned to me and began to raise her voice. "I don't want to see you do that ever again. You look dumb calling after her and she's not worried about you! That girl is making it very clear to you that you are not important to her like that. She is using you and you're sitting over here not speaking to your captain for her? I've told you before, pay attention to the people who strive to be your friend and those who pretend to be one. And you of all people are destined for greater than them so don't stoop to their level." I knew just about everyone sitting in that room could hear her and she didn't care. I had nothing to say back. I knew she was right in so many ways. I looked over to my captain who looked down, as I apologized to her. She accepted. I got up to leave passing by my big sister and her sisters. I decided to speak simply because I was passing by, but I definitely didn't want to after what happened. They just looked as I walked out.

As I made my way back onto campus I received a message from my big sister.

"Hey, I hate I didn't get a chance to come up to you when you called me. I had something to get to."

"It's cool."

"I heard your mentor talking but I didn't know if she was trying to talk to me. Was everything okay? What did she say?"

All I could think in my mind was that once again she was proving what my mentor said to me. I read the message a few times, thinking on how I would respond.

"She was just making me aware of some things, but if you would like, I can see if she can call you if there's a concern."

"Oh no don't worry about it. Just wanted to make sure everything was okay."

I didn't respond. I was again stuck in a position of what really was right. How was I supposed to handle this? Especially with someone I looked up to. I knew I didn't want to accept the fact that maybe this was all I was to her.

School came to an end and summer was finally here. My roommate and I were due to move into our new apartment off campus in a few weeks so I stayed with my boyfriend for the time being. Despite the school year just ending, summer was moving by quickly and auditions were vastly approaching. We eventually got settled into our new apartment and things continued to go as normal. Because my captain and I began to get closer as the days went by, we spent a lot of time with each other. I invited her by to hang out and talk, with no specific reason, just quality time. We grew to trust each other and we spent a lot of time venting to one another about many things. As we talked, we laughed and went back and forth.

During our conversation she said, "I think I want to come back one last year."

"I'm sorry, what?"

She caught me of guard. She was good for being random with me. I was used to it, but not news like this. She confided in me about how she felt, and although I had personally never seen it done before, I could only support her as a friend, with small concerns.

"What about my big sister? How do you think she's going to feel?"

"This has nothing to do with her. I don't want to purposely take anything away from her. This decision is for me."

I understood that. Despite my big sister being in the back of my mind, I wanted my captain to know that as her friend and her baby, I had her back. I looked down at her knee.

"What are you going to do about your injury? Do you think you'll be ready in time for auditions?"

"I'mma get ready!"

I loved that about her. When she set her mind to do something, she strived to achieve it. I was the same way so it was naturally in me to believe her. We came to an understanding that we wouldn't say anything until she was ready to move forward.

I looked down and said, "Can I just tell you one thing...if God blesses you with the opportunity to be captain again, do it differently. Learn from your first time."

I anxiously awaited her response because I didn't want her to take it the wrong way. She looked back at me.

"I got you. I promise."

My captain officially decided to audition for another year and the news was out. She made it known to me it was no longer a secret, but my main concern was if she was okay. We spent a lot of time talking about her doubts and I knew I wanted to be there to reassure her every step of the way. The days grew closer and closer to audition. I was sitting at work, bored, going through my phone. As I scrolled through my social media I came across a video of my big sister and our drum major. She was dressed in our team wardrobe and our drum major was dressed in his attire as they made an appearance to an event. I sat up and watched the video a few times. All I could think was that no one informed me of a performance, so what was going on. My captain and my crab sisters seemed to be in sync this day because the moment I watched the video, I received a message from my sisters and a call from my captain.

"Girl, did you see-"

"-Yes girl I was just watching it and then you called. Did I miss the memo about a performance?"

My captain responded saying no one knew about this specific appearance. As I hung up from her I sat thinking. Part of me wondered what my big sister was doing, but whenever it came down to her, it was hard for me to think that anything she did was wrong. I hated to think that my mind could think any less of her. Ironically, as I messaged my crab sisters back and forth and continued to watch the video over and over, I received a message from my big sister. "Hey, just wanted to say there is a lot going on right now. I know you probably seen the video and there is much more to the story, but it does not concern the team. I know God is going to work this whole thing out, but I don't want you to worry." As I read the message, I became confused. Why was she telling me this? Why would I be worried? I already had no clue what was going on and this made the situation even more confusing. Was I the only one who received the message? I decided to leave it alone and responded, "Yes, God will work it all out. Keep your head up." I proceeded to lay my phone down and it began to ring. As I turned it around I saw it was my big sister. I squinted my eyes, looking at the phone wondering why she would be calling me after our conversation.

"Hey, can I ask you a quick question?"

I said, "What's up?" in a haste to know what the call was leading towards.

"Do you know if your captain will be auditioning? I heard a few things, but everyone is telling me they don't know so I didn't know if she didn't want anyone to know or not." I didn't hesitate.

"Yes, she's auditioning. And it's no secret so I don't see how no one knows."

With that, I knew something wasn't right, but I didn't say anything. I answered the question and left the conversation where it was.

It was now the day before auditions. I, along with my crab sisters and captain, were invited by my mentor to her daughter's graduation. Because we had grown a good relationship with her through the organization, I always looked forward to being present anytime she needed anything or wanted to do anything because she was always there for me. After the graduation we all went out to lunch. We didn't talk much about dance because other guests were present, but I was itching to ask her a specific question. I waited until we made it outside alone with just her and my sisters.

As she walked to her car she said, "Good luck tomorrow at auditions," as she gave a slick smile and kept walking.

I looked at her with a side eye. "I know you know something we don't know."

"I don't know what you are talking about."

I moved to the side of her, nudging her in the arm, laughing saying, "Who is judging for auditions tomorrow?"

She turned around and stopped us before we made it to the car.

"It shouldn't matter who the judges are, as long as you all have been working hard and doing what you are supposed to do you shouldn't be concerned right?"

At this point, I knew for sure we were getting no answer out of her, so we left it alone and got in the car.

That night my roommate and I invited our crab sisters, and our captain over for a sleepover so we could all be together before auditions. We laughed and clowned one another as we always did. We quickly got up and moved around the furniture to dance to the band music as we recorded ourselves. It was like a moment of Déjà vu. Afterwards, we began to get ourselves together for auditions the next morning. We packed our bags, curled our hair, laid out our audition outfits, and in no time, we were all in our designated spots sound asleep, anxiously waiting for the big day.

Audition day was here at last. We all moved around the apartment putting on our makeup and gathering our things to head out. I'd grabbed all of my bags to head out the door when my phone rang with a message. It was my big sister. She sent a long message with a scripture and a passage. I thought to ask everyone if they received a message as well, but I decided to keep it to myself. Once I pulled up to the band hall, we all parked in front, being introduced to a line of girls already standing outside. I sat in my car as I got ready to go into prayer. I called my aunt first, then my mom, and lastly my dad. They all said their own prayers, but I loved for my dad to go last because he always said the best prayers.

"Baby girl, you got this. You keep God first in every move you make and every thought you think, and I promise He will direct you and you're going to love the outcome."

I could see him in my head smiling and his one dimple forming in his cheek. I knew I was going to do well. I got out the car and met my sisters and my captain on the sidewalk. We walked up to the line together and this time the feeling was different. I was nervous, but I felt seasoned. We walked past as girls eyed us and I kept my mind on one track. As we made it to our room I reminisced on being in the same room, same spot from my first audition. It felt surreal. My captain, crab sisters, and I settled in our space and prepared our things. As we settled into our spots, propping our mirrors up to touch up our makeup and primping our hair, we decided to see if any of the other team members made it yet. As we walked in the hallway to find the other team members, we saw they were in the room directly across from ours. I walked in to speak, and saw my big sister standing next to her sister, the same girl who I encountered in the club who previously had relations with my now boyfriend. No one really showed much enthusiasm. As I observed the room the team sat in, something felt off. I didn't speak on it. I wished everyone good luck and walked back to my own area. Auditions began and our sponsor called everyone into the band hall. As I walked in, the first place I looked was the judging table. I looked over to see both of my mentors sitting at the table, beautiful as ever, along with the other judges. I looked their way smiling, but they wouldn't catch my eye. I didn't let it bother me though. I knew they had a job to do. As we began to dance I made sure to pay close attention. I watched as the current team went across the floor. Everyone looked amazing, even my captain. I prayed she could make it with her injury. My dad's words played in my head as I went across the floor. "Keep God first in every move you make." I continued to be observant as I stood next to my roommate and captain. We were all in line together on one side of the room, but my focus was suddenly drawn across the room. I watched as my big sister and my teammate stood next to one another laughing and talking. I looked over to the judges as I watched them look towards one another and then towards my big sister and our teammate. One judge motioned for my sponsor to turn the music down as she spoke. "Ladies, we are watching you. All of you. This is an audition so let's be respectful." My captain and my roommate eyed me as we all took small glances towards my big sister and our teammate. The technique portion was now over and we were all dismissed to our specific dress rooms. My sisters, captain and I gathered in a circle, but we didn't discuss so much of what had taken place, but more of how we all agreed something felt weird. As we waited in silence for the first cut, I sat in my small space with so much going through my mind. I consistently stayed in prayer. I didn't know what was going to take place. "Ladies, if you could please make your way to the band hall door." As we walked up amongst all the girls, my roommate and I grabbed hands, with our shoulders pressed against each other and I put my head down. I tuned everything out except for the sound of my number. The moment she called it I lifted my head and walked forward. As I walked in the room to line up amongst the rest of the girls who were called, I looked towards my mentors hoping now they would make eye contact with me. Still no connection, but I didn't worry about it. I was excited to see the team return but especially my sisters and my captain. I looked over to my big sister because I didn't see her sister. I surprised myself because I would've thought it wouldn't affect me, but it slightly did.

179

Because she had been on the team before I figured she was good enough to make it again. The simple fact I cared about my big sister, I knew it was hard for her being the only one left from her class of dance sisters and I couldn't imagine.

It was now time for the choreography portion of auditions. Because I experienced this point before, I was ready. I stood to the front, making sure I took every step and every note, detail by detail. After we finished learning we were given our time to rehearse and then it was time to perform. I stood in my own area going over the dance in my head as I anxiously waited for them to call my number. Once they called for my group my heart began to beat fast. Each step I took to the band room felt slower and slower. I took my position and waited for the music to begin. As much as I wanted to watch the judges to see their reactions, I centered my attention on my performance. It was time for my solo. I focused on every movement, every facial expression. As I moved across the floor I ignored everything and everyone around me. I took the last move of my dance and leaped over the girl crouched down next to me strutting back to my spot and hitting my pose, making sure I looked every judge in the eye. The music faded as I watched them look at me then look at each other, shaking their heads and smiling.

As I walked out, I felt good about my performance. I sat in anticipation with my sisters and captain, waiting for the sponsor to announce the results. "Ladies, please make your way back the band room door." I moved quickly. This was a big part to me. I knew the biggest cut would be made, down to the top few girls. They called my number and I let out the biggest breath I held within me. As the final girls walked into the room I noticed my big sister didn't come in. My captain and roommate were already looking at me. I knew we all thought the same thing. We were all directed to get ready for the interview portion of the audition. As soon as we made it out the door the team immediately went to the room where my big sister was. As I walked in I hadn't realized another teammate was cut with her. I walked to my big sister hugging her as I watched tears roll down her face. I looked at my other teammate, who had already quickly packed all her things, chucked up two fingers saying, "I'm out this hoe," as she walked out the door. I looked back over to my big sister, who slowly packed her things, with tears still rolling down her face, walking out as each of us hugged her.

The mood was evidently different at this point. I knew I needed time to process what had just taken place, but in the meantime, I kept my mind on track. I prepared myself for my interview understanding I couldn't let the situation change the way I personally presented myself. As I sat and waited amongst the team for my number to be called, I observed everyone. Of course I didn't know what anyone was thinking, but I had a pretty good idea based on facial expressions. They called my number. I walked into the band director's office. I sat across from the director, the sponsor, and her assistant. I crossed my legs, placed my hands on my knees and smiled. My band director grabbed the tissue box and placed them next to me.

"I got this box of tissues just for you!"

Everyone in the room began to laugh, but then their faces turned back to being serious. I continued to look each of them in the eye until my band director spoke up asking how I was feeling.

"I feel good, thankful to have made it to this point."

I could tell he was thinking something as he squinted his eyes and asked, "What would you say, 'building your own brand' is and do you agree with it when you are a part of an organization?"

As I explained my thoughts all I could think of was my big sister. I had a feeling the question was based on the video I saw before auditions, but nevertheless, I answered based on my understanding.

He nodded his head, "Smart girl, you get it."

The sponsors continued to look at me but didn't say anything.

"How would you handle being a leader on this team? The drama? The backlash?"

"I can tell you what I believe I would do and that is handle the good, the bad, and the ugly and everything that comes with it the best possible way I know how, until I find a better way to take care of the situation. I'm not perfect, and ultimately I will make some mistakes because I don't have all the answers, but what I can tell you is that I strive to be the best at whatever I do so I can guarantee that you're going to get the best out of me."

As he lifted his head, squinted his eyes and smirked, no one said anything. For a moment there was silence. As the sponsors began to ask small questions about being in leadership, general questions, and what I wanted to see from the team for the next season, I could see the director still watching everything I did or said.

As I looked into my sponsors eyes, she ended with, "Don't ever lose your spirit, it's needed."

As I smiled and got up to walk out, the band director called after me. "Glad we didn't need the tissue box this year." We all laughed and I proceeded to walk out.

I sat down next to my sisters, feeling good about my interview and under the impression interviews were over. They informed me the judges were also giving an interview. The moment they told me, my number was called.

As I walked in, I smiled, "Well hello darlings."

They all smiled as they spoke back to me. "Here's the diva!" I sat down in front of them. My mentors made it clear they were not going to say anything because they already knew me very well personally.

The judge looked at me, "I just want you to know that you kilt your audition. There is just something about you and I don't know what it is, but you've definitely got it."

As I smiled, they all looked at one another as they began to ask me questions.

"What is the role of a captain, and what would you do differently if you were appointed the position?"

I had no time to think why they were asking these specific questions because my mind was occupied on formulating the answer. As I responded they all continued to smile.

"If you were given the position, how would you handle the hatred and the backlash?"

"I can only be honest and say that it will affect me, but in me knowing that, I also know how to remind myself of how strong I am. It definitely won't be easy, but anything worth having won't be easy, but working hard is what's worth it and I have that in me."

The judge looked me in my eyes.

"You think you can captain this team?"

"I know I can."

The judge to the end reached her arm out as she looked to the other judges and back to me.

"I see why you would make a good captain. You are so intelligent and articulate."

I nodded and smiled, wanting to shed tears of joy of course, but I held them in. I guess I needed that tissue box after all.

"We don't need to hear no more, we've heard all we needed."

I walked out and fixed my face. I knew my sisters and my captain would ask me about my interview time so I kept it brief and kept the majority of what took place to myself. It wasn't because I wanted to hide it, but simply because I myself didn't want to read into the things I was asked, so I didn't want anyone else doing so. I knew I was capable of everything talked about in both interviews, but in the back of my mind, I knew whatever was coming my way, God was already setting the motion to prepare me for it.

This was the first time I experienced being released from auditions before the team was picked. We were informed we would receive a call if we made the team. Weeks went by and I was still anticipating a call that I made the team for a second year. I was still in constant communication with my sisters and my captain, but my captain and I mainly spoke daily about when the results would finally come. I had just come home from work. I walked straight to my room, jumped in the bed looking at my phone. Minutes later my roommate ran in my room with news that she got a call. My heart dropped and as we screamed together in excitement for her, all I could think about was where was my call. She could see the look on my face. "They'll call you bud," and she walked back to her room. Moments later, I received a call from the sponsor. "Hello, sweet girl! I'm calling to let you know we would love for you to return to the team for another year." I tried to keep my composure as I jumped up and down holding my hand over my mouth trying not to make too much noise. I hung up and ran to my roommate's room as we celebrated together again. I walked back to my room and called my mentor.

"I made the team!"

"Congratulations, but I wasn't expecting anything different."

I paused, then my tone changed.

"I made it as a regular member though."

I thought it was necessary to tell her that because a part of me felt like I let them down. I knew she could hear the sudden slight tone of sadness in my voice.

She responded, "That doesn't mean you are not a leader. Having that position is already destined for you, so you just stay ready, because when it's time, it's time and they'll be no more 'getting ready.' Use this next year to learn all you can. Gain some thicker skin and keep your relationship with God close because something is coming for you."

As we exchanged our final words, I hung up from her and laid there thinking. I asked myself, "If they would have told you you made it as captain, can you honestly say you were ready?" As much as I, myself wanted to say yes because I felt that was the best answer suiting my personality, the answer was no. I knew I would be able to get ready, but I also believed in allowing life to happen according to how God wanted it to. But my mentor was right. My job wasn't to worry about a position. I was already a leader. I knew the moment I began to realize on my own it didn't take a position to spot a leader, would be the very moment I was rewarded with greater. As I laid there I received a phone call from my captain asking if she could come over. The moment she walked into our apartment my roommate and I ran into the hallway. Our captain stood at the door staring at us with an awkward smile on her face. We looked back at her, as I braced myself, preparing to charge into her arms. She continued to stand there driving us deeper into suspicion. I put my hand to my hip, dropped my head to the side, and said, "Cut the foolishness heifer, are you gonna be captain?" As she nodded her head me and my roommate wasted no time as we began to scream, running into her arms. I was honestly happy because I began to trust her. I took her promise serious. So in my mind I was going to get the chance to see the woman I knew she could be. Because I cared and loved her so much, I was anxious to experience every moment finding out.

It was still summer and my captain was already working with her new crabs, as she did with us when my sisters and I first got started. We talked on a regular. She always confided in me about anything on her mind. One day she asked me if I wanted to meet her to look at the new girls and help out. I agreed. As I walked in to sit next to her I thought about a few things. I thought about how I was really sitting next to my captain as a veteran. Then I thought about how the new girls were so beautiful and I could call these three my little sisters. I watched as my captain had them go across the floor while I reminisced on when it was me. One I paid close attention to because she reminded me of myself. As I sat in my chair I mouthed corrections to her as she nodded with a determined look on her face showing she would strive to get it. I gave a slight smile as she walked across the floor. I would glance over to my captain through the mirror, just to pay attention to her mannerisms and how she communicated.

Once she would catch me looking she'd look to me laughing saying, "What?"

"Oh nothing. Keep teaching your new crabs," as I smiled and watched.

I still felt slightly reserved because I was new and I didn't want to say too much, but my captain insisted I speak up. She encouraged everything that came out of my mouth. Once she finished we stayed to talk.

"Should I explain to the team why I chose to come back. I mean should I bring it up?"

I looked at her, raised my eyebrows, and sat back in my seat. She laughed as she waited for my response. I looked back to her.

"You don't owe anyone an explanation. You were picked for a reason whether they like it or not. But if you feel as though that is what you need to do, I support it."

I could tell she was thinking about it. We continued to communicate about anything that came to our minds.

A few days later my captain called the entire team to the dance room to meet the new girls. We all sat against the wall with my captain waiting for the girls to walk in. While we waited, I looked through the mirror at myself. I could finally do it without someone yelling at me saying I wasn't cute enough to look at a mirror. Everyone sat, laughing and talking amongst themselves, then my captain brought up our conversation. "I just want to know how everyone is feeling. What is your outlook on this new season?" My crab sisters and I sat alongside each other as we went down the line stating our take on the question asked. As each one of my sisters spoke, I smiled agreeing with everything they said. I personally loved the fact we were all strong enough to say how we felt and do it with confidence. It came down to the other teammates. I directed my attention to them, anxious to see what they would say. I could only imagine how certain things affected them. My other big sister spoke up. As she said her peace one part stood out to me and I could feel my heart drop. She looked to my crab sisters and I, then to my captain and said, "I feel as though they just got here so they shouldn't even have much to say. Me and my sisters have been

188

here longer so we know." As I clinched my teeth, trying not to allow my facial expressions to get the best of me, I looked over to my captain. She briefly responded to the statement with what I thought was done with class and grace. The room was then silent. The new girls walked in. I could feel myself unconsciously taking on the mannerisms of the team when they first called me and my crab sisters into the hotel room. I watched as they walked in with their makeup on, hair done, and dressed up. I said nothing as I simply watched them, listening while my captain spoke. They stood on their toes and I could tell by their smiles they were nervous. Their eyes became glassy and I could see their bodies shaking. While my captain read the rules, I looked over to the girl I gravitated to. Because I was the same way, I could read the attitude on her face instantly. I opened my eyes wide, trying to get her attention so I could help her to calm down, but it was too late. The moment my captain questioned her she responded with a smart comment. I laughed on the inside because it was like watching myself. While they were wiping off their makeup I could see the frustration and I could only feel for them. But at the same time, I was slowly learning how necessary certain tactics were. Once she finished reading them the rules they walked out. The team sat in silence for a moment then exchanged a few words and we dismissed.

High school band camp was set to take place the very next week. I decided to split my time between working my everyday job and still participating in helping for the camp. It was the beginning of the week, and with everything going on my captain and I were long overdue for our daily talks. My phone rang and it was my captain. I always knew she had something important to tell me whenever she called me. That meant it couldn't wait. I answered the phone anxiously, waiting for her to tell me what I knew she longed to get out. As always, she sat in silence, leaving me in suspense. She knew I was done waiting when I smacked my teeth. That's when she finally started to speak.

"She quit."

I took a moment to respond. I genuinely did not know who she was talking about.

"The crab you liked, quit."

"What? Why?"

As she explained as much as she knew, I was already thinking ahead. She quickly finished telling what took place and we hung up from one another. Although it seemed surprising as to why I cared so much for this girl barely knowing her, it was simply because I thought of myself when I first saw her. I knew how she could possibly feel being new. The very next day on my way to work I called my captain. "Would you be okay if I talked to her? I know she quit already, but I feel like if I talk to her maybe she will change her mind." I didn't know if it would affect me in the long run, and part of me didn't care. I wanted the young girl to know she had somebody in the beginning because that's all I wanted. She told me she would check with the sponsor. Once she got the approval she informed me it was okay to proceed with what I wanted to do. That very moment I gave the girl a call. "Hi, my girl. Are you busy?" As she expressed to me her decision to quit, I posed to her before she completely made up her mind, if she could just give me a moment of her time. After that, whatever she chose to do would completely be up to her. She agreed and we planned to meet on the final day of high school band camp.

The day came for us to meet up. It had been a few days since we last spoke, but I wanted her to have time to gather her thoughts. As I pulled into her driveway, I sat in my car briefly and said a quick prayer. I didn't know what was going to become of this decision, but what I did know was I wanted God's stamp of approval. She welcomed me in. Instantly I could see the expression of defeat on her face. As we walked to take a seat her mother greeted me. "I am so glad you are here to talk with her because she needs that. I don't want her to quit, but at the end of the day I want her to make the decision for herself." I completely understood. As we sat down I looked into her eyes and could see them watering.

"You can talk to me. Tell me what's on your mind."

As she expressed to me how she felt tears rolled down her face. I wiped her face as she continued, making sure she knew I was listening to every word.

"I just don't think it's for me. I can't do this."

I continued to look her in her eyes as I waited for her to finish. When she was done, I sat for a moment and then responded.

"I don't want to ever hear you say you can't. I don't want to tell you how you should feel because you have every right to feel how you want, but do you know how talented and special you have to be to make this team?"

I could see a slight smile form on her face as she looked down, but quickly pulled it back.

191

"I don't want you to look back and say, 'I should've done this.' I was in your position just last year. Do you know how many times I said I was quitting? But I stuck it out and I believed God could get me through. Guess what? He can do the same for you."

She continued to stay steadfast to her original answer as I spoke. I didn't let that defeat my purpose for speaking with her. I said one more thing.

"Do you think you're good?"

She shrugged her shoulders, still looking down and said, "I guess I am."

I quickly cut her off.

"Look at me. You ARE good and you need to speak that over your life. No matter what decision you make, believe that."

Everything was quiet. As she sat there looking out the window, I prepared myself to get ready to leave. She looked up. "I want to stay."

I tilted my head down and put a small smile on my face. "Don't just say it because I want you to. Are you sure it's what you want to do?"

"I really want to."

We both stood up and she leaned in to hug me saying, "Thank you." As I walked out, I looked to her and smiled. "You got this."

Once I made it to the school I informed my captain of the good news. I wasn't sure of my captain's plans afterwards, I was just happy the new girl made the decision to stay. The band camp performance was over. My captain, crab sisters, and I all met in the dance room. She called the new girls in and they stood shyly in the corner. I didn't know what was going to take place, but I looked towards my girl, winked, and nodded as a gesture to show she was okay. She gave a slight smile. My captain directed for them to wait in the car. As they walked out, she looked over to my roommate and I saying, "I want to make sure she is really here to stay, that she really wants this." As we looked at her, questioning what she had in mind, she asked if we could all go back to our apartment, including the new girls. My roommate and I agreed. We all got up to leave, heading for our apartment.

We all made it to our apartment. We popped some popcorn and found our spots we would occupy in the living room. We talked for a minute before our captain called the new girls to come inside. No one spoke except for my captain. As they stood on their toes, I didn't take my eyes off my girl. I was praying every time my captain said something to them for her to push through. I watched as she smiled, resembling an air of confidence. My captain continued to talk. "Give me a skit." As much as I wanted to mimic the same behavior the team gave us when we did our first skit, these girls were funny. I couldn't hold it in. Everything was going well, at least that's what it seemed like. Although my captain was calling the shots, she spoke to them very sweetly, mainly just talking to them. But then she did what I thought she wouldn't. "Give me fifty kicks." I didn't think that was that many, so I didn't see the harm in it. However my girl instantly looked at me. I could see the frustration begin to build on her face. "Plank." As they crouched down slowly, my heart began to beat fast, but I really didn't know why, so I didn't say anything. My captain continued.

"Kick. Last fifty so get them up."

As I watched them I could see my girl giving up, so I spoke up.

"C'mon push through, you got it."

My captain didn't say anything. She sat, just looking at each of them with no form of expression on her face.

Suddenly, my girl stopped, and began to walk off crying saying, "I can't do this."

She ran into my room. My captain got up to go after her. We all sat in silence in the living room waiting. I eventually got up to see if I could speak to her again, but she had already made her mind up that she was done. She grabbed her things and walked out.

It was a week away from our team band camp and it was now finalized there would only be two new girls. My captain gave me a call asking if I would come in to help her. I wondered what she would need my help on, but nevertheless, I showed up. As I walked in, she stood staring at me with her two crabs standing next to her not knowing where to look. I was used to it, but I also got sick of it.

"Girl, what is it?"

"So, the sponsor said that she basically wants me to bring in all new things."

We both sat down in our seats looking towards the mirror. I took a deep breath and looked over to her.

"So, what you gonna do?"

She insisted she was up for the challenge, but she needed to get started ASAP. We stayed for hours coming up with new ideas and new dances. As I watched her teach her crabs certain things, all I could think to myself was that the game was about to change.

Band camp began and practices seemed the same as I would've known them to go from the past. The only difference was, I was no longer "less than" in the room. It wasn't as much tension as before, but the divide was obvious. Not in a physical sense though, but mentally it was known we had our captain and the rest of the team had theirs. Because we were under the leadership of my captain, it was understood that everyone had to fall in line. There were days where we all spoke and things seemed normal, and other days I battled my own internal issues, not with the team, more with my roommate. Although she was my best friend, I began to feel a sense of "looking over my shoulder" when it came down to our relationship. I loved her, but I always had a feeling in the back of my mind that I was more invested in our friendship than she was. I tried to look past it because we were always together: school, practice, home, and then do it all over again, together.

It was the weekend of our first performance as a team. Everything was going well. I was excited for this performance.

Personally, I felt as though I had something to prove. I wanted to come back better, so that was my focus. I was driven by the thought of not returning the same, while physically being the same person, but mentally being better in every aspect. I was becoming the person who didn't care so much about what everyone thought. I did value the opinions of the people I truly cared about and looked up to. Besides my parents, I made sure I always had my mentors' approvals. They were seasoned with knowledge I believed was beneficial to me. After the performance I stepped outside to call both mentors on a three-way call. Besides dancing, they were big on physical appearance. They were also brutally honest at times. I didn't mind because I took it as preparation for any point and time in life. As I asked for their opinion, they voiced a few of their concerns. I listened and let them do what they did best. Then the conversation changed into what I would always expect to come. It was normal for them to bring up the role of captain from time to time. Whether it was telling me stories from the past or preparing me for what they knew was to come.

"Right now you are being put in a place where you need to start getting your house in order."

I knew what they meant, but I listened to hear exactly where they were going with their statements.

"And that means cleaning house everywhere. That girl is not your friend and you continue to place yourself around her."

I knew they were talking about my roommate. Yes I would tell them the struggles we would have, but it was just to vent. I never thought to stop being friends. I stood in silence as they continued to talk.

"She is not a bad person, but she is not the friend for you; not for where you're about to go."

I stopped the conversation. As much as I hated to cut them off, it was natural for me to take defense for the ones I cared for.

"We have our good times, and we have our bad times, but she is my best friend. Y'all don't know her like I do. So I'm sorry, but I can't agree with you and I'd rather not talk about this."

Because they were very straight forward and blunt, I didn't expect them to respond in an understanding manner, but it never offended me. I knew how they were, and they knew how I was. I took the knowledge I wanted, and what I didn't I respectfully left it alone. As for them, they said what they wanted. They knew I would eventually find out for myself.

"Fine. Do what you want. I'm just telling you so you won't be out here looking stupid. But it won't be on us when that girl does you bad."

I laughed as I hung up from them. I knew from the surface I could hide what I really felt inside. I stood outside a few more minutes alone. Although I defended her, why did I believe their outcome more than mine? I knew I wanted how I responded to be true. But the truth was, I didn't even believe it myself.

The season continued and seemed to move rather quickly on certain weekends. This particular weekend seemed to be the weekend that slowed the time down. The bus had just pulled up to the school where we were due to perform. We had only a few minutes left to finish primping ourselves. Everyone moved around grabbing last minute things to prepare. My captain and assistant sponsor sat towards the front of the bus. We realized we had yet to pick a certain lipstick color and we were due to perform at any minute. As everyone quietly asked each other, I looked to my captain and the assistant and then back to the team. I could tell my captain and the assistant sponsor knew everyone was whispering in frustration amongst each other about what lip color to wear. To some, one would think, "a lip color?" But it was a big deal, especially because we could go out and dance flawlessly, but the first thing people would notice and critique is our physical appearance. It was important to always be on point when it came down to wardrobe, hair, and makeup. It was minutes before we were due to line up and my captain had yet to pick a lip color. The team continued to whisper amongst each other, voicing concerns privately. I whispered amongst my crab sisters, as well as with the other team members. Once we finally concluded, we lined up, to get ready to perform. We wore a dark purple lip color with a hint of pink in the middle. Despite the small dispute before the performance everything went well. That night my roommate and I sat up talking about the situation. As we talked to each other from our rooms, yelling our responses to one another, laughing and joking, we seemed to be on the same page. She yelled, "Girl, that was so stupid how they handled that, and that color was ugly. A hot mess." I laughed responding to her comment agreeing, adding on my opinion on how the situation should've been handled, and she agreed.

The next day at practice I could see the situation floating in the air. Practice still moved as normal, but knowing my captain, I could tell it was on her mind. Around the end of rehearsal the assistant sponsor walked in the room. She had us all sit down as she pulled up a chair in front of us. I had a feeling of what she was going to bring up, but I waited until she began to talk.

"I'm here to address the situation that happened on the bus this past weekend. Who had a concern or felt some type of way about what took place?"

A few seconds went by and no one said anything. I raised my hand.

"I did think that the situation could have been handled a little better", and as I stated my piece she responded.

"Thank you for being honest. Anyone else?"

Again, no one said anything. I looked over to my roommate briefly and looked away. Although she wasn't obligated to say anything, all I could think of was how we had so much to say last night, but instantly we turned into me. Because I thought we always seemed to be on the same page when it was just me and her, I expected the same amongst the team. We always had moments where we would stop talking to one another for a certain period of time, but this was my reason why. I found myself becoming distant unconsciously in moments like this. Publicly, her distance from me was evident, so I returned the favor in private. Besides having to deal with certain issues, I was learning to remain steadfast in who I was, however, each day I grew an understanding of how I wanted to carry myself in the room. I learned from my teammates, who were a year ahead of me, to relax your second year. They never really taught this specific gesture, but it was naturally picked up through my observation of behavior from my first year. I battled with naturally being a person who spoke up when I believed something needed to be said. Although I seemed to be content in my behavior, I was slowly making changes to what I knew I could have possibly done better.

Chapter 9
Growth in Setbacks

It was close to the end of the week. Practice on this day seemed to be lasting longer than normal as we ran the field show over and over. I was already not feeling well and going through personal issues with my boyfriend. So I sat in my seat comfortably waiting for my turn, but I wasn't in the best of moods. It was now my turn to perform the dance. My cue hadn't come yet and I had already decided it wouldn't be my best that day. I barely looked myself in the mirror as I flopped through some movements. While I performed some movements clean, there wasn't any enthusiasm. And for the finish, the moment it was time to hit my final pose, I found my spot and after what seemed to be a long performance of "mess," I stood in my pose for a second with enthusiasm. I gave a smile of sarcasm and walked off to sit in my seat, indicating, "that's all you're going to get out of me today." No one said anything, but my captain looked at me, and with a straight face she said, "What was that? Because that was not it." I went from just directing my attention to her, to sitting up and directing my attention to her.

Sarcastically laughing I said, "Excuse me? I'm not one of your new crabs, sweetheart."

"I can't tell based on the way you just performed that dance."

I went back to crossing my legs, sitting back in my seat, and throwing on my blanket as I laughed saying, "Watch yourself sweetie."

She rolled her eyes turning away. I sat there trying not to let the situation bother me, but all I could think of in my mind was that she really checked me, and in front of everyone. I knew she could see and feel my energy from where she sat. I wanted her to. Minutes went by and she called a team break.

She looked over to me and in a stern tone she said, "Can I talk to you for a minute?"

We walked into the restroom and she turned to me.

"What's the problem?"

I instantly took on a greater defense.

"Don't come at me like that. That's my problem. Don't ever call me out like that. You don't know what I could be going through."

She looked at me as she dropped her hip.

"We're too close for this. I wouldn't do anything to intentionally hurt you, and you know that, but what kind of captain would I be if I didn't correct you when you were wrong. I just wish that if you were having a bad day you would have come and told me so I would have known."

I looked down, because instantly after she responded, I knew I was wrong. It only convicted me. I saw I was now talking to the woman I knew she could be and the woman she was growing into, but the problem was I became the girl I strived to grow away from.

I looked up to her as I said, "You know what, I apologize. I honestly didn't have to come at you like that so it's on me. I was wrong. I just let the things I'm going through interfere with my emotions then. I should have handled it better so I'm sorry."

She looked at me smiling, making a face as we walked off laughing. We walked back into the room together. I felt embarrassed because I knew that despite how she approached the situation, she still wasn't wrong for calling me out for it. I knew I needed to accept the fact I allowed my personal situations to interfere with the way I chose to respond.

The season continued to move along. Although most of my time and days were spent being amongst the team practicing, my headspace was occupied with only a small percentage of the team. Most of my headspace was occupied with my boyfriend and my roommate, but being that my birthday was around the corner, I tried to use it as a distraction from the things I didn't want to worry about. I was excited because I was finally turning 21. I didn't really express too much excitement for it publicly other than to my boyfriend. However, my roommate knew to some capacity my eagerness for that day. It was a week before my birthday and we were preparing to head to an away game. My roommate had just finished whispering to me about a team member, and as her best friend, I believed it was my responsibility to co-sign anything she said. In my mind, that's what best friends did. You talk about her, I talk about her with you. You don't like her; I don't like her. Besides me knowing when something was taken too far, I saw my roommate whispering to me about others rather small, especially if I didn't have much of a relationship with the particular person we spoke about, so I didn't feel the need to end our normal gossip. As I walked onto the bus I watched as my roommate laughed and giggled in her face. The same teammate she had just told me about. It was hard to understand why it bothered me so much, it just did. I didn't know how to explain it. Once my roommate made eye contact with me, I rolled my eyes hoping she saw me, but still wanting it to be subtle and then I turned away. I tried to stop my reactions, but before I could take a deep breath to ease my thoughts, she called to my crab sister who stood next to me. "I'm going to sit with you sis." I figured she caught my attitude towards her because we always sat together. My immediate thought to change my attitude went out the window. The bus ride between us was quiet but tense. Despite us not sitting with one another, I could feel the energy between us. Even during the game. We would normally smile and snicker with one another from time to time, but this time, there were no words between us. As we headed back to campus from a long, but successful game, all I could think about was what took place with my roommate. I made up my mind again that I wasn't going to talk to her, but one simple question kept coming to me. "Does she even know or understand why you're upset with her?" Instead of really thinking through the question, I always answered it, telling myself that as my best friend she should know me so she should understand why. That was the notion in my mind. It made it easier for me to have a reason not to speak to her.

A week went by and it was finally my special day. I had just left from being with my boyfriend and my day was already starting to go downhill, literally. Besides everything I had to deal with on a regular, one of my major problems was my car. It was old and used. I didn't know how much longer it would last. The way I drove it you would think it was brand new. As I drove up the hill to get onto campus I could feel my car begin to lag. "God not today, please. It's my birthday!" talking out loud. I pressed the gas as it began to pick up a little speed. Thinking I was good, I turned my music back up. The moment my car hit the top of the hill... it shut off. I banged on the steering wheel,

"No, no, no!" as the car began to roll backwards down the hill. As much as I wanted to panic I turned around to make sure no one was behind me, remaining as calm as I could while the car slowly rolled backwards. As I got to the beginning point of the hump I called my sponsor informing her I would be a few minutes late due to my technical difficulties. As I hung up from her I cranked my car thankfully pulling it to the closest spot I could get to. I walked up and the team was already finished practicing outside. My best friend and I still weren't speaking, but a big part of me thought maybe this would be the time. I purposely walked next to her as everyone walked in the room to see if she would say anything, but she moved over and said nothing. I walked into the dance room to find a cake, flowers, and balloons sitting in my chair from my family. As everyone began to wish me a happy birthday, my captain pulling her phone out hugging me, I didn't put much of a smile on my face. I subtly glanced over to my roommate who still having said nothing, sat in her spot on her phone. As I told everyone thank you, I walked out of the room to give my mom a call.

"Hey ma, thank you for the cake and everything."

I knew she immediately was going to know something was wrong.

"You're welcome sweetie, happy birthday! What's wrong?"

I was silent, trying to hold back tears I knew were on the way.

"Sweetie."

I began to let out all my tears. "Mom, she said nothing to me. No happy birthday. Nothing. I'm not upset, I'm angry! I go out of my way to be a good friend, and THIS is what I get."

She was quiet and just listened as I cried. When I calmed down she began to talk.

"Sweetie, you have to gain thick skin, even with the people you care deeply about. Is it right? Maybe not. But what can you do about it? Now I don't know what is going on, but this is your day. Don't you let nobody take that away from you. Clean your face up, go back in there, and enjoy your gift from your family."

I did as she told me and walked back in, hoping they wouldn't see my eyes red from crying. No one said anything. Either they didn't notice or they did but chose not to say anything, but within no time practice was dismissed.

It was now the day of the game. My boyfriend surprised me and invited my cousins down. I planned to go to the club with my family, my captain, and my crab sisters. After the game my cousin pulled me to the side. "Where's your roommate? I haven't spoken to her yet. Is she coming out with us tonight?' I told her I received a message from my roommate the other night wishing me a happy birthday, but I wasn't sure. I walked away, only to see moments later, my cousin speaking to my roommate. I walked up to her looking to find out what was said. "She said she wasn't going. I'm just surprised because she helped plan for us to get here." I looked over to my roommate not knowing she had anything to do with my birthday surprise. I let it go and decided to just enjoy myself with the people I didn't have to beg to come. A few days went by and my roommate and I were still walking around our apartment in silence. I was usually the one to

206

initiate conversation. As we both stood in the kitchen fixing our food in silence, I asked if we could sit in the living room to talk. She agreed to it. As we went back and forth I looked at her, scrunching my eyebrows while she spoke. "I saw you roll your eyes and then you stopped talking to me so I figured I would just leave you alone until you were ready to talk." I decided not to explain to her the real reason why I stopped speaking with her. A big part of me felt as though yes, she should understand, but because of her very response, I didn't think she wanted to understand. After that, we went back to us as usual.

The season was now winding down and performances became a little more hectic. Normally we would receive news in advance if we were asked to do a specific performance in the middle of the week, but this week, we were informed right before the day of the performance. It was okay with me because I saw it as something that came with being on the team. You always needed to be ready to perform. My roommate and I came together and met up with our crab sisters, our captain, and the two new crabs. As we made it to our dressing room we began to get ourselves together with less than thirty minutes before it was time to perform. Our other three team members had yet to show up. I could see my captain getting frustrated. She walked over to me and whispered, "At this point, I can't." I shook my head continuing to get dressed as the remaining three teammates walked in together. I looked to them then looked over to my captain who wore her frustration on her face. I didn't blame her. Nevertheless, the show went on. Everyone was dressed and ready. While we stood in the back waiting for our cue, we all talked and no issue seemed evident. Once the performance was over, my captain came to my roommate's car asking if we wanted to go out to dinner with her and the crabs. We decided to go. Meeting them at the restaurant, as we sat down our captain stared at us with the look we were used to. My roommate and I turned and looked at each other laughing because we already knew what was going through our captain's mind. As we ate the new crabs sat and listened as we reminisced about some of the things our captain did when we were crabs. Our captain began to discuss her frustration for what took place at our performance that night. I looked around the table then to her.

"So, what are you going to do?"

"I already talked with the sponsor, and along with some other things, I asked if y'all could lead for Bayou Classic."

We all stared at her as I said, "You think that's a good idea?"

"Yes. I mean one of y'all could honestly lead this team next."

I could agree with her statement, however, I could only imagine the problems it would cause. No one said anything. As we continued to eat we moved away from the subject. We began taking pictures and carrying on conversation, but in the back of my mind I honestly became nervous. We never talked about any of us physically leading. Although captain seemed to be a relevant topic, this was the first time it seemed as though it was really going to be set in motion.

It was practice time. We all sat in our designated spots as normal waiting for practice to begin. We greeted each team member as they walked in. As my captain turned the music on she looked over to me, "You're going to lead." It was normal for her to ask this from our other teammates who were a year ahead of us, but this was the first time she asked anyone amongst my crab sisters. I did as she asked and after, we began to stretch. I stood in my own area as our captain advised everyone to get a good stretch on their own. As I stretched my big sister walked in from using the restroom and came to stand directly in front of me. Normally I wouldn't mind, but this was a problem to me because she stood an inch away from my face as her hair slightly touched the tip of my nose. I looked over to my crab sisters and my captain, just to make sure I knew someone else saw what was taking place. I leaned my head to the side so she could see me looking at her through the mirror as I said, "Girl have you lost your mind," stepping back in front of her the same distance away from her face as she was from mine. I had no intentions on moving because the way I saw it, she came into my space and I had no clue what the problem was. We both stood on top of each other stretching until she began to move over. After we finished everyone sat down as our captain dismissed for dinner.

As my crab sisters, my captain, and I stood up getting ready to walk out, my big sister and her sisters remained seated as my big sister said, "What's y'all problem?"

Calling out all of us including my crab sisters, my captain, and myself. Before anyone could respond, she spoke again.

"Actually, it's just you two!" Directing her attention to my captain and I.

I looked over to my captain and then back to my big sister as my captain snickered asking what she was talking about.

"This vibe y'all giving. I don't like it. I'm not scared to address an issue. I'm also not the one."

As much as I wanted to tell her I was the one, I tried my hardest to respond respectfully.

"I don't know what you are talking about. I was under the impression everything was fine until you came and stood in front of me like you lost your mind."

She continued to go on and on as I looked to my captain to see if she was as confused as I was. As my big sister's voice got louder, my defense increased levels every breath. She was still sitting down and at this point I was tired of talking. I could see her crab sister sitting next to her trying to calm her down so she could get a word in, but before she could stop her sister from speaking to me and my captain, I said my last words as I walked towards the door. "I don't know what the issue is and frankly I don't care, but when you're ready to really solve it, I'm right here." I walked out slamming the door behind me. I waited to see if any of my sisters would come, but the only one who came looking for me was my captain. As she walked up, she began to laugh. She looked at me and continued to laugh saying, "It's okay. She clearly is not going to do nothing. She's probably just feeling some type of way because I let you lead, so don't worry about it." As we walked back to the band hall we stood outside waiting for practice to begin again. I decided to call the sponsor and let her know what had taken place. Mainly because I was still disturbed by the situation, and didn't want my feelings to take me to a place I couldn't get myself out of. As my crab sisters walked outside, no one asked if I was okay, but only speaking on what one of our teammates said the problem was. While I looked at them in confusion to the explanation, I laughed in sarcasm. "So, you mean to tell me, all of this because they said I gave them a look when they walked in late last night?" As over it as I was, I returned to the room with my sisters and captain. I sat in my spot looking straight ahead and said nothing. Minutes later I watched as my big sister walked out. A big part of me had already convinced myself to follow her. I felt as though her response to me was one way in front of the team, but I was curious to know what it would be like with no one around. I waited a minute to walk out, hoping she was in the restroom. As I opened the door, I walked right into her as she was walking out. Immediately she smiled, stepped back and tilted her head to the side saying, "C'mon, I'm your big sister. We shouldn't be acting like this." And as she apologized she leaned in to hug me. As she walked away, I smiled in confusion because I prepared myself for a problem. However, I expected just what she gave me. The next day I walked into practice with the surprise of the sponsor and the assistant sponsor sitting against the wall. I greeted them and continued into my normal way of doing things when it was time for practice. Minutes later my big sister walked through the door. I continued to stretch. As she came to stand next to me, she reached for a hug. I looked over to my captain and my sponsor as she hugged me, making a joke with me and laughing. This behavior was brand new.

It had been a long semester, but Bayou Classic weekend finally made its appearance. Although it was no longer my first time, it was still just as emotional because it was now my first time as a seasoned vet. I no longer held the pressures of being new, so I became relaxed like I had been at this point before. The weekend was going great, but the only thing that clouded my mind was the fact I could possibly be leading for the first time. It was a big deal to me because it was almost like being a crab again; never being in the position before and having to deal with however it came. I had no clue if she was really going to do it. If she did, when would she call me to the front? What song would the band play? I had experienced the hype of marching into the arena before so I used this time not to revel in the moment, but to get my mind right for what was about to come. As we sat in the stands, she called my roommate to the front first. My heart dropped as if she called my name. I knew this was a big moment for all of my sisters because in my mind it set the tone for our class. I felt the same pressure for them as I did for myself. I held my breath every count she threw, hoping neither of us messed up. As she called my other sister to come up, I found a spot in the distance to focus on and get my mind together. "Just be yourself, and have fun,"" I kept telling myself. After my sister finished we left the stands to prepare for our field show. I tried to use this time to relax myself. My captain walked behind me and whispered, "You ready?" I looked at her smiling as she smiled back saying, "You got this."

We had now made it back into the stands and she immediately called me forward. Everything I could possibly think, I thought of in that moment. As the music played and I danced, all that played through my head was, "be you". As soon as the moment began, it ended. I walked back to my spot. As I prepared to dance again, I took a deep breath and smiled. It seemed like it was the hardest part of the game and it was finally over. But just as soon as it ended, I imagined reliving it again. As we marched to the buses to meet with family and friends after the game, the first person I ran to was my boyfriend. He picked me up, spinning me around. For just a few moments everything was perfect. But just like the performance, as soon as he came, he left. I longed for the moment with him to last into another great moment because the weekend was going great. It wasn't evident so much on the outside that things weren't going well between us, but I felt every ounce of it on the inside. Nights went by, leading into the new year. I would sit in my prayer closet and ask God, "Why is being on this team and being

212

in this relationship so hard?" I thought for sure I'd be prepared to go into 2018 ready to take on the world. The night before the new year I prayed. "I don't know what You have planned for me or how You're going to do it, but take away from me whatever is not needed in my life. Do whatever You want. Can You just make it evident because I'm bad with signs?" It was now a new year, a new day, and despite the baggage I knew I needed to get rid of, I could see Him preparing me for what I was praying for.

PART III

Be Wise

Matthew 10:16, "I am sending you out like sheep amongst wolves. Therefore be as shrewd as snakes and as innocent as doves

Ecclesiastes 8:1 Who is like the wise? Who knows the explanation of things? A person's wisdom brightens their face, and changes its hard appearance

Chapter 10
Becoming Who I Need, Without Becoming Who I'm Not

It was the very first day of the year. As much as I would love to say I made changes, I realized my idea of change needed some work. My boyfriend and I broke up the night of New Year's Eve. Instead of using this as a sign from God answering the prayer I prayed, I took advantage of the idea of "working on the relationship without the title." I thought it would go well due to the simple fact I loved him and he loved me, but I began to find out just how much that mattered.

Due to the spring allowing more free time, I decided to get a job. I didn't expect to stay long, but I figured it would keep money in my pocket and it would help change up my regular day to day schedule, which had become normal and redundant at this point. I'd just finished with my last customer and was looking forward to one, getting off my feet, and two, heading to pick out an outfit for Valentine's Day. Although I no longer had an official boyfriend, I still felt as though he was obligated to do something for me, even though technically he wasn't. As I made it onto campus, upon waiting on his call to meet up, I encountered a girl who I would say wasn't a friend, but she was more than an acquaintance. I met her through my captain and because I trusted my captain, I saw no problem in getting to know this girl. There was only one dilemma I thought I could look past, but it always came to my mind when I saw her.

* * * * *

I'd invited her over to my apartment some time ago for a small kickback my roommate and I were having. This was our first time associating in person so I looked forward to getting to know her. We took a few pictures, laughed, and talked.

217

Everything seemed to be going well. As we all congregated in the pool, her and I sat off to the side talking and getting to know one another. "I'm hoping my boyfriend will come, but he claims he's tired so I'll leave him alone I guess." She looked up at me asking who he was. As I responded with an explanation her eyes opened wide as she changed the direction of her body looking away from me.

Because I picked up her response through her face and her body language I asked, "You know him?"

"I'm familiar with who he is, but I don't really know him like that."

I let the conversation go, taking her for her word. As we all made our way back to my apartment I excused myself and stepped outside to call my boyfriend. He said a few words and I realized the tone in his voice seemed strange. As I asked if something was wrong I waited until he began to speak. "Are you alone?" I moved further away from my apartment, curious as to why he asked me that question. I answered nervously, scared to hear what he was about to say, but anxious to hear at the same time. "I wanted you to hear it from me before you heard it from anybody else, but the girl you have there, we slept together...But it was before I met you." As I explained to him the conversation her and I had just had, he denied her responses to me. He explained to me the only reason he thought to tell me was because he saw a picture of the two of us she had put up hours ago. I stood outside in silence, pondering on how I should go about the situation. What played in my head was how she smiled in my face with another story other than the truth, and he would have never told me if he didn't think someone else would get to me first. As I hung up from him I walked inside finding an excuse for everyone to leave. My mind was still trying to process it all. I didn't want her around to find out where my mind would be when it finished.

* * * * *

I found a table to sit and eat as she asked to join me. She sat across from me. This was the first time since the last we would actually speak. Because I never told her I knew, I used this as my opportunity. "I know it's in the past now, but I never got to tell you that I found out about you and my boyfriend." Instantly it felt like a moment of Déjà vu because she made the exact same face she made that night in the pool. I continued my statement sarcastically saying, "I'm not mad or anything, I just want to know why you felt the need to lie if it was before me?" As I watched her face change back to normal, I briefly listened to her response as I was directing my attention to the message my now ex-boyfriend sent me telling me to meet him at his apartment. As I stood up grabbing my things, she said, "Girl that's all you. If you're happy, I'm happy." Paying less attention to her, I walked off excited to get to him, not realizing I left my purse sitting on the table.

As I pulled next to his car in front of his apartment, I looked around realizing I didn't have my purse. I called her asking if she could bring it to my boyfriend's apartment. As she said yes with no hesitation, I looked past the fact she failed to ask where he stayed. I got out of my car fawning over the Valentine's Day gifts he had gotten me. Minutes later she drove around the corner and parked her car in front of ours as she got out to hand me my belongings. I watched as she spoke to him briefly before making her way back to her car. I noticed how he didn't look her in the eye once. I tilted my head up squinting my

219

eyes with a slight smirk on my face, I chose not to say anything. Good moments like this between he and I didn't come easy with us anymore so whenever they were presented I did my best to make them last.

A few weeks passed and everything seemed to be going well. It was a Wednesday. Every Wednesday meant everyone got pretty. It was a day for everyone on campus to get dressed up and enjoy the many festivities taking place on campus. I never really participated in this particular day much because it wasn't new for me to get dressed up, as it was something I did on a regular. Besides the music and dancing, it was a regular day for me. I decided to meet up with my ex-boyfriend while he and his friends participated in some of the events taking place. As I stood next to him, taking part in what I could, the girl I encountered on Valentine's Day came and stood on the other side of me, complimenting me on how good I looked. As I responded she pulled out her phone to take a picture. I was already late for my next class so I said my goodbyes, kissed my ex-boyfriend, and walked off.

I walked in class and began to prepare my things. A few minutes later my phone rang with a message from my captain. She told me she needed to tell me something. I stepped out leaving my things on my desk. As I walked outside I gave her a call. "Hey bud! I'm just going to tell you to stop talking to her." I asked who she was talking about. As she explained, my heart dropped. "She just put a picture of both of you on her page and when I saw it I thought to tell you to watch your back." Like Déjà vu I thought back to the first time my boyfriend called me because this same girl posted a picture of the two of us and the news immediately following. I instantly began to get upset and frustrated because I was still trying to figure out why my captain was telling me what she was telling me. Every time I asked, she responded to me saying it wasn't her place.

I took a slow deep breath shaking my head, "Don't play with me right now. Tell me what is going on."

She waited for a moment in silence. My body became warm as my heart beat faster and faster.

She finally spoke, "You know they slept together?"

As my heart calmed down I responded saying, "I already knew that."

She cut me off and with relief in her voice she responded saying, "Okay good! Then there is nothing to worry about."

I then finished my statement saying I knew they slept together before I knew either of them. Suddenly she became very quiet.

With a shy faint voice she responded, "Bud, this was three weeks ago."

I stared forward in silence, clinching my jaw and fighting back tears as she called my name. I hung up from her and immediately called him. He instantly answered the phone as if he was expecting my call and in a stern emotionless tone I said, "You have three minutes to get to where I am now." I still stood there, not moving. I focused my attention to the parking lot across the street, waiting to see his car. Two minutes went by as I continued to stare in the distance. His car sped around the corner parking in the exact spot I focused my attention on.

As I walked to his car my heart beat faster and faster. I sat in the front seat looking down at my hands as I balled one into a fist. I could feel him looking at me.

His voice shook as he asked, "What's wrong?"

I looked up. For a moment, all I did was stare him in the eyes, then I spoke, slowly and clearly, making sure he heard and understood exactly what was coming out of my mouth.

"Did. You. Sleep. With Her?"

I knew he knew exactly who and what I was talking about because he looked down at his hands.

Quietly, but comprehensibly he said, "Yes."

With no thought or hesitation of my reaction, I reached back and socked my fist into the side of his face, as his head hit the window.

He yelled, "Get out!"

I didn't move. I cried, yelling and screaming as I picked up the drink that sat in the cup holder, throwing it as whatever was in it landed on him and his seats. I slammed my hands on the front dashboard.

"You got me out here looking stupid, all in her face and you knew! You're a coward and I hate you!"

He grabbed me, trying to hug me, crying saying, "I'm sorry, I'm sorry."

For a brief moment I laid in his arms crying. I then pushed away, snatching the necklace he gave me from my neck throwing it at his face. Shaking my head, I looked into his eyes.

"You never deserved me."

As he looked at me crying, I called my classmates to bring me my things. I walked to meet them halfway with my makeup running down my face. This was the first time I couldn't care less about my appearance in public. I got back into the car. While he sat with his face in his hands, I looked forward wiping my eyes and said, "Take me to my car." I refused to walk all the way to my own car, in my heels, feeling the way I did. Once we pulled up, I grabbed my things and proceeded to get out as he called after me. I threw my things in the backseat of my car, laid my head on the wheel, and began to cry. I looked over to see him opening my passenger door, in motion to sitting in the seat. I immediately began to bang my hands against the steering wheel with tears rolling down my face as I screamed, "Get out!" over and over again.

The moment I made it home, I lost it. I screamed and yelled as I fell to the floor. I felt stupid and disgusting. He was the first man I gave a piece of me to and in that moment, to know I could never get it back due to his disvalue of it made me feel stupid and disgusting. As I laid down I thought about everything that had taken place. I felt like I couldn't trust anybody. The man I loved toyed with my heart. My captain, who I thought I was so close to, all I could think about was how long she knew and said nothing to me until she felt the need to. Trying to forget everything I closed my eyes and let my tears put me to sleep.

Not realizing how long I had been asleep, I woke up just in time to hear my roommate come into the house.

As I stood in my bathroom, staring into the mirror at the puffs that formed on my face, she yelled, "Bud, I'm home."

She knocked on the door and walked in.

"Hey bud."

I turned around to face her. I could see the concern on her face and as she asked me what was wrong. I began to cry again, falling to the ground. She grabbed me as she began to cry falling to the ground with me. I laid my head in her lap as we both cried.

She put her hand on my head as she asked, "What's wrong?" while tears rolled down her face.

I looked up to her and with my eyes practically swollen shut I said, "He slept with her."

I briefly explained the situation and then she looked at me and said, "Why didn't you tell me that you lost your virginity to him bud?"

I didn't respond right away because I honestly didn't know how to answer. I thought it was love, and maybe it was, but what felt right then, felt so wrong now.

Weeks went by and I continued to cope with slowly pulling myself away from him. It helped I had a job and still danced with the team in the spring, so I had things to occupy my time. My big sister had taken over leading, and all I could say was thankfully something was going right at a time where it seemed as though everything was going wrong for me. We remained busy due to the fact we were preparing for a performance coming up. The night before, my roommate and I prepared our things as usual. I brought up to her how it seemed as though my crab sister acted differently with me than she did with them and how I felt as though I treated her the same as everyone else. Thinking maybe my roommate would tell me if my crab sister had said anything about me to her, she didn't. I couldn't be mad at her for it, especially since she said she hadn't heard anything. She began to say things about our crab sister. As she talked about her I shook my head laughing, but I didn't say anything, not knowing this moment would be the start of a severed friendship.

The next afternoon we prepared ourselves to head out for our performance. Being that we normally rode together, I was under the impression I was riding with her until she stepped in my room saying, "Hey bud, I'm going to head out to the performance a little early." I thought to ask why but decided not to worry about it and continued to get myself together. Once I finished with everything, I had a few minutes left to spare. I headed to the school early seeing as though my roommate was already there, but when I made it, her car was nowhere to be found. I left it alone and walked inside to begin getting ready for the performance. Moments later my roommate walked into the dressing room with my sister. The same sister she talked about the night before. I looked towards her and then turned away. I knew it was obvious I was avoiding her because as we moved around each other before the performance we didn't speak. When it was over, I watched as she drove off with my sister. In that very moment I decided our friendship was no good for me.

I knew if she could talk about our sister with me, what was stopping her from talking about me to our sister. Because I didn't have an answer to justify her actions and didn't care to find one, I knew it was time I backed away.

Days went by. Going through life at this point in time seemed so difficult. I spent nights sleeping in my prayer closet crying, asking God why He wasn't answering my prayers. I guess I didn't read the fine print when I signed my prayer off to him because I didn't ask for anything happening to me. I promised him I'd do right if He sent me a man who was worthy of having me and I was worthy of having him. I didn't know who he would be, but I began to pray for him and his well-being in advance. Everything going on with my life at the time, I prayed about, manifesting that it was already done. One night I decided to call my aunt to tell her what happened between my ex-boyfriend and I. Besides calling my mom and telling her the day after the situation took place, I hadn't talked about it with anyone. As I explained the story to my aunt, she was unaware I slept with him. When I told her, she stayed quiet for some time. I waited for her response.

"I knew something wasn't right when I first met him, but I knew you had to see for yourself because I knew you really liked him. I just wish I would've told you what all comes with taking that step. I'm going to be praying for you every step of the way, but you need to use this time to really lean and depend on God because you're going to need Him for whatever He is preparing you for."

I didn't truly understand to what capacity her statement reached, but I just listened and then I said, "I haven't told daddy yet."

Because she knew how her own brother was, she laughed a little saying, "We all know how your dad is, but you need to talk to him. He can be a big help to you right now."

As I thought about it, ironically my dad messaged me saying, "I want to talk to my daughter."

I knew he knew something was going on. They moved to the same city and I went from visiting a lot, to coming over very little. When I did come over, they knew I had been crying. My attitude was bad, I was distant, and I barely wanted to look my dad in the face because I felt ashamed. The very next day I went to my family's home to see him. He was sitting on the bench in the backyard. As I sat next to him he asked me how I was doing, but despite my answer of being fine, I knew he knew what was real. He started to tell me I needed to figure out my priorities and responsibilities. I began to get frustrated, crying and raising my voice.

He knew it was deeper than what we were talking about because he cut me off saying, "I know something is going on. Did you sleep with him?"

As much as I wanted to lie, I knew all my dad had to do was look into my eyes and know the truth. I looked away, waited a moment, and said, "Yes," as I began to cry harder.

I could see him out of the corner of my eye look down as he wiped his hand down his face.

"I told your momma you did. I knew it. I just wanted to wait to see when you were going to tell me."

As I continued to cry, looking away, he continued. He grabbed my chin and motioned my face to face his.

"I told you, don't you ever let no man dictate your behavior. You are better than that. You are God's child, and although I am disappointed in you, you are still my baby girl and I'll love you no matter what. But because you are my child, I don't ever want to see you hurting like this; especially over no man, because he's not worth it. God put too much joy in you for you to allow some man to steal it."

As tears continued to fall, I looked away as he kept talking.

"Baby girl, I can't help you with what you're about to go through. God is taking you through something and I have to get out of His way and let Him do it. I'll be praying for you the whole way through because I'm your daddy." He turned me back to look at him, pointing to his chest, "And this man loves you and would never hurt you."

I continued to cry as I stood up and walked away. I really had no clue what was going on with me, but I knew I wasn't myself.

Time was slowly passing by and although I still hurt, I did my best to suppress the pain. I started communicating with a guy who I loved to speak to. He was a good guy. He listened to me and I didn't feel the pressure of intimacy, but rather intellect between the words we exchanged on a daily. He was smart and kind. Although I had yet to meet him in person, I figured it was best that way. It was simply just good to have someone to talk to. I was happy I had someone to call and tell my day to. It had been about a month since we started talking and this particular week he informed me he would be in town. He called to let me know he was here. I was just getting off work and he had just made it to his hotel. I was nervous about seeing him. Seeing as how I was recently out of a relationship, I wanted to make sure I wasn't moving too fast for what I was ready for. I decided to meet him at his hotel. As I walked to his hotel room I took every step slowly. Once I made it to the door I said a quick prayer, knocked, and stepped back. As he opened the door, my eyes started from his feet to the top of his head. He was tall, dark, and handsome. I didn't realize I had a new type until that moment. He reached for a hug as I stepped into his arms. I sniffed his shirt closing my eyes as I took in every scent. We sat on the couch and talked for hours about everything; laughing and simply getting to know one another and enjoying each other's company. I felt good about him. It was the fact that all I needed was conversation, and he gave it to me. He knew how to listen. Without knowing one another for a long period of time, he was interested in everything I wanted to talk about. For once, I stopped thinking about my ex. The man who sat in front me seemed to fulfill exactly what I needed.

The spring semester was coming to an end. Although I spoke with my ex-boyfriend from time to time, I spent my days with the new guy I was now talking to whenever he came to visit. He occupied a lot of my time and I was very happy when speaking to him, but it felt so hard to completely let my ex go. It was the second to last week of school and I was excited because the new guy planned to come to town. It was also the day of our end of the season band banquet. It was my second time attending and I always seemed to get there a few minutes late. As I walked up, I noticed everyone stood congregating outside, including my band director. I didn't think much of it, so I made my way into the banquet room to sit amongst the team. Time passed by and still the event had yet to get started. The team stepped out to take pictures and as we all gathered, my roommate and I passed by one another not speaking as she stood close to our crab sister.

While we occupied our time with pictures, a band student walked by saying, "There's police cars parked outside. The band director is held up at his office because they locked his office door and all of our awards are in there."

All of us looked around, wondering what was going on, as I walked away to speak to a former band member. "Do you know what's going on?"

He looked down and then back towards me and said, "I'm not sure exactly, but I heard they could possibly be letting him go."

As we exchanged final words I said, "They'd be a fool to let my band director go."

I walked back into the banquet room and sat with the team. An hour passed by and still no start, and no sign of our band director. Minutes later, everyone began to clap as he walked in from the back door. I clinched on my tissue, not knowing if I was going to shed tears of happiness or sadness. As he made it to the podium, he asked everyone to stop. He looked down for a few minutes in silence and then back up as he began to speak.

"You all are my family, so I have to be real with you. I don't know everything that's going on, but it's going to be alright. I will say they are giving me two options: to resign or be fired, but because we are family and I would never choose to leave y'all, they're just going to have to fire me."

As the band began to make noise and everyone yelling and talking at once, I looked over as some of the other dancers began to cry. Tears formed in my eyes, but it wasn't until the moment he came from the podium and began to cry, that I let my tears fall. This was the strongest man I had met since I'd been there. He was my first band director and I had never seen him cry, so it hurt me. In that moment, they ended our band banquet. We all stayed standing around our table crying. He walked up to us as we gathered around him. He made eye contact with each and every one of us as he said, "My girls," smiling. As he continued to smile giving small words of wisdom, he looked over to my big sister, "You're going to be my next captain, and I don't care what happens, you're ready." As he hugged us all, we crowded around my big sister congratulating her as she cried. I walked to my car with the thoughts of everything that had just taken place playing in my mind. I said to myself, "My band director was seemingly fired and he just appointed my big sister as captain." This year was about to be interesting.

The very next day, once I finished classes, I decided to spend the evening with the guy I was talking to. We laid, enjoying a movie, when my phone rang with a message. I looked over to see my ex-boyfriend's name on the screen. I knew he had a special event that day, but I was exactly where I wanted to be. I didn't respond and turned my phone face down. Later on that evening, the guy and I decided to go out to eat. We were just walking out of the restaurant when I looked down at my phone to a message that read, "So you're out here messing around on your ex-boyfriend. I'll be sure to let him know." Because the number was random, I looked around trying to see if anyone was watching me. As we walked to the car, I asked the guy to drive, dismissing the message I received. I directed him to my apartment. I planned to pick up a few games before heading back to his hotel room. As he turned into my complex, pulling right in front of the gate, my heart dropped. My eyes opened wide as I saw my ex-boyfriend's car parked right outside the gate. I looked over to the guy I was with.

"That's my ex-boyfriend."

He could hear the anxiety in my voice and saw the worry on my face.

Calm and with ease he looked at me, placed his hand on my knee saying, "Relax, it's okay."

I took a deep breath as he drove past the gate. Being that he had never been to my apartment before, he missed his turn and had to drive all the way around. I looked to the rearview mirror to see my ex following us.

I turned around and then turned back saying, "He's following us."

He could still hear the worry in my voice as he looked over to me, and with a stern strong voice he said, "Calm down."

He pulled up to my apartment and as he parked I said, "Don't get out of the car, please."

I watched my ex step out of his car as I walked towards him. He walked up close to me, crossing his arms looking down to me.

"So this is what you do? I call you all day, you don't answer because you with this dude? Who's in the car?"

I dropped my head to the side and lifted my eyebrows.

"We don't talk like that no more and you know that. I was very clear when I said I was hanging out with a friend, and he's the friend."

As we exchanged words, I could only think on how I was simply confused as to how he could sleep with someone, but when I hang out, the world ends. He started to walk towards my car to the driver's side. I watched as the guy I was talking to opened the door and placed one foot on the ground.

I looked over to my ex-boyfriend as he said, "I don't want no problems. Y'all friends?"

The guy responded saying, "We vibin bruh."

"Cool, that's all I needed to know."

As he walked into the middle of the road, he called after me.

"Come here."

"Don't talk to me like that."

He raised his voice and again he said, "Come here."

I looked to my ex and then over to the guy I was talking to, hesitating on what I should do and then the guy called my name.

"Get in the car, we're not doing this."

It was the assertiveness in his voice.

I began walking to the car and my ex followed me as he yelled, "So you gon' listen to this dude?"

He held on to the door as I tried to close it, pulled out his phone and proceeded to say, "Look at this hoe y'all," repeating himself as I pulled on the door, closed it in his face, and drove off. We headed back to his hotel room. The car ride was silent and he placed his hand on my knee again.

"You okay?"

I had no words. I replayed every moment in my head over and over again. I mainly worried because I blamed myself. If anything had happened, I felt as though it would've been on me. Once we were in the hotel room I stood off to the side. It was hard for me to know how to function because I didn't know what he was thinking. He sat on the bed and called my name. As I walked towards him, he pulled my hand and motioned for me to sit on his lap. I laid my head on his shoulder as he kissed my forehead, wrapping his arms around me.

"Talk to me."

I couldn't control the tears that fell down my face. He let me cry as he held me. I moved over to sit up against the headboard and he sat next to me. I looked over to him.

"Honestly, if you don't want to talk to me anymore, I'll understand."

As much as I didn't really want that, I felt as though I put him in a bad situation. It was on me.

He continued to look at me as he said, "You couldn't have known that was going to happen so stop worrying about that. I like you a lot, and I know love doesn't go away instantly, but if we're going to continue to pursue one another, you have to make a decision because these types of situations can't keep happening."

I wanted things to work with him, so in that moment I officially decided it was time to leave my ex alone for good.

Summer started and I did my best trying to cope with the changes. Besides losing my boyfriend to a situation that still devastated me and with my roommate and I no longer talking as best friends, let alone friends, I began to find other ways to adjust. I worked a lot to occupy my time. As hesitant as I was to make new friends, I met some girls who seemed to be genuine. When we were together, we always had a good time. I invited them over after work one night. I didn't know much about them, but I wasn't as concerned about it because I was learning to see people for who they really were, so I figured any negative motive would present itself. As we all sat in the living room talking and laughing, a piece of information within the conversation stood out to me. As their words continued, my mind was still on that one part. I looked up from my phone. "Wait, who are you dating?" I didn't think I would hear her say it was my captain's ex-boyfriend. I shrugged the comment off and directed my attention to something else. I knew they figured I would probably tell her, but the way I saw it, it had nothing to do with me. We were all grown. I felt as though the status of their relationships was none of my concern. I began to get closer with them as the time moved along. I didn't think too much about my captain when it came to them because we never

235

discussed relationships. That would have been the only relevancy she remotely had.

I was heading out from my job on a lunch break when I received a message from my captain. "We need to talk." To my surprise I didn't think she would address me about my "new found friends" and anything she heard about their relationships. As close as we were, and as many things we saw eye to eye on, I would think she would understand why it was not my place to tell someone else's business or even lead her on making her think there was something going on. Even if that was my motive, I didn't know anything to be able to tell her. I decided to take a step back. I had the opportunity to decide how I wanted these new friendships to go. Because there were many things I decided I needed to change, my tolerance for the drama was becoming very low.

Chapter 11
Unbalanced Expectations

It was now the week of high school band camp and my big sister and her sister took over, leaving the rest of the team to follow accordingly. Because I decided to continue working my day job, I assisted in the evenings with what I could. The day before the big camp performance the girls were scheduled to practice out on the field. As I walked around assisting with whatever needed to be done, a parent approached me. She called out my name. I walked up to shake her hand, proceeding to ask what I could help her with. "I don't want to cause any issues, but I have been very disappointed in how my child has been feeling these past few days. She called me crying yesterday telling me the young lady in charge has been very rude, and threw her and a few other dancers to the back because they weren't doing the dances like she wanted them to. I have a problem with that because there is a way you talk to people, especially a child." I explained to her I hadn't been present most of the week, but didn't mind helping her get to the bottom of the situation. I walked over to my big sister.

"There is a parent who would like to speak with you about some concerns she has dealing with her daughter."

She looked over to me briefly and then back to what she was focused on as she waved her hand saying, "I don't have time to be dealing with petty mess like that right now."

I decided not to go back and forth with her being I knew it wasn't the time or the place, and walked back to the parent. "She is busy right now, but I can help you on talking to your child, making sure she is okay."

It was now the final day of the camp. I walked to our dance room to see our captain standing in the door.

We hugged as she whispered in my ear saying, "Can we talk?"

This was the first time we would speak since last we stopped talking due to my "new found friends."

We stepped to the side as she looked at me saying, "I just want to apologize because it was childish for me to come at you about something like that. You were right."

As we went back and forth, agreeing to leave the situation alone, I asked if she was staying for the performance.

"Girl I'm not staying or I might catch a case."

I laughed, not really knowing what she was talking about until she explained that her crabs, which were my little sisters, complained to her about how the camp was going. She then asked if I could look out for them. I had no problem with checking in. I felt as though we had a different bond than some of the other team members being we had the same captain. I pulled my little sister to the side.

"Everything okay?"

I knew there was a problem when she rolled her eyes, took a deep breath and said, "Me and my crab sister have been doing all the work. Your big sister and her crab sister haven't been doing anything and the dancers have been complaining."

I could only figure there was some truth to what she was saying seeing that someone had just approached me the day before about an issue.

"Do I need to say something?"

She looked at me with a slight smile, then sighed saying, "Thanks sis, but I already told the sponsors."

Despite the stories I had already heard, the performance seemed to have gone great. Up until now I had not witnessed my big sister doing wrong, other than hearsay, so I tried to dismiss it. We all walked back to the band hall from the field. I was just focused on getting off my feet from walking in my heels the entire day when a parent of one of the dancers tapped me on my shoulder.

She was furious, raising her voice as she said, "Can you direct me on who to speak to because at this point I'm going to make my way to administration."

I looked over to her daughter who had tears rolling down her face. I laid my hand on her shoulder as her mother continued.

"She messed with the wrong child," as she gestured over to my big sister.

Immediately I answered, "I can understand your frustration, but there's no need to go to administration ma'am. You can speak with our Assistant Band Director," as I took them to him.

A day went by and it was now a week away from auditions. I wasn't doing much when I received a call from the sponsor. Because it was so close to auditions I didn't expect to hear from anyone.

I knew something was going on when she said, "I just have a few questions about the camp."

I didn't think much about the things I experienced during the time because I wasn't as present as everyone else.

"Did anything take place that you witnessed?"

I stood quiet for a moment, then responded.

"I don't think that it's my place to say anything."

"Every last one of you are responsible, so you need to tell me what went on."

I informed her about the parents who approached me.

It was now the day before auditions. I prepared for weeks with one of my teammates who made it on the team before me. She was gorgeous and I didn't mind being around her because her spirit always seemed to be positive. After weeks of practicing together, we decided to end with dinner and then head straight to the gym to get in one last practice. As we rehearsed our choreography and technique, I looked into the mirror to see my roommate and my crab sister come in together through the back door. My heart dropped. I guess my teammate could see and feel the tension because she looked over to me, opened her eyes wide for a quick moment, and then turned her head. Although I had informed her briefly that my crab sister, my roommate, and I didn't have the best relationship, I didn't think to see them the day before our auditions. Nevertheless, we all practiced together. Still nothing changed between my roommate and I. We moved around one another with very little words. I couldn't help but be in my head on how we got to this point. I just knew things were supposed to work because we were sisters. That's what we were taught. "Your crab sisters will be your only true friends. They're going to have your back no matter what." For a moment I isolated myself, sat close to the mirror, and took random glances at myself and my teammates who danced behind me. It was funny to me how my idea of "team" and "sisterhood" began to show its true identity, but why now?

This would be the first year I wouldn't talk to my roommate before auditions. It seemed almost like a ritual to me, but I figured maybe it was for the best that it changed. As I meditated to the gospel music playing through my car speakers on my way to the band hall, I focused on calming myself and getting into the right frame of mind. Being on the team seemed easy when you compared the process to auditions. Because I had experienced drastic changes to auditions two years in a row, I wouldn't dare leave this year exempt. It felt like stepping into a time capsule of the unknown going from one year to the next not knowing how. After I finished saying my prayers with my family, I walked to the door with the team. My crab sister and my roommate walked ahead of me together. We all settled into one room with just the current team members. I sat next to my teammate who I'd been practicing with. Although there seemed to be no tension, it was evident everyone's mind was focused on the same thing.

Auditions started off as normal. As we walked in, I prepared my mind for technique across the floor. This time I watched no one, but remained focused on every way I presented myself, whether it was the way I positioned my body to every expression on my face. As we returned to our assigned room after finishing the first part of auditions, we waited. It seemed normal to wait with anxiety. Although it was still present in me, it didn't seem as bad as my last auditions. Luckily, once the first cut was made, everyone from the current team walked into the band room and it was now time for choreography. I found an area to myself as I took every step of the dance and found a way to make it my own. Time seemed to go by quickly when rehearsing individually. Before I knew it my number was called to perform. I lined up with my group, standing as the first in our lineup. Although I stood further to the side, I still thought of every way to get the judges attention and keep it. "Ladies, once you finish the choreography, please freestyle until the music fades out." This was a first and I was just glad I had a dance combination prepared. The music was on and I hit every step and every beat they taught. It was now time for the freestyle portion as the sponsor yelled, "Improvise ladies!" I began to perform the dance I created. The moment I felt myself growing comfortable, my mind drew a blank. My mind raced as I told myself, "don't stop." I started to spin and leap, throwing in a funky move every moment I connected with the judges. As I caught the sponsor walking over to fade the music, I dropped to the ground and proceeded to lay out. I stood up at attention making eye contact with every judge. I felt good. With that, we were dismissed.

I could finally sit and relax as the rest of the team took their turns to perform. Once everyone had gone, we all sat, waiting for instructions and then the unexpected happened. It was common for callbacks to take place, but through my past experience of auditions, I'd never seen it happen, especially to a current dancer. One by one they began to call back every member on the team to do the routine again except for myself and my teammate. Out of her crab sisters, she was the more reserved one, so she didn't say anything, but I could see the concern in her eyes because I wore the same expression. They then called a few of the team members back again for a third time. My concern came from the fact that in the past I would've thought not getting called back was a good thing, until it came down to the point where it seemed like more against less in this case. The majority were called back, two weren't, and I was one of them. I walked over to my crab sister. She looked nervous as she waited against the wall. "You got this." She shrugged her shoulders as she responded to me. "Yea I'm fine. They're probably just calling us because were the stronger dancers." I didn't respond because I figured maybe her seeing it that way was her way of coping, but part of me took it and internalized her words. Seeing as though I never seen something like this happen before, I didn't know what to believe. As everyone made it back to the room, we waited. Although I knew interviews to normally come next, I didn't really know how to move at this point, so I focused on staying ready. Time went by as we continued to wait, and then the sponsor made an announcement. "Thank you, ladies. You can gather your things and leave. Be on the lookout for further information."

Despite getting use to waiting for results, this time felt different. The preparation process was over and there was no longer room to "get ready." It was a few days after auditions. I had stopped to pick up some food before heading home, when I received a call from the sponsor. Whenever we spoke it was very rare that the call was formal because majority of the time we talked as girlfriends, but this moment came unexpectedly. I answered the phone with excitement, thinking it would possibly be a normal conversation, but I was immediately corrected. Her words and her tone told me everything I needed to know.

"Good evening ma'am. I hope your day is going well. I need you to write a letter on what leadership is to you, what are some ideas of yours' to enhance the team, and what is one thing you would like to bring, or see done differently? Please have this to us no later than tomorrow evening. This call is to stay here. Do not speak of this conversation with anyone."

We exchanged goodbyes and within minutes the phone call was over. My heart sat at my feet and my mind raced. I lost my appetite, which was very rare, and I then decided instead of going home, I needed to talk to someone about what took place. I decided to go to my parents' house. I rushed to their room and told them the news. My mom looked up and stared at me for a moment.

"What if they ask you to be captain sweetie. You believe you're ready?"

Before I could respond, my dad jumped in.

"Of course my baby girl is ready and they will pick her to be captain."

I laughed at his comments, shaking my head.

"Maybe co-captain if anything daddy, but my big sister is next in line."

I knew it was about to get serious when he sat up and leaned forward.

"Do you believe you can lead this team?"

"Yes."

"Then that's it. You need to speak that thang as if it's already done. I'm sure the other girls are good, but there is something special about you that only you possess, and that's why my baby girl is going to be the captain of that team," as he smiled from ear to ear. "Now you have a letter to write. Don't rush it. Say a prayer, let him speak to you and then give them who you are."

I walked to the dining room table, prepared my things and did exactly what my dad told me to do. I wanted to make sure that with everything I was required to write about, they still saw me.

Two days had gone by and all I could think about was what the band director and the sponsors thought about my paper and when I would receive a response. I decided to go to the gym when I received a phone call from my roommate's mother. I hesitated on answering because her daughter and I weren't talking. I was sure she knew we weren't. It had been a while since we last spoke, and although I had my doubts, I decided to answer. As we spoke briefly on how the summer was going, the questions I expected came next.

"So have you heard anything regarding auditions?"

"No I haven't, you?"

I knew she was looking for answers, so I continued to keep my comments brief.

"You haven't heard anything from anyone? Neither have we. This is strange."

I picked up her motive when she failed to ask about her daughter and I's relationship. Minutes later, ironically after hanging up, my roommate called me.

"Girl, have you heard anything?"

"No"

"Me either."

Although there was no bad blood between us, we hadn't spoken since auditions, but I decided to play along.

"That's crazy, your mom just called me."

"She did? What she say?"

I rolled my eyes and laughed within myself as we finished the conversation.

It was normal for things to get weird and uptight whenever audition results came around simply because no one knew who knew what and when they were going to know. That evening I went to work, still with everything on my mind, not really focusing on my job when my crab sister messaged me.

"Hey sis, did you get a call?"

Out of all my crab sisters, her and I hung out the most that summer. We checked in with each other every now and then, so part of me felt like maybe I should tell her. All I could hear play in my mind was everything the sponsor told me during her call, including her words about not telling anyone. I didn't know what her motive was for asking me, if she even had a motive, but I knew I didn't want to lie to her.

"No I have not received a call regarding the selection."

I didn't lie, but I just didn't tell the full truth either. I didn't trust anyone to tell them what I was told not to. I didn't see why I had to put myself in a position to have to choose between a friendship and an opportunity.

The very next day I received a message from the sponsor stating my interview would be the next day along with all the instructions I needed to prepare. The day came and it was now time for my interview. I changed my outfit multiple times just to make sure it was perfect. I took a deep breath, said a quick prayer, and then took one last look at myself through the camera. My heart began to beat fast as I watched the band director and the sponsor reveal their faces. I smiled as they began to ask questions. They could see me looking into the camera, but my vision showed me a glance of the girl I was when I first interviewed. It almost seemed as though the moment and feeling were the same, except this time I didn't shed a tear and my mindset seemed broader and more experienced. As they continued to ask questions based on leadership, I answered, enhancing the words I wrote in my letter. No one cracked a smile. I had no clue what to think, but I continued to answer each question to the best of my ability, smile and give them just who I was. That same night I invited my coworker over for a girls' night to take my mind off the interview when I received a call from the sponsor.

"Are you alone?"

I stepped outside as my heart began to race. The phone stayed silent as we waited for a moment, which seemed like forever. As I heard the first word come out of her mouth my body froze. I wanted to make sure I didn't miss anything.

"We regret to inform you that you will not be returning as a member on the team."

Silence. I couldn't even bring myself to cry. All I could feel was my body going weak. Before I could gather my words to respond, she began to speak again.

"You will be returning as the Captain!"

I let out a loud, quick scream, and dropped to the ground. I covered my mouth hoping no one would respond to my commotion. I had no clue what to say or how to feel. I couldn't cry because my body and emotions were in shock. I believed I always had the potential, but there was always a little doubt in me that underestimated my ability to take on the task, so I always seemed to dismiss the idea.

I could feel my sponsor smiling through the phone as she said, "It was a unanimous decision. You earned this and I am so proud of you, but things are about to get real for you now. You display strength, and that is a big reason for why we chose you. This is by far not about to be an easy journey, but me, including the other sponsor and the band director are going to be behind you 100%. I know you're going to be okay because you're smart. You have a strong family and strong faith. You'll be good."

It was hard to know how to feel. I had so many questions.

"Who all made the team? Who didn't? Why wasn't my big sister picked as captain? Who were my crabs?"

I received not one answer for any of my questions.

"Can I tell anyone, at least my mom?"

"You are not to say anything to anyone. If word gets back to us that you have said anything, you will lose your position indefinitely. You can tell your mom tomorrow, but that is it. The real work begins now, so don't let us down."

I honestly didn't have the option of excitement. From that moment on it was go time. I knew this would be a battle that in the moment, I didn't know how to fight. To my surprise, I hadn't cried or showed any major expression. I couldn't. I wanted to share the news simply to see if I felt the form of emotion I believed should have been displayed. Not that I needed anyone to be happy, but at the same time, I felt like I did.

The very next day I gave my mom a call. She answered the phone with question in her voice and I knew she was waiting on any news. I put on the saddest tone of voice I could.

"They just called me mom...They told me that I wasn't returning as a member of the team."

She was quiet for a moment, then said "Sweetie...that just means God has something greater for you."

I could hear the disbelief in her voice. Before she could continue, I finished my statement.

"They said I would be returning as Captain!"

For the first time I felt the exact emotions I wanted to feel when I first received the news. I began to jump around with tears falling down my face, trying to stay as contained as possible being I was still at work. I could hear the excitement in her voice and I felt her energy.

"You are the captain? I am so proud of you!"

I didn't need to tell anyone else for the time being. I got to tell my best friend and that's all that mattered. I figured after being able to tell my mom the news, the day would be a good day until quickly I was reminded why people say, "It gets lonely at the top." I received a call from my sponsor minutes later informing me that she contacted the members on the team. Still not knowing who was on the team or who had what position other than myself, I asked broad questions to see if maybe I could get closer to certain answers. "I'm not telling you who made the team, but I did let them know you would be captain." I could only assume what the responses were based on her silence. I didn't want to form any opinion of my crab sisters just yet because I knew everyone was told to keep the information to themselves, but I only hoped that at least one would have reached out. However, my biggest concern was my big sister. Although we weren't close, it still mattered to me what happened to her. Despite the fact I was excited for the position I received, I could only imagine how she felt. It was important to me to know if she received any position.

"She doesn't have a set position, but we don't want her to feel slighted. As of right now she will be assisting you when needed."

I didn't like the sound of that too much.

"Would it be possible if we could share the captain position or she at least be co-captain?"

"You can have her assist any way you would like, but there will only be one captain position as of right now."

Because I had never been in this position before, I didn't know how far things could get, or how deep, but I could foresee where everything was headed. Although it was meant to be a secret, I knew the news would be out before anything truly got started.

That night I sat around packing for a vacation I along with some coworkers planned for, when I received a call from my teammate who I worked out with during the summer before auditions. The moment her name came across my screen, a sting hit my heart and I could feel something was wrong, but I didn't want to jump to any conclusions. I let the call go to voicemail as I messaged my sponsor to see if she knew why she was calling but she didn't answer my question. The phone rang again. This time I answered. "Hey, you know what is going on? The team said that they received a call but no one called me." It seemed like my heart stopped. This was the first team member I spoke to since I received my news, but I still didn't know anything regarding the team, and because I spent time over the summer genuinely getting to know her, the news she gave shocked me. I wanted for it not to be true. I didn't know how to respond as she continued to ask if I knew anything. I wanted to tell her the news about myself because I didn't want her to think I was lying about anything. I had no clue about her, but my mind fought against telling her about me so I could keep a friend, and not telling her to keep my position. It seemed to always happen this way with me. I meet a potential friend, I receive something I can't share, and because we're not friends to that capacity, I don't feel the need to share, but if I don't, then I'm "not a real friend" or a "liar." I could hear the anger in her voice. My voice became faint as I pushed to answer what I could without saying what I wanted. She hung up the phone and I immediately called the sponsor.

"She didn't make the team?"

She was silent and then responded with a single, yet still "No."

I didn't say anything. She then continued.

"We have not called to speak with her yet."

I was hating the position this was putting me in.

"Can I please call and tell her what's going on? I'm sick of losing friends and I'm sure I don't have the support of my crab sisters. She was the last teammate I was forming a relationship with."

She wasted no time in responding.

"Your position or friends? It's up to you. This is going to show you who your real friends are, and if they can't support you when things don't go their way, then you need to decide if that is really a friend."

As adamant as I was on telling my teammate, my sponsor was right. It bothered me at the simple fact I was possibly going to have no one, but I was starting to see things based on the prayer I prayed. I was slowly realizing everyone is beneficial, but not everyone is beneficial for you.

As I prepared to head out for my trip, I thought about everything that took place. The fact that now I knew the team had spoken, but no one reached out to me. It's not that I expected it, but the situations were really forcing me to toughen up. I was a strong person, so for the life of me I kept wondering why I felt everything and why it bothered me. It's easy to say what you will and can tolerate until you're actually in the situation. I had already encountered the best and worst of the experience my first two years, so why did I feel like I was back at square one? My friends and I made it to our location and all I could think about was what my next move was. I continued to push for my big sister to be a captain, only to begin to see the reason why it was better off being left alone. My sponsor gave me the permission to speak with my big sister and see what would happen. I called and immediately I could feel every bit of her emotion through the phone.

"Hey girl you busy? I just wanted to talk to you about the team and about us working together going forward."

She kept her responses short and snappy.

"For what?"

I took a deep breath before I continued to respond. Although I was now in a somewhat higher position, it didn't change the fact

I never minded taking it there, but I knew that's what they expected from me and every move I made was being watched.

"I was hoping we could get together and discuss everything."

She waited, then said, "If we get together, it won't be nice."

I was starting to feel as though the position was causing me to be someone I wasn't because every part of me wanted to know exactly what "wasn't going to be nice," but in all actuality it was only bringing out the best of who I already was and molding certain aspects of me. Later on that evening, I received a message from the sponsor saying she, along with the band director and the assistant sponsor, needed to speak with me. I stepped away from my friends to find a secluded area. The band director, who served as interim for the time being, began the conversation.

"How are you feeling?"

"I feel fine, what's going on?"

I could sense there was a problem. The sponsor cut in.

"We don't want you to be alarmed or worried, but the team reached out to us and had some things to say about our choosing you as captain."

"What did they say?"

My heart was beating fast as tears began forming in my eyes. I never experienced anything to this capacity where I was able to know the things others said about me, not know why, and not be able to do anything about it. It seemed like the worst feeling I could possibly feel. The sponsors continued.

"They mentioned a few things about your work ethic and how you weren't the best choice."

My tears uncontrollably rolled down my face. I knew they knew I was crying. No one said anything. For a moment, they listened to me cry. The band director broke the silence.

"We're not telling you this to hurt you. We're telling you this because we want you to be strong and know that no matter what they say, you are going to remain the captain. We stand on our decision and we're standing behind you. It's not going to be easy, but you're strong and we know you can handle it."

As I hung up I wiped my tears and just sat there. Besides for my crab sister who I didn't have the best relationship with, I never heard of anyone having a problem with me until now. No one came to me to talk about it, not even my crab sisters. Was I not supposed to take the position? Regardless of me not having the closest relationship with everyone, I still loved my teammates, but was I supposed to turn away from the position to prove it?

A day passed. I tried to put on a brave face for the rest of the trip, but it was far from easy. Every thought went through my mind. It wasn't like I could vent to anyone because I couldn't talk about it. It was just hard. As my coworkers and I rode to our destination I sat in silence, looking out of the window thinking on everything taking place when my friend handed me his phone with a post on social media releasing the news of me being captain. *The Shambles Poem*. The news of my position had now been released through the form of a poem along with comments expressing the feelings of the selection. I knew social media would play a big role in my everyday problems, but once again it was like I was a crab again. It was hard to pull away from watching and caring about what other people thought. I knew it wasn't good for me, but I couldn't help it.

That night we all went to dinner. I was in hopes of finally having a moment where the situations left my mind, but they didn't. It seemed like every moment something presented itself, it added on to the issues, making it worse. We stood waiting for our table when I looked over to see my captain's ex-boyfriend walk through the door. I looked over to my friend as he looked back to me, opening his eyes wide. I knew we both thought the same thing. I had no clue he would be coming, but I knew the moment someone took out a phone, panned the table, and posted on social media, assumptions would come from everywhere. Sure enough, it was done. But what was I supposed to do? I was in no control of who others invited. I didn't have a relationship with him so I left it alone, knowing it was going to cause a problem with my captain once again. The very next day I called my big sister one last time to ask if she would like to meet up to discuss ideas about the team. She agreed and I could only hope things were going to go better than what was already taking place.

I made it back from my vacation. It was now the day to meet with my big sister. As I walked to our location I waited, thinking on every possible way the conversation could go. Minutes later she walked up and sat across from me. My heart was beating fast. I didn't know what to expect. I wanted everything to go well, but all I could think of was her words, "If we get together, it won't be nice." I did my best to dismiss it as I began our conversation.

256

"So I just wanted to start off with a quick prayer in hopes this meeting will go well."

Once we prayed I continued.

"I want to begin by talking about us. I just want to know how you're feeling and you can be honest with me."

"I don't have a problem with you because you didn't make the decision, others did, but I did lose respect for you."

Although I asked for honesty, I tried to understand where exactly she was going with her statements, so I continued to listen.

"I came in before you. You really learned from me and if I choose to come back you can't tell me nothing. It's called deference and you should understand that," but I didn't.
I mean I understood her timeline, but what did "deference" have to do with the decision that was made? I waited for a moment, then responded.

"I agree with some of what you said, and I understand that you came in before me. I have learned a lot from you. You're an amazing dancer and I am sure I can learn so much more from you. That is why I wanted to meet with you. I want us to be able to work together as a team. My goal is to get the team to come together."

She gave a slight chuckle, looked away, and then looked back to me as she responded.

"I can tell you now, that's not going to happen this year. The entire team has animosity towards you. I personally feel like you don't deserve to be captain. You don't put in the work others do. Because we're in the room 24/7 we see what each person does and brings to the table. I would have been okay if my sister got it or one of your sisters because I know they work hard. And I still won't have any input. You don't need me. And if I do choose to come back, I'm still deciding whether I'll have a positive attitude or negative, but either way it goes, however I come in there is how the team will respond. If I come in not caring about you, they're not going to care about you.'

I lifted my eyebrow and stared into her eyes with a slight smirk. I figured she was waiting on me to jump out of character. I looked around trying to gather the right words, and then I looked back to her.

"What made you or the team feel entitled to decide who deserves what spot on the team? You would have been okay with others and that is fine. Bottom line, I'm in this position for a reason. Because God opened this door for me, none of y'all can close it. All I wanted you to know is I want to involve you and your input would be appreciated. I do remember the last time we spoke you said you would not have input and that's completely up to you, but your reasons are why I am trying to get things between us worked out. If we are on one accord, I know the team will fall in line."

She wasted no time in responding.

"Well that is just not going to happen and I'm sorry, but the team is not going to be how you want it. But I will give you one input. You may not want to talk to your captain. She is very hostile towards you right now."

I laughed not knowing what the purpose of that particular comment was but her energy enticed me to respond.
"Oh girl, I am not worried about her or anyone being hostile towards me," as I concluded my statement with a laugh.

She responded with a smile on her face.

"The team is not hostile, they just don't like the decision that was made. So from a leader to a 'leader', you need to find a way to talk to them about all of this."

As the conversation came to a close I stood up.

"Thanks for the input and I appreciate you meeting with me. This was a very productive conversation."

We went our separate ways. I didn't think after that moment it would lead her to quitting the team, but the very next morning the sponsor called me with the news. I continued to try to understand why things were getting so bad. I wanted to talk to the team because I truly didn't know where this was coming from. Was I really not fit to be captain in their eyes or was it that they saw me in a position they wanted? I straddled the fence with both questions. That evening I called the sponsor. What my big sister didn't know was that my intentions were for her to be co-captain, that's what I wanted but judging by how things went during our conversation, only to lead to her quitting, it was back to the drawing board. I expressed to the sponsor I still wanted a co-captain.

"Who all did you consider for the position other than myself?"

"We mainly looked between you, your big sister, and your roommate."

This was the first time she inched to any other information I tried to get in the beginning. I waited to respond because I contemplated my decision in my mind. I wanted to make sure I didn't make any decisions based on personal feelings.

"I think my roommate would be a good choice. I know we have our differences right now, but I believe we would work well together. I think it will bring a great dynamic to the team."

She quickly responded.

"Spoken like a true captain. I will give her a call and let her know the news."

Later that night the sponsor set us up in a group message asking if we could get together to come up with some things for the season. I gave my roommate a call and said, "Congratulations on getting co-captain." She said, "Thank you," with nothing else to say. Once again I found myself expecting from her what I should have known she wouldn't supply. I let it go. I began talking about the ideas I had for the season. As I watched her take notes, I stopped.

"I just want to make sure everything between us is good before we continue. I figured we should get some things clear so we can move on with a clean slate, especially since we'll be working together now."

"I'm good. I don't have anything to say. So is that all for your notes?"

As much as I wanted to say I was beginning to regret my decision, I tried my hardest not to allow my emotions to take me to that place. Last we spoke everything seemed fine. Now it was a different story.

The next day I made my way to the dance room to get some things situated for the season. I stepped outside of the room when I watched as my big sister's crab sister walked through the front door. As I spoke she briefly responded and kept walking. Everything in me contemplated asking if we could have a conversation, but I decided to leave it alone because it seemed as though no matter what I said, no one understood the situation from my point of view. Granted I wanted to know from their point of view, but it seemed like no matter who it came from, the answer would be the same. "It just should've been somebody else." I walked back into the room and sat in the spot my captain normally sat in. I stared at the mirror, doing nothing other than simply looking. I didn't know what to think or what to do. It seemed as though I was just there. My daze was interrupted as the band director walked in and stood next to me.

"How are you feeling?"

"I guess I'm doing okay. I'll be better though."

He took a deep breath, looked down, and for a minute he didn't say anything. As I continued to look down I could see from the corner of my eye him looking at me through the mirror.

"We just lost another teammate."

I had a feeling my big sister's crab sister was going to quit, but I really wasn't sure. He paused for a moment as I took a deep breath, then he continued.

"You know this is not easy for me either. We were both given something we didn't ask for, but God doesn't put more on us than we can bear. You were given what you have for a reason, and you have to believe that. I've seen the way you carry yourself since you first made this team. You're a strong, beautiful young woman, and you carry yourself like a lady everywhere I see you. I knew you had it in you from the very beginning. I know it hurts, hearing the things that are being said about you, but it doesn't matter what they think. Anytime you need to talk you can come to me. I'm going to be here for you every step of the way."

It felt good to know I had people who were there for me, but the team is who I would spend the majority of my time with. I wanted to get things right with them. I finally got permission from the sponsor to give everyone a call. One by one, I started off with my little sisters first. I figured with them being freshman they wouldn't have much to say. We never had any negative encounters so what could go wrong. I called the first one who was more vocal of the two. After a brief conversation I got right to it asking how she felt about everything. "I just don't think you deserve it. Others work harder than you and I believe it should've been them." It didn't add up to me. This was the same person I checked on when it seemed as though she was having trouble with my big sister at high school band camp. As I responded, trying to fend for myself, the conversation escalated as her tone of voice grew aggressive. "You're lazy. You don't do anything. And there are girls on this team that can dance better than you and work harder than you. Simple as that. But regardless, I'm still going to do what I gotta do in the room for

262

the team." I hung up and called her crab sister. With no time in between, she wasted none in telling me how she felt. "I just don't believe you deserve it. Nothing against you. I could see if they gave it to your crab sister, but that's just me. I'm going to do what I have to do in the room for the team though." For a moment I sat the phone down, laid my head on the back of my headboard, and stared into the ceiling. I needed just one minute. I sat back up and returned to making calls. This time calling my crab sister. I was nervous. We already didn't have the best relationship, but we were cordial. I asked her the same question I asked the first two as I anticipated her answer. "I honestly don't care. Do I agree with it? No because you did something I don't even care to get into." My heart dropped. The only thing I knew of that could possibly be what she knew was the incident with our crab brother, but that was a year ago. If that is what she was referring to why was it coming up now and how did she know? The only person who knew was my roommate. Other than that, I didn't know anything I did to her because we didn't talk much. I asked, "What did I do to you?" I didn't want to say. I didn't know for sure if she knew or not, or exactly what she was talking about. "Don't worry about it, I don't want to talk about it. But I'm going to do what I have to do in the room for the team." I saved my next crab sister for last. I figured since we hung out a few times during the summer and kept in contact with one another, there surely wasn't a problem with her. Being that up until now, everything seemed good. I decided I would see if she wanted to grab a bite to eat while we spoke, but there was no time wasted in me finding out how she truly felt about me.

"No, I'm good on hanging out."

I could hear through her tone she was upset, but I didn't want to jump to conclusions on why.

263

"You know why, so don't act stupid."

I pulled the phone away from my ear and looked at it. I contemplated cutting her off because I already felt like I was taking too many shots, but I continued to tell myself "Just listen."

She continued, raising her voice with each word, "You're just so fake, and I don't mess with you."

"What exactly did I do to you?"

I figured maybe she would give me a valid explanation, unlike what I had been hearing already.

"You know what you did. You are evil and you deserve everything that is happening to you right now because you don't deserve that position. But I'm going to do what I have to do in the room for the team, because I am a leader."

I let out a small breath but didn't say anything. I honestly didn't expect it. Not from her. But I asked to know and regardless of if it was a valid reason to me, I guess that's how she felt. I knew I had to take it for what it was. But how was I evil? And fake? Those were the questions that never received an answer. I guess she figured I was supposed to know, but I didn't. I was still trying to figure out. If everyone was so real, and I was fake, why was this my first time hearing there were issues with me? I genuinely wanted to know. Having these problems didn't feel good. It was hard to believe if it was part of God's plan for me because why would He allow it to happen the way it was? If He really was helping me, why allow everyone to turn against me when I felt like I needed people the most?

That same night I received a call from my captain. I was half sleep while on the phone with the guy I had been talking to, but I still chose to answer. I figured maybe she would want to talk like we normally did when we used to speak on a regular. Up until now, we hadn't spoken directly since the summer high school band camp, so everything I heard or thought about our relationship was based on either an assumption or words from others. Never directly from her. So I was anxious to see. I was quite sure she knew about the decision of me being chosen as captain, but instead of putting my mind in a place where I would think she wouldn't support me, I forced myself to think away from it, hoping it wouldn't be true.

I answered and the whole dynamic of what I had hoped the conversation would be, went left as she said, "Is there an issue you have with me?"

"Excuse me?"

It was one o'clock in the morning and I wasn't here for where the conversation seemed to be heading. I could hear laughing and commotion in the background as she continued to carry on as if she was intoxicated. She started mentioning my co-workers, or as she would like to call them "my new-found friends", and her ex-boyfriend. I cut her statements off.

"Look, it's too late for this and I don't have time. We can talk when you can address me a better way."

With that I hung up the phone and proceeded to call my co-worker.

"Is my captain's ex-boyfriend over there? I don't know what has been told to her from him, but she just came at me and I don't have time for it. So please let him know to leave me out of it."

He heard as I spoke to them. Because we all began to get close, they grew to be very protective over me and didn't mind escalating situations if needed.

"Is she there? Do we need to come? If there is an issue she can call my phone because I talk to him, not you."

That was my point overall, but my captain didn't seem to understand. I could only guess her ex-boyfriend said something to her because minutes later she called again, this time loud and belligerent cursing me out. I hung up mid-sentence. Who knew our friendship would end over a guy and an assumption, but it seemed as though there was no fixing the situation. She thought what she thought and no matter what I said, her mind seemed to be made up.

A few days passed and every situation continued to come back to back. I received a call from the sponsor stating the team was needed at the school the next day for a meeting with administration. I received word the team reached out to them about the decision made regarding me, signing a petition against my being captain.

"Everyone?"

I knew the sponsor could hear the shock in my voice.

"Your roommate is the only one who didn't say anything."

"But was she on the phone with the others?"

"Yes."

In my mind, being a part was just as bad, so saying nothing was pretty much the same to me. These issues were the last thing I expected. I showed up the next day to the school ready. Not knowing what it was going to bring me, simply just ready. I sat in the dance room as the team walked in one by one. I briefly spoke, then remained quiet. They asked questions about what was about to take place as they talked as if there was no issue. I wanted to address the fact I knew they were behind a lot of what was going on, but I left my comments to myself and answered their questions as if nothing was the matter. It was now time for us to make our way to the administrative office. Once we arrived, we walked into a room with a long table with chairs around it, just like a board room. I sat between the band director and the sponsor. The team sat together across from us. The President of the school sat at the very end of the table along with the two other school officials sitting to his sides. We got right to it. To my surprise, the team didn't have much to say. Along with the band director and the sponsor speaking, I responded to one comment the President made. "Let's just bring the girls back who left, and things will be fine." I raised my hand to speak. To me, it wasn't that simple. They walked away. As much as I didn't want things to happen the way they were, these situations were happening for a reason and I had to come to grips with that. Either I was going to allow them to run me out of my position or fight for what was rightfully given to me.

After the meeting, on my way to make a few stops, I received a call from my little sister. Last I spoke with her was when she told me I didn't deserve the position and that she could see my sister getting it over me. Because she wasn't as vocal as what her sister was, I questioned why she called me. Being that I figured she said all she wanted to say. I answered. To my surprise, her tone was the complete opposite from when we first spoke.

"I was just calling to see how you were doing?"

I let out a slight snicker because I couldn't believe she was serious.

"I'm doing fine, everything okay?"

"Yes, just was checking in and wanted you to know that I support you no matter what."

"Well thank you. Everything is going to be good. I appreciate you for calling and checking in. It means a lot."

I didn't know whether to believe every word, or look deeper into it. After everything they had already said to me, it was honestly hard to believe anything positive that came from any of my team members. I decided to leave it alone. If it was real, I would see. If it was fake it would do like everything else and present itself eventually.

About a week went by and we were preparing for our team retreat before the season officially began with band camp. It was a day before we were due to leave. I was at work when I received a call from my roommate. I hadn't spoken to her since we talked when she received the position. The way things had been going, I stopped expecting calls or even support. Regardless I answered. "Hey, just calling to check on you and see if you're doing alright." Because I wasn't expecting anything particular, this shocked me. Although we were now technically partners, being I was captain and she was co-captain, I still felt as though it was something she didn't want, at least not with me, so I didn't think it mattered to her how I truly felt. What she probably didn't know or realize was I didn't care about anyone else's support on the team as much as I cared about her's. Because she was my best friend, my love for her didn't just go away because we stopped talking. It mattered to me what she thought. "I'm doing good! I'm excited for our retreat and just the season overall. We're going to get through it and I'm glad we're doing it together." I found out quickly just how much we were on the same page with my comment.

It was the day of the retreat. I was excited, yet very nervous. I looked forward to meeting my new crabs, but nervous to see how the weekend would go with the team. As I pulled in front of the band room, I sat in the car, saying a prayer in my spirit. I got out to meet with my new crabs. They were beautiful. I could only help but reminisce on my days as a crab, seeing the innocent but scared looks on their faces. We all walked into the dance room as we laid our things down. I occupied my time by going through some boxes sitting around the room when my crab sister began to help me. She asked if I needed her to do anything. I tried not to think too much into it, but being that everyone else began to speak made me think between if something was up, or if they were really coming around. The only one having nothing to say was my roommate. I watched as she laughed and played around with the team, but never seemed to make her way towards me. I figured maybe I read too much into her call the day before, giving it a chance that she possibly did care. Nevertheless, I continued to do what I needed to do and tried not to let it get to me. We packed our things in the van

269

to get ready to leave. The team rode with the assistant sponsor. My crabs and I rode with the head sponsor. I turned around to take a look at my three girls sitting close to one another, looking around as if they were in another world. I couldn't help but smile as I turned back to face the front. These girls were really my babies. We were a few minutes into driving when my sponsor began to speak to them.

"Do you all know who this is?" as she looked at the girls through the rearview mirror.

I turned around, laid my elbow on the middle partition and rested my head on my hand, looking from them to the sponsor. One of the girls said my name. As I smiled, the sponsor continued.

"This is your captain."

The girls began to smile as they looked at one another and then back to me. I turned back around and looked at the sponsor as we smiled at one another. As excited as I was, all that raced through my head was if they had pre-judged me. I knew everyone saw the things being said on social media about me. I kept wondering if they saw or even expected my big sister to be their captain. I wanted for them to love me because I knew they could possibly be all I had amongst the team. Hours passed as we continued on to our destination. I looked back to find my girls stretched different ways, sleep.

I looked over to the sponsor as I whispered, "I was planning on taking them through a process tonight. Is that okay?"

Naturally I thought about when I was a crab experiencing the start of my process at our retreat, so I wanted to do the same. However, my main focus was that I went about certain ways differently and essentially better. I asked her what were some things I should and shouldn't partake in.

"I trust you will make sound decisions. Just always make sure they know you love them because they are coming in blindly putting their trust in you."

Once we made it to the home we would be staying in, we all got situated in our rooms. My roommate and I were assigned a room together. As we walked in she laid her things on her bed and walked out to be with our crab sisters, still not saying a word to me. Later on that night, after we all gathered for fun and games, I went to my crabs' room as we all sat down on their bed. I asked them how they were feeling. Just as I had figured, their responses were simple smiles and shrugging of the shoulders as they said, "I'm a little nervous...I don't know what to expect...I just want y'all to like us." I smiled as I listened to their small voices. "You all are going to be just fine. We are all in a position where this is new to us, but I want you all to understand that throughout this entire process, I have your best interest. It's not going to be easy, but out of everything I tell you, always remember to be strong, be smart, and be wise. Everything you need to know falls in those three things. I'm going to be hard on you, but it's because I care. In whatever I do, I want to make sure you understand. You can always come to me no matter what. I'm always going to be here. I want you all to get your minds prepared and stay ready at all times, and no matter what, always be...?" In their small, sweet voices they responded. "Be strong, be smart and be wise." I gave each one a hug as I walked out.

271

I walked into the room amongst the team to discuss some of my plans for the crabs' process and to get some of their ideas. I guess it made me happy to see everyone laughing and adding input, but it was hard to really know how to feel for sure because I didn't know what to believe with them anymore. We all gathered in my room to begin the crabs' process. I put them in a group, messaging, "come to my room and knock eighteen times". Of course I proceeded to mimic the way my captain did us until I finally let them come into the room. "Stand at attention." As they stood on their toes it seemed so surreal to now be experiencing the process through a captain's eyes. I had each crab introduce themselves as I let the team chime in asking their own questions. After, no one said anything as I studied each of my crabs. I watched as one of my girls let a tear roll down her face and I could see her hands shaking on her hips as she displayed a small form of attitude. I squinted my eyes, lifted my head, and with a calm voice I asked, "Why are you crying?" She shook her head trying to get it together. I kept my eyes on her. "Look at me...You're okay...Do you remember what I told you?" She nodded her head. "Then pull it together." She took a deep breath, proceeding to stand higher on her toes as she looked forward smiling. I didn't crack a smile, but I smiled on the inside because I was proud of her. Once they left the room, the team stayed for a few more minutes to discuss what they thought about the new girls. After they finished they all walked out together, including my roommate. We still had yet to speak. It wasn't until the moment everyone prepared to go to sleep that she returned to the room. Although the lights were off, I turned over and pulled my phone out to indicate I was still up, hoping that maybe we could talk. She got in her bed, turned over, and still, it was nothing.

The very next morning I could see the way the crabs were feeling simply based on their faces. All I could do was laugh on the inside because I remembered that exact look. I chose not to say anything to them just yet because I needed them to feel it just a little longer. This particular day the sponsors planned for us to take a dance class with an alumni dancer who was a captain in the 90s. Once we finished, she sat us all down to speak. She began to touch on certain things such as being close as a team and supporting one another. No one said anything. I began to ask questions based on being a captain and how to handle certain situations. As she answered, addressing me as well as the entire team, I looked around to see that the energy changed from everyone based on how things were at the start of the conversation versus now. Instead of getting into trying to figure out how they felt about it, I left it alone. As we all walked out, the alumni dancer stopped me. Being she was so legendary in my eyes, and a part of the panel of judges who contributed to my recent accomplishment, I held a commodity of respect for her. "Continue to add to this legacy beautiful" and then she hugged me. It felt good to know I had her support. That evening I chose to speak with my crabs about the start of their process. As I walked into their room they all sat around me; their faces like little babies. "So, how do you all feel about yesterday?" They always caused me to take my mind back to when I was in their position. I listened while they gave their responses and then looked each of them in the eyes and said, "I'm very proud of you all. I know it is an intimidating feeling. It's not easy, but you stuck it out and you need to be proud of yourselves for that. The process is only going to get harder, but it gets easier for you when you pay attention and begin to learn from each experience." I sat a little longer with them as we laughed and talked. I could feel them really leaning on me and I didn't want to let them down.

It was our last night of the retreat. The sponsors set up a sit down with my mentor. We all situated in the living room as she began her presentation. Little did I know she would talk about a lot of things pertaining to certain situations going on. I knew she was very direct, however I knew anything could come out of her mouth at any time with no fair warning. She began to speak on how people will hate you because of who you are and what you can do, but to continue to be you. She also touched on how to carry yourself as someone in the spotlight, especially since she wasn't too pleased with what she was seeing on the internet about other dancers within the organization. What she said she made no apologies for. My crabs sat next to me and the team sat together across from us. I looked over to them as I watched some roll their eyes, and others directed their attention elsewhere. I didn't let anything bother me. I was use to the way my mentor was. Did I think she would be as blunt around the entire team? Not confidently, but I always knew she never had a problem speaking her mind. After she finished the team got up and walked away together. My crabs went to their room. I stayed where I was. As I sat alone occupying the free time on my phone, my little sister came and sat next to me. The same one who called me the day of the meeting.

"Hey, you okay?"

"Yea, I'm fine."

She took out her phone proceeding to get comfortable. I guess indicating she wasn't going anywhere. I continued looking at my phone but peeked over to her out of the corner of my eye. She put her phone down and looked at me.

"You think I would make a good tail?"

Bingo! I figured it was something. Even though I hated to think that way, sadly this was the way it was.

"I mean what do you think I can work on? Do you think they would pick me?"

I knew I had to get out of my own way and respond as a captain rather than someone who was hurt or felt used.

"I think you have the potential. I don't know much about the position, but I would say to work on confidence. I believe you would look good."

She nodded her head as she smiled, giving me a hug and then returned to be with the rest of the team. I looked over to them as they sat at the table laughing and talking with one another. I contemplated walking over just to be able to say I tried, but it was obvious there was a divide. It was me and then it was them. It didn't have to be like this, but the way I saw it, I wasn't going to go out of my way to be-friend girls who I knew couldn't care less about me.

The next morning we made a few stops and then headed back to campus. For the most part my car ride was silent. All I could think about was how the very next day was the start of band camp. I had crabs who barely knew me and a team who didn't want to see me in my position. Once we made it back to the school I got into the car with the assistant sponsor. Everyone left and it was now just her and I.

"How did you feel about this weekend?"

I looked over to her, shook my head, and snickered as I said, "It went okay I guess. I just need to find a way to handle certain things when it comes to the team, but I love my crabs." She paused her questions for a minute, looked out of the window and then back to me.

"How do you think your roommate's behavior was?"

"If I'm being honest, I don't think it was all that great. There are girls on the team who had a better attitude than her this weekend and they don't even have a position. I just feel as though being that she is co-captain she could have set herself apart. Instead she tries to blend with everyone. I'm not saying it's all on her, but it's obvious there is a divide and I just believe she could've been that person to step up and try to help bring everyone together."

The assistant sponsor nodded as she responded to my comment.

"Me and the sponsor talked about the same thing. I agree with you. She's just not ready right now, so I think we're just going to leave it at you being captain."

It's not that I wanted her out of the position, but I didn't want someone around who I believed felt ashamed of doing what was right. That night as I settled in, preparing for the next day, which would begin the first day of band camp, I received a call from my mom.

"You okay sweetie?"

"Yea I'm fine, why you ask?"

She explained to me that she had just gotten off the phone with the moms of two of my crab sisters, my roommate's mother and my crab sister's mom, the crab sister whom my roommate had become so close with after parting ways with me. My mom informed me they reached out to her because my crab sisters expressed to their moms how I didn't have their back when my mentor was talking at the retreat and how I didn't deserve the position because I was lazy. My crab sister's mom also expressed that her daughter mentioned about me doing something really bad to her. She couldn't say, but if she was in her daughter's position and I did something really bad to her, she wouldn't be my friend either. Naturally I had no response for the lazy comments because they seemed to have made that their go to problem with me. I decided I would dismiss that notion of myself. However, I still had yet to know what I did that was so bad to my crab sister. A big part of me was starting to feel that my roommate had told her more than what truly happened, but I just wasn't sure. It also caught me off guard to hear that I didn't have their back.

"My mentor didn't call out anyone specifically. She spoke to all of us as she addressed certain issues she felt the need to touch on. I had no control over that. Furthermore, it's funny how they look for me to have their back and when I don't, it's a problem, but since I got this position no one has had my back at all. Have I asked for them to? No. I've just begun to learn how to manage on my own."

I knew my mom was upset with the mothers, being they felt the need to call her phone and talk about her child and I hated the fact they felt the need to assert themselves by addressing my mom based on issues between me and their daughters.

"Sweetie don't apologize to me. I can handle them. I want to make sure you are okay. Regardless of what they say, what goes on amongst you and the team is between you and them. I know you don't talk much about what goes on amongst you all, which is why I didn't know much of what they were saying anyways. I just let them know that if the shoe was on the other foot, I would not talk about their child because that's just what they are, children to me. We, as you all's mothers, are adults."

She could hear the frustration in my voice as I responded. Since my first year on the team, besides for my crab sisters and I, our mothers had set a new standard of dance moms for our crab class. They did everything for us and made sure we remained close because they were also close. It was never a moment that a mom didn't look out for another mom's child, whether it was food, money, a ride, or simple encouragement. We all had each other's back and to see it come down to this made me think if any of it was real or was everyone residing in a role until they could get ahead of the next woman.

"I know this upsets you sweetie, but regardless, you treat them right. They will get exactly what is coming to them, but let God handle it. Don't worry about the moms, and don't worry about those girls. Handle the task God has given you and He'll take care of the rest. And don't worry about me either. I have this handled over here."

I knew she was right, but it didn't matter what way I turned, I was a disappointment to somebody. It was just nothing I could do to get out of the situation I was in other than quit. I tried to stand far from that option. My concern wasn't even my crab sister, it was my roommate and her mother. It seemed as though they had the most to say, but my understanding led me to feel as though I was only good enough for what I could do for them and how I made her feel until I was of no use anymore, or better yet, until I got ahead.

Chapter 12
Visible Trials, Invisible Triumphs

It was the first day of band camp. We all met on the track to begin outside workouts led by our sponsor. Of course I was used to working out, but the sponsor was a different type of beast when it came to exercising. She had us line up as we Indian trailed around the track multiple times. Being that it was the first day I could feel all the pain in my body, but what motivated me to keep pushing was not just my crabs, but the simple fact I felt as though I had something to prove. We wrapped up our workout as we ran up and down the bleachers multiple times and then laps. Crabs were always to do a few more than vets, so once they finished their sets, they ran with me as I talked with them. Being that the football team came out on the field to practice around the time we began to wrap up, we would make our way to finishing up our workouts. My crabs and I continued to jog and as we turned the corner the football came flying down, knocking me in the head. I fell to the ground. For a moment I had no clue what was going on. I looked up to see my crabs helping me off the ground. I knew everyone saw what happened because the entire football team looked over to me. I looked to the team who I saw looking at me, but no one said anything. They continued to walk as if nothing happened. Out of embarrassment I hopped up and said, "I'm okay", laughing it off, but on the inside, I wasn't. I was just ready to go home. As we made it into the dance room, I continued our process of conditioning. Aside from everyone taking part in the exercises, I had the crabs sit on the wall a little longer as we placed weight in their hands in the form of bags. Just when I got ready to tell them to relax, the band director walked in the room. He looked at the crabs and then over to me.

"What is going on?"

I didn't see anything wrong being that we were conditioning, however the way it looked, I would imagine the scene was seeming questionable. He stared at me a few seconds longer.

"Wrap this up and then come to my office."

I took a deep breath and walked slowly to his office a few minutes after he walked away. My first day and already it seemed as though I was failing. As I walked in his office to sit down, he took a deep breath and just looked at me before he began to talk.

"Do you know how many people don't want to see you in your position? Do you know those girls don't want to see you in your position?"

I looked down at my fingers, nodding as he continued.

"They are waiting for you to mess up. What if administration were to walk in? You would be done. I want to see you come out on top. Don't give those girls a reason because they are waiting on one thing and that's a wrap. You don't want that, and I don't want that, so you need to be mindful of everything you do."

I understood and accepted everything he told me. I did have to be smart. I just hated the fact I had absolutely no one. I had to stand in a room, expected to smile and do everything right, while the people around me had other plans and there was nothing I could do about it.

I walked into my bedroom that night dropping my body to the bed in exhaustion. I pondered on how I could make the next few days work to my favor when I received a call from the sponsor. She informed me she would pick a few of the team members, including myself, to be at practice early to film a potential show they were looking into making centered around the team. As excited as I was, I kept my composure because I knew it wasn't set in stone.

Just the thought of being a part of something to that magnitude, and being the captain was big to me. That next morning, as the members of the team walked in, we waited for our turns to interview with the creators. In that moment I forgot about everything that took place outside from where I was sitting. I simply allowed my love for the organization to shine through the things that tainted my idea of what I believed we were. The day went by smoothly, but I figured the camera had a lot to do with that, being as though everyone made it their duty to put on a good face. The next day came and we continued to film. An alumni doll came as a guest to teach a jazz routine. While they filmed, we moved around the room learning the dance and executing every movement as if we were on the field performing. Everyone talked and rehearsed and in the middle of the room she whispered to me.

"How's everything going Ms. Captain?"

"It's going okay. I'm having a little trouble with the team, but I'm working my way through."

Once I made the statement, she pulled me outside to talk a little more about what I stated to her. She was an alumni captain from the 90s and a person whom I looked up to and admired her place in the organization. Minutes later as we spoke, the sponsor stepped outside to see if everything was okay. The guest alumni looked up to her.

"Can I sit down and have a talk with the girls?"

My sponsor looked at me and I could tell by the look on her face she hated I said anything. As much as I wanted to listen to everything they asked me to do, one thing I had a problem with was being muted. The way I saw it, trying to simply let things go when they "seemed good" was not my idea of solving problems. Granted, maybe to her, telling other alumni dancers wasn't the way either, but I was determined to get to the root of the situation. Plus, I trusted this particular alumni dancer. She was once in the position before, so I saw no harm. The team sat down in another room with me and the guest. The crabs stayed with the sponsor. She started off by asking what the issue was. One by one they all went down the line and said the exact things they said to me on the phone. As the guest alumni dancer listened, she nodded, looked over to me and then responded.

"Where is all of this coming from? Have they told you any of this in the past?"

I responded shaking my head as some of them rolled their eyes or looked at me as if I disgusted them. I began to speak.

"I just want to know where it is all coming from. Before, everything was fine, now suddenly, everyone feels a type of way as soon as the position is announced. I just want to know what happened in between to make everyone feel the way they do."

A tear began to roll down my face as the alumni rubbed my back. My crab sister spoke up.

"Is it okay if she leaves the room while we talk to you?"

The alumni looked to me. "Are you okay with that? If not, you can stay. It's up to you."

As much as I didn't see why they wanted me to, I left, hoping that maybe she could get some answers without me. As I stood alone, waiting, about fifteen minutes later she walked outside. She walked up to me and just looked for a moment, shook her head, and then hugged me. I was waiting for her to tell me what had been said. She pushed me back as she began to speak.

"It sounded to me like others wanted the position. I still didn't get anything from what they were telling me that would cause everyone to be in agreeance with you not being captain. But what is this about you being lazy?"

"That is something I never heard before. Now suddenly everyone is saying it. I've just stopped responding."

She looked down, laughed, and then looked back to me. "You may not believe it, but I went through exactly what you're going through when I was captain. It happens every year. They can say who they prefer, but for most, they'll never be satisfied unless it's them. Your job in that is to do what you are supposed to as captain and to the best of your ability. Knock them dead with everything you do. They don't want to help, you do it! It's going to be hard, but that's the way you gain their respect unconsciously. Let them say what they want about you, but if you do what you're supposed to do now, whether you were

284

doing it before or not, people will see, and they will not be able to deny it when others start to see. You tear this season up like they have never seen it before and let everyone hate. You just do what you need to do because you already came out on top. Now you just have to stay."

I smiled as she hugged me. "Call me anytime."

I watched as she walked away as I stood there for a moment. My mind began to flow with ways of how to show MYSELF that I was worth it.

It was now Friday. The last day of the first week of band camp. I was just glad I made it through. As normal, we started off outside that morning for workouts. The sponsor informed me to take over because she would be late. I continued with the workouts she set in place for us. The sun was beaming and it was getting close to the time to wrap it up. Before we left, our workout ended with bleachers, going up and down the steps. I had everyone line up in front of each step and the crabs lined up together. Vets were assigned to go up and down the steps thirteen times. Crabs were assigned to do sixteen. As the vets finished, the crabs continued. I watched as one of my girls kept stopping. "Come on, push!" They continued until she stopped again. I walked up to the steps and stood next to where they began.

"What number are you all on?"

"Thirteen."

"You have three more. Encourage one another and push."

I could hear two of my crabs encouraging the sister who was giving up. As she got to the top of the steps she began to cry and whine.

"No ma'am. You can do this. You are psyching yourself out."

As she continued, she began to stumble on the steps as she came down.

"Grab onto the railing."

I yelled up to the other two to help her. "You don't have to run down the steps, you can walk, but you have to finish."

I knew she began to draw a crowd when the football team started to look from the field and a trainer came walking up to me.

"Is everything okay?"

"Yes we're fine."

Before she could walk completely away my crab began to slide down the steps, scrapping her leg as her head slightly dipped to the side. I ran up the steps and grabbed her, putting her arm around my shoulder, walking her down the steps. We sat on the bleacher as I yelled to the team to grab her water. The trainer ran to get her medical equipment. My crab looked up at me with tears rolling down her face as she cried hysterically.

"I'm so sorry! I tried, I promise! I don't want to let you down!"

"Shhh calm down, relax. You're okay. You don't need to apologize. I just need you to keep your eyes open and your head up."

The trainer came back to check on her as I called the sponsor to come quickly. It hadn't been five minutes and I watched as the sponsor booked it around the corner. She stood and watched as my crab laid in my arms. She continued to fade in and out as she drank her water. I had the team go for breakfast as I walked with her to the football training room to see the medic. Her crab sisters and one of my sisters followed behind. She lay on the cot as I rubbed her head.

"What did you eat this morning?"

She looked at me and then looked away. "I had half of a granola bar."

I smiled at her and in a sarcastic tone I said, "What did I tell you about eating?"

She smiled a little and laid her head to the side. Her legs had a few scratches and blood. The medic walked over as she took out a needle to take some blood. My crab grabbed a hold of my hand. "You'll be okay." As he stuck the needle in her arm, blood began to gush out. The medic immediately plugged it as I fought against walking out of the room. I was not for all the blood, but I knew I needed to be there for her.

I'd be lying if I didn't say I believed the situation was exaggerated, but regardless of how I felt, the moment seemed like Déjà vu. All I knew was I didn't want to do her like my captain did me. I consistently reminded myself I wanted them to know I cared. As we returned to the room everyone sat at the mirror doing their make-up for photos when an alumni dancer walked in. This was the same one who consistently told me I was too short to be on the team. I looked through the mirror as she walked through the door, then turned around. I wasn't expecting any visitors nor was I given the memo of having visitors, so it caught me off guard. Nevertheless, I did what I had to do in front of the team and spoke. As I greeted her, I had my crabs stand to introduce themselves. As they finished, she cut the last one off. "Which one of you made a scene outside this morning?" I instantly looked at her because I was trying to figure out how she knew already. My crab spoke up shyly, revealing she was the one. "Who do you think you are coming here causing scenes like that?" As she continued to raise her voice, saying different things to my crab, I looked at her and could tell it caught her off guard. Naturally it made sense for her to feel that way because it caught me off guard. I didn't know what to do. I felt as though I couldn't say anything to the alumni because I didn't feel as though it was right to address her in front of the team, let alone address her period, but I also didn't agree with the way she spoke to my crab. I stepped outside of the room to find my sponsor standing by the door on a phone call.

As she hung up from her call I said, "Did you know that she would be coming? She's in there confronting my crab about the situation and how does she even know what took place?"

She waited for a moment before she responded.

"I called and asked her to come. I wanted her to shake them up a bit. They'll be okay."

Being that the alumni dancer was my sponsor's crab when she was captain, I guess I kind of understood a little of where she was coming from because she knew how her own crab was, but to a certain degree it offended me. I was their captain, and no I wasn't the hardest on them, but it was the first week. Despite me feeling as though the situation was forced, I still had my own reasons for why I chose to let the situation go. I returned to the room. As I got everyone situated and in place to practice stands, my sponsor walked in and stood at the back of the room by the door. The alumni dancer sat in the corner towards the front. As I got up to throw the first count my captain walked through the door. The entire team, besides my crabs, ran to give her a hug. I stayed in my seat as I smiled, but looked over to the sponsor with a look on my face that read, "did you call her too?" She looked back to me shrugging her shoulders and eyes wide indicating she had no clue my captain was coming. I didn't know who to believe. I guess my crabs and I shared the same feelings that day. One was sent to rattle them. My captain randomly showed up to fluster me. I hated the fact she did, but it seemed as though she was one of my biggest enemies. She stood to the back looking at me. I waited for my sponsor to ask her to leave but she didn't. I just knew my captain knew exactly what she was doing. I turned around and faced the mirror, taking a deep breath as the music began. I looked out of the corner of my eye to her and the other alumni dancer. They didn't crack one smile, just stared at me. As the music stopped, I looked around to see how the team looked. My captain walked up to my crab fixing her posture. I clinched my teeth as I tried not to allow it to bother me. Once we finished practicing our stands, I directed my crabs to put the chairs up as the sponsor and the alumni dancer left the room. My captain walked up to me as we hugged. I did my best to mask how I was truly feeling. I looked over to my crabs.

"Come line up in the middle of the floor at attention. Who is this?"

As they began to speak, one stumbled, and everyone turned their heads to look at her as I spoke again.

"You don't know? If one doesn't know it then you all don't know it." I looked over to my captain. "What would you like them to do?"

"Kick."

As I watched them kick, I thought about my decision of letting her be a part. I didn't want her to be, but again, I tried to think as a captain and not as someone trying to get back at her. I looked to my crabs, "Last ten. Get them up."

I had officially made it through my first week with so much on my mind to fix. It was Sunday and every moment I thought on how I could be a better captain. My one crab who had the incident that day was on my mind so I decided to send her a message. "You can do it. I believe in you. Stay focused, pray, and you will be fine." Little did I know the minute I sent that message, the next day would bring unexpected events from that moment on.

It was Monday, the second week of band camp. We all met at the track and continued our regular workouts from the week before. The sponsor led as normal as we did sprints back and forth on one side of the track. We were halfway through our workout session when my crab began to walk off in the midst of everyone running. I could tell by her demeanor that morning she wasn't feeling it, but I knew that was a normal feeling being a new girl. I looked over to the sponsor. She continued working out as if it didn't bother her that my crab was leaving. I stood there looking back and forth from my crab to my sponsor.

"Are we just going to let her go?"

"You can say something if you want, but I'm not going to force no one to be here."

I wasted no time and ran after her. I called after her until she turned around.

"Where are you going?"

She shook her head and looked down as a tear rolled down her face. "I can't do this anymore. I tried. I didn't want to let you down, but this is just not for me."

Before I responded, I thought back to the first girl I tried to convince to stay. The truth was I learned that people are going to make their own decisions at the end of the day. I can encourage them, but ultimately the decision is theirs and I have to be okay with that. I looked into her eyes.

"Regardless of your decision, you didn't let me down. I don't want you to go, but I also don't want you to feel as though you're doing something your heart doesn't desire."

As I continued to speak, the same alumni dancer who said something to her the last time walked past on her way to the track.

"Let her go", as she kept her eyes forward, not taking one look at my crab. I ignored her and looked back to my new girl.

"Just tell me this, are you making this decision because it's getting hard, or is this something you really don't want to do?"

"I really don't want to do it anymore. I'm sorry."

I reached forward to give her a hug, and then she walked off. After breakfast the team and I made our way back to the dance room. In the middle of practice my sponsor walked in and called me into the hallway. "Your crab's father is here. They're in the band director's office and he wants to speak with us. She's saying someone was mean to her and bullied her." I wasn't worried, but then I was. I knew I hadn't bullied her, but I also knew all it took was something to this capacity and I could be out of my position. The sponsor and I walked into the band director's office to find my crab sitting next to her dad crying. As the band director asked different question about how she was treated she hesitated to answer. I spoke up. "Was I ever mean to you or bullied you?" She shook her head and the band director looked at me. I was still confused on what happened. Because she didn't say much in the meeting, I didn't know what bothered her. I had regular talks with my crabs and I would always ask them what they learned that particular day or how did they feel. She never said anything to the magnitude of feeling hurt or bullied. Being that I believed the situation was said and done, the sponsor and I walked out, leaving the band director to finish speaking with the young girl and her father.

"So what is going to happen now? Am I going to get another crab?"

"We'll talk about it. For now, don't worry about this situation. You did nothing wrong. Go back to the team and continue to lead practice."

I already knew I did nothing wrong, I just hoped she would be honest about it.

Practices went on as normal and by Tuesday it was set in stone I would have another crab on Wednesday. Wednesday afternoon I met up with my new crab. The team went to lunch. I stayed in the room to get to know her and teach her a few things we already learned. I could tell she was overjoyed about being a part of the team. She couldn't stop hugging me and telling me how excited she was to have made the team. The team returned. I introduced her to the team briefly and we immediately jumped into practice to catch her up. We didn't have the time to hesitate on anything. Our first game was around the corner and things needed to move quickly. I decided to have my crabs stay after practice to work with them a little longer. We were there for about two hours after the team left. Once we finished I headed straight to my apartment, only to park and find some of the team there helping my roommate carry her stuff down from our apartment. My heart dropped. We talked in the past about moving but not like this. I got out the car and walked up the steps as each one passed me with her things. No one said anything. I walked into the apartment to find her room cleared out. I walked into my room, shut the door, and called the guy I'd been talking to. As I whispered, "She's moving her things out and she called the team to help her." I could hear them in the kitchen laughing. My heart pounded. I didn't know whether to be angry, upset, or not even care. He tried to keep me calm as I stood in the bathroom to see what they were talking about. Minutes later I sat on my bed and my roommate opened my

293

door as she poked her head in saying, "I'm out," and then shut my door. It was silent. I couldn't even cry. I truly didn't know how to feel. I didn't want to think they did things on purpose, but it was hard not to the way events seemed to take place back to back.

The week slowly made its way to the end and my biggest focus, besides everything else that seemed to be taking place, was getting my new crab on track. As we worked on everything pertaining to our first game, I noticed how she would get tired very quickly. I called them to the middle of the floor.

"Give me fifty kicks."

She stopped at twenty-five and walked over to her bag. She pulled out an inhaler.

"Sorry, I only usually need to pump at least once."

I watched as she got back into place with my other two crabs.

"If we're in the middle of a game you can't stop like that. Did you inform the band director of this because that is something you shouldn't take lightly?"

She looked back to me and didn't hesitate to respond.

"I'll be fine. I'm just getting use to this, but I want to be here. I'll be okay."

I stood in front of them just looking as I squinted my eyes.

"Give me another fifty." To see how she would do one last time.

As they began she stopped again asking if she could take a break. I had the vets continue practice as I walked to the band director's office.

"I don't think it's the best idea for her to stay on the team."

He directed his full attention to me.

"I love the fact that I have a new crab and she's an amazing and beautiful girl, but I don't believe she told you all anything about her having to use an inhaler. I don't want that to cause any problems in the future."

"I agree with you. Thank you for telling me. Monitor how she continues to work, and we will all have a talk tomorrow."

They decided it would be best to let her go. I was now back down to two crabs. The way I saw it, it was God's plan for it to be those two all along. I had gone through four and only two came out standing. They would officially remain my babies for the rest of the season.

We hit the ball rolling as school began and we were in our first official week of the season. As we began to learn the parts the team brought in for the field show, the assistant sponsor walked in the room. She stood next to me as I told my crabs to do a certain part again. She looked over to them.

"Stop...how many times has your captain asked you to do that part?"

"Twice."

"After her telling you once it needs to be done right. She should not have to repeat herself."

She stepped by the door as I made them kick. It seemed to keep happening. No one allowed me to discipline my own crabs. I didn't know if it was because they were trying to train me on how it was done without deliberately telling me, or if they felt as though I genuinely couldn't do the job on my own. That night as the team practiced the assistant sponsor and I went to the room across the hall. She assisted me as I got her opinion on how I decided to put the dance together and some of my ideas. The next day we were due to practice the dance with the band. The assistant sponsor sat on the sidelines watching. I tried to study her face to see what she thought, but she didn't say anything, nor did she crack a smile. Just stood there. We all stood on the sidelines as I watched the team huddle together talking and my crabs standing at attention, looking forward smiling. Once we made it back to the room, everyone sat down. The crabs strutted around the room to the band marching in. The assistant sponsor walked in. "Ladies, you all cannot go out there preforming the dance like that." She began to take over, cleaning the dance piece by piece. Time went from 10:00pm to 12:00am instantly. I could hear as some of the girls spoke under their breath. Some were rolling their eyes or saying things like, "This is how it should have been cleaned before." I didn't say anything because the last thing I wanted anyone to say was that I was playing the victim, but my blood boiled on the inside. I just knew they were counting down the things they could complain about and it seemed as though I was helping fill their list up.

That weekend I decided to stay with my family because I didn't want to be alone. It was the weekend before the week of my first performance and I wanted to be around people who I knew supported me. Everyone was occupied in their rooms and I laid on the couch as I scrolled through social media. Instantly my heart dropped. I stared at the picture of my captain and my crab sisters out to eat together. I looked down to the caption. "My girls." That very moment my mom just so happened to be walking into the living room. "Sweetie everything o-." I immediately burst into tears. She came over and held me in her arms.

"Talk to me sweetie."

"I don't want to do this mom. I don't want it anymore. I don't even care about anyone else. My former roommate was supposed to be my best friend. I told her everything. I trusted her. And then my captain knows exactly what she's doing. No one told me it was going to feel like this. I don't even want to stick around for more. Why should I? They don't support me. They don't care. I hate I ever allowed myself to be a best friend to my former roommate and I hate I ever stood by my captain through everything."

As my mom waited for me to finish and dry my tears, I sat back as she began to speak.

"Don't say that sweetie. Regardless of how they are treating you now, they were placed in your life for a reason. I know it hurts. I hurt seeing you hurt. No mother wants to see their child in a position where they can't do anything. Every moment I wish I could take on everything that you are going through, but I have to remember that we serve a God that sits high and looks low, and He sees everything that's going on and trust me, no one will get away with it. So, you love them; despite what they do to you. It won't be easy, but there is something God has for you sweetie, but you can't get to it until you complete the path that He has set out for you. Sometimes I wish I could go back and do things differently in my life because maybe you wouldn't have to go through these things, but then I think about how blessed we are and how anointed you are. They will not win. I can promise you that. The tougher the battle, the stronger the soldier."

She hugged me as I cried in her arms. I guess God was looking out for me. I was right where I needed to be.

It was now the week leading to our first away game of the season. We were in the beginning of the week still preparing. We had finished practice and I had everyone try on the uniforms I picked out to wear for the game. Regardless of names being in the uniforms marking who had what uniform from the previous years, I distributed them out based on who would fit them the best when it came to my crabs. Although the rule in the past seemed to be that crabs get leftover uniforms, I didn't care for it so much if it meant they would go out with something that didn't fit them correctly. I decided to give one of my crabs my little sister's uniform. I could hear the team mumbling and my little sister stood in the corner and said nothing. I ignored it, continuing to make sure everything was in place how I believed it should be. A few minutes later my little sister asked if she could speak with me outside. "I don't think it's fair that you gave her my uniform. It's about seniority." I looked at her for a moment thinking on how weeks ago she expressed to me how I had her support. Only for me to really believe it was all for a spot, and then once she achieved her goal of getting the tail position, it was back to being against any move I made.

"I understand that it has your name in it, but the uniforms don't belong to us and I have to worry about who fits what better."

298

She stood with her had on her hip.

"I want my uniform."

"Well, I'm sorry but you're going to have to be okay with the one that I gave you."

She stared at me for a second, and then walked away, slamming the door behind her.

A few days later I decided to get to practice early to get uniforms situated for the performance. I stood in the costume room going through our many outfits when the assistant band director peeked his head in the room. "I need to speak to you." Being that I was occupied, I didn't look to him until I heard the tone of his voice. I stopped what I was doing so I could get a look at his facial expressions.

"Okay, I'll be there in a minute, let me just put this stuff down."

"Now!"

At this point I was concerned. Before this moment I seemed to have a good relationship with him. My captain was very close with him her years of being on the team and outside of the team as well, so I picked up a relationship with him through her. Was I as close to him as they were? No, but I still saw him as someone I could joke with or talk to, so I didn't think much of his tone until I made it into his office. I always called him by his first name. I figured he didn't mind it since he never said anything and he was only a few years older than me.

"What's going on?"

"I don't know what you think you're going to have going on around here, but understand something, you take directions from me. You don't come into this organization thinking you run anything."

"Excuse me? Where is this coming from?"

"Some concerns were brought to me from some of the team members that you were treating them unfairly when it came down to the uniforms and I have a problem with that."

I let out a small breath as I lifted my eyebrow responding, "With all due respect, if there is a concern I will speak to the band director about it."

He wasted no time in snapping back.

"I'm your superior and if there's a problem with the team information is brought directly to me. So when I ask you about something I expect an answer! And when you're talking to me it's Mr. We're not friends like that. My position is above you."

"Okay then, 'Mr.', if there is a concern you have with me and the way I run the team, you can take it up with the band director."

I then walked out and immediately stepped outside to call the sponsor to tell her what had just taken place. I was angry and it didn't make it any better that she tried to tell me to leave the situation alone and that she would talk to him when she came. She was also angry, but what was waiting to speak with him going to do for me? Who was really for me? I knew my sponsor meant no harm, but I felt as though she could not possibly understand an ounce of what I was going through. I was in a building where I felt like the walls caved in on me every minute of the day. The last person I felt like I could completely trust was the band director. I walked to his office, knocked on the door, and I wasn't surprised to see that the assistant band director was already there, expressing his concern for my place on the team. I sat in front of the band director and the assistant band director stood next to his chair as I began to tell the band director what took place. Immediately the assistant band director walked away from where he was standing and began yelling in my face about how I was going to respect him because it was his band and he had authority over me. Because he was basically my height, I had no problem with taking him myself because I was past the point of angry. I looked over to the band director because he sat there. He just sat there and let the assistant band director speak to me the way he did. I waited. I waited for the band director to take defense for me because that's what they said. "We will have your back 100%." But my back was being beat and stabbed, and the only thing I saw done was watching and talking. Once the band director dismissed the assistant band director, I looked the band director in his face.

"Why would you let him treat me like that?"

A tear rolled down my face.

"I would never let someone hurt you in my presence. I will take care of him, but he is your superior and you do have to respect him."

"I don't have to respect no one who doesn't respect me. My own father doesn't even treat me that way."

"Go get yourself together. I will take care of it."

I walked into the restroom and cried my eyes out as I slammed my hand against the stall door. No one knew. No one could even imagine because no one wanted to. What was the purpose of having a team if I had to experience everything alone? What good was it doing? I tried my hardest to pull myself together as I walked back into the room. We were minutes into running the dance when the assistant band director knocked on the door.

"Can I speak to you for a minute? It's about your music."

I walked out trying not to show that I was bothered. He walked me across the hall into a room.

"Look, I didn't mean to come at you like that. I do apologize. I just want some respect you know?"

"You have to give that to get it."

"I understand. That's why I am coming to you, but I know you need to get back to the team. You okay though? Do you have everything you need for your performance? Let me know if there is anything I can do."

I didn't know if the band director had spoken to him, if he had a change of heart, or this was a part of some plan, all I knew was that I couldn't trust anyone.

The next morning I received a message randomly from my captain. She informed me that she would be stopping by our practice that evening. We hadn't talked since our last conversation. Because I was at a point where I didn't trust anyone, I automatically assumed there was a motive. A big part of me convinced myself she was behind everything that was going on, but what I hated was the fact I wanted her approval. I wanted her support, so instead of brushing her off, I chose to respond and give things a try. I set up a time for her to come. That evening, when I watched as she walked through the band room door, my heart began to pound. This was my first time seeing her in person since high school band camp. I had no clue what the moment would be like. As we both walked in the dance room, the team crowded around her like they'd never seen her before. I didn't say much, but I did my best to engage so a problem wouldn't seem evident.

As the commotion died down, I walked next to her and whispered, "Can I speak with you in the other room?"

We walked in the room, and as I shut the door, she stood a few feet across from me as I began to speak.

"So what is really going on?"

She shrugged her shoulders as she smiled, "Nothing. Everything is good."

"If I'm being real, I'm asking that you be real. It honestly just seems as though you've been egging certain things on. I saw you went out with my crab sisters, and to be honest, if you were being the person I know you could be, you could have sat all of us down, or even came to me so we could talk," as I referred to the picture that she posted on social media.

She continued to sarcastically respond as if the issue was irrelevant.

"They reached out to me and said that they didn't want you involved, and they just wanted to talk to me. I couldn't do anything about that. I never asked to be involved. When you got the position, the team reached out to me and asked me to help them come up with a plan. We all met and I just showed up in support for them. It had nothing to do with me."

I stared at her and nodded my head, because I didn't know if she realized everything she had just said, but I had all the answers I needed. It sent a sharp pain to my heart because this was the same woman I grew to have so much love for. I stuck by her side when it was her turn, but the minute my turn came, my side became empty. I didn't want to fight, argue, or go back and forth. I just wanted to cry out of hurt and anger, but quickly, the very moment I listened as the words flowed out of her mouth effortlessly, I realized she didn't deserve to see my tears. None of them did.

It was now the day of our first performance, five in the morning to be exact. I had barely gotten much sleep because I honestly couldn't. All I could think about was how this would be my very first performance as Captain and I wanted everything to go perfect, but that was just the problem. I filled my mind with everything I could possibly do to make everyone else love me, not really thinking about how I wanted to love myself. As we pulled up to the school we would be performing at, my mother sent me a message. "Hello sweetie, I hate we can't be at your first game, but I want you to know that we are praying that God is with you every step of the way. No matter what happens you shine and do what God has called you to do. Do everything unto Him. We all love you and are so proud of you." A tear formed in my eye. I tried not to get so emotional, especially before my very first appearance, but I couldn't help it. I would hear stories about how the teams in the past were so close, and how they would encourage one another. I longed to feel an ounce of it, but my reality was that that wasn't a part of my story. I was trying to hold it together before getting off the bus. It seemed like everything I was dealing with sat in the front of my head. The moment I began to walk and lead the team in, the nerves went away but it seemed like all the problems I was facing laid on my body. As we stood in place still strutting, waiting to enter the stadium, I could see everyone cheering, but I couldn't hear anything. All I could think about was what I was going to look like? What did the people think about me? Was I going to be what people wanted to see? Once we began walking into the game and we made our way to the stands, it seemed like things couldn't get any worse. The sun beamed down harder than I had ever felt it before, and the space we were placed in was extremely small. My mentor, who wasn't a dancer, but someone I met through my being a part of the organization, sat a few seats in front of me. Every moment she would mouth to me. "I'm right here sis. Do your thing." I could feel the energy from behind. Every moment I would get up, it seemed as though something pulled on my back. I looked over to my mentor who had been with me since my sophomore year on the team. She kept mouthing "smile." It was hard. Every time I sat down tears filled my eyes. I would fan them to keep them from falling. No one knew because it was already hot, so I knew that would be the best way of hiding it. The game didn't last long, and before I knew it, we were heading straight to the bus. It seemed like the longest strut ever, but once we made it, I immediately wished the walk would have lasted longer. As we all walked onto the bus each team member walked past me. No one said anything. I looked at my phone immediately to messages from friends and family saying how good I looked, but I didn't believe them. I hated the fact I wanted that validation from my team. I immediately called my cousin. I knew she would be honest with me.

"How did I do?"

"Was something wrong cousin? You didn't do bad, but I could just tell you were holding back."

I waited for all the girls to get off the bus, then I tucked myself in the corner of the seat and began to cry. I still didn't respond, but she could hear me crying.

"Don't let those girls get to you like that. You're allowing the way they feel about you to mess with your head and that's exactly what they want. You know what your best is. If you're not satisfied, change it, and dare any of them to stop you! You were the most beautiful one up there. Don't let them take that away from you."

I wiped my eyes, took a deep breath, and stepped off the bus. As much as I didn't want to, I walked up to my crab sisters' moms to speak. My mom's words played in my head. "You continue to treat them right and let God handle the rest." As I proceeded to speak and put the best smile on my face, they simply looked at me, gave me a hug, and watched me walk away. Still none of my teammates said a word to me. I continued to walk to meet my mentor who sat in front of me in the stands. She could see my eyes were glassy from crying.

"Pull it together sis. Don't let them see you like this. They don't get the chance to win."

As she spoke, the tears rolled down my face and she stood in front of me as I cried. She patted my face with my gloves.

"Cry sis, let it out. I'm right here."

She began to make me pose for pictures, doing her best to make me laugh. I put a smile on my face, but as I looked at the best picture she took, I could read every emotion on my face and through my body language. We walked to get some food, talking as we sat on the curb. I called my other mentor who prompted me to smile during the game. Her and her husband did most of the talking as they could hear the emotion in my voice.

"You just needed to smile. You looked beautiful and did amazing. Don't let those girls and the fans mess up what's for you. They don't have what you have and when people see that, they try to pull from where they know you're weak. You show them that they don't get the chance to do that. It is jealousy, but mark our words, you're going to come out on top."

As I walked back to the bus, I promised myself I would hold it together until I made it to the hotel.

My former roommate and my crab sister were assigned to sleep in the same room as me. The moment they made it to the room, they laid their things down on the bed and left. My family and friends continued to call my phone, but I didn't want to talk to anyone. I walked to the sponsors' room. I sat on the couch as they walked around getting their things situated.

"So how did you feel about your first game?"

I couldn't help the tears that kept coming down my face.

"How do y'all think I did?"

"We thought you did good. It's going to take a minute to really warm up to the position so don't beat yourself up about it. You are doing an amazing job and don't let anyone tell you differently."

I wiped my tears as she continued her statement.

"The team did have some concerns, so we do have them coming in the room." Minutes later the team, minus my crabs, walked in together as they all packed on one couch across from me sitting alone. The sponsor opened the floor.

"How did you girls feel about the first game?"

I looked over to them, waiting for someone to speak up, trying to hold in my emotions and tears.

"I just feel like we weren't prepared. There were things she forgot, and it just could have been better."

My crab sister and little sister seemed to be the spokesmen for the team because everyone else simply agreed. Once again, my former roommate said nothing, simply went along with whatever the team had to say. As they got up to walk out, I continued to sit there.

"It's good to get feedback so you know what can be worked on," the assistant sponsor said, but it wasn't that for me. I was expected to be perfect in their eyes. If I wasn't a leader to them, or captain material, why did they expect so much out of me? It seemed like everything I did was scrutinized from people who shared in the same practices I did. If everyone else was such a leader, why not step up and say what you think is missing, rather than just telling someone how wrong they are with no direction. And although I didn't look to take any direction from them, I never minded getting ideas or opinions, but it was their choice if they wanted to give it.

As I walked back to my room, I laid on the bed and called my mom. Everything came out. Every emotion, every tear, every feeling, along with reiterating everything everyone had already said to me, she sent her aunt to the hotel to make sure I was good.

"She should be there in a few. I just want her there to make sure you're okay. Keep your head up sweetie. When you perform tomorrow, don't hold back. You pray tonight that God takes all the doubt away from you, and I promise you it's all going to work out."

The moment I hung up, a video from the performance had been posted. Sadly, I didn't even want to watch myself perform. I just went straight to the comments. Tears rolled down my face as I read and internalized each one.

"She's a placeholder."

"She stole the position from who really deserved it."

"She was better off in the back."

I knew I shouldn't have, but all my mind cared about was what other people thought. In the midst of reading the comments, I received a message from my band director.

"Are you okay?"

"Yes I'm fine."

"You did an amazing job today. I'm so proud of you."

"Thank you, means a lot."

"It should, because my opinion and the sponsors opinions are the only ones that matter. Don't read that garbage online. It's only haters trying to destroy you. Be strong. If you need to talk, I'm here if you need me."

After I finished speaking with my mom's aunt, I decided to call my crabs over to my room to speak with them. They sat in front of me and I did my best not to cry.

"So how did you all feel about your first game?"

"I think I could have done better...Some things just don't seem right."

I looked at my crab when she made the comment and questioned, "What doesn't seem right?" A tear fell from her eye.

"We see how you're being treated. We just don't like it."

It honestly made me want to cry and smile, just to know that they cared. What blew my mind was that I had never spoke on the team to my crabs. They just seemed to see it on their own.

"It means so much to me, you're concern, but I'm going to be okay. Regardless of how you see me being treated, I want you all to form relationships with them for yourself. Don't base it off of how people treat me. I want your relationship with the members on the team to be your own. I don't want to talk about what goes on between us and them because that's not your concern. Your concern is to be the best you can be on this team. All I ask is that you always pay attention. Give everyone a chance but watch and pay close attention when you get involved with anyone. I will always have your back and I hope that you will always have mine. I can only trust that what you do outside of me, reflects positivity. You both have been through so much these past few weeks, losing a crab sister then gaining one and then back to losing, only to still end up with each other. Always have each other's back and be real about it. Don't talk about anyone, just observe and things will be revealed to you."

They hugged me and went back to their room. Despite how it made me feel to see that it hurt them to see me hurt, I took the good out of it. I made it my duty to do what I had to do from that moment on because I had two women who were pleased with the woman I was and that's what mattered.

The next day, before the last performance of the weekend, which happened to be a battle, we stopped to get food and then went to the mall. Besides my crabs, my best friend who was also in the band, made sure he always stayed by my side. I loved having him around because he made me feel like I didn't need the others to have a good time. I introduced him to my crabs during band camp week and they seemed to get along, so I never minded them being around him. As we walked in the stores, I walked away from my crabs to look around. Once we all met back up, it was time to head to the performance. As soon as we made it, my adrenaline began to take over my body. I was ready. Once we made it into the stands, I couldn't wait for the

311

first song to come on. It didn't matter how the team felt about me, or how they looked at me, I knew they weren't going to hold back, so why should I? They didn't even know they were helping mold me into a captain they didn't see coming.

I had officially made it through my first game as captain. As much as I would love to say that it was a success, it didn't feel like it. It was Monday, the start of the week leading into our next away game. I was getting myself situated at home when I received a call from the sponsors. Once they asked me if I was alone, I knew something was wrong.

"We don't want you to get alarmed, but there are a few things that will be taking place today."

I never could catch a break, but then again, I stopped expecting for good times.

"The team gave us a call yesterday with some concerns. They said apparently you told the freshman not to speak to them."

To be honest I'd be surprised if the team didn't have any concerns, but once again, I had no clue where a lot of their accusations came from.

"I don't know what that is about because I have never talked about them to my crabs."

"Well, we're going to have a meeting today. Please just have an open mind and hear out what they have to say."

I stayed quiet. I was getting tired of having to just take it. Was that the job as a captain? Since I'd never experienced being in the position before I didn't know what a captain was supposed to take, however, for myself, I wasn't that person. I stood quiet as they continued.

"Also, there has been an accusation brought to the band director about hazing."

"From me?"

"Based on what we were informed, apparently your best friend was hazing your crabs."

There seemed to be no moment where I could simply just work on being happy. If it wasn't one thing it was another.

"I am in complete shock because I am not aware of any of this."

"Your crabs did say you were not present when the incidents took place, however an anonymous tip was brought from someone in the band that being that you are his best friend, you had something to do with the situation."

"Yes he is my best friend, but I would never condone anyone hurting my crabs. If I had any knowledge of it, I would have stopped it, but I promise I don't know of anything you are talking about."

I immediately suggested that I give my best friend a call to see what was going on. They immediately stopped my gesture, leaving me to only be able to assume the worse. It appears everything that took place that was shown in a bad light, someone always made sure to attach my name to it.

Once I made it to practice, the team sat down, and the assistant sponsor sat in a chair in front of us with the sponsor on video call. As we began, each girl spoke on how I was a problem. Everyone. Including my former roommate. Every time I would try to speak up, the assistant sponsor would say, "Just listen." My crab sister, the same one who called me evil began to speak.

"You are just not captain material. I am a leader. I do things for the team. I look out for the team's best interest."

I was confused. Was this a moment to express concern to me about how to better the team, or to speak on how someone else had better attributes of being a captain?

My little sister stood over me and said, "We all tried to let it go until you sat in the room with the alumni dancer and said that you were better than us and you didn't even think to apologize."

I dropped my head and my faced changed to a look of someone beyond confused.

"What are you talking about?"

That didn't even sound like anything that would ever come out of my mouth. All the girls started sarcastically laughing as they all made small comments at once.

"Still lying...Don't act like you didn't."

I looked up to my little sister, as she continued to stand over me.

"I'm not apologizing for something I didn't say."

The assistant sponsor cut in and directed her comment to me as all the girls began to shake their heads, rolling their eyes at me.

"That is not the right way to handle this. I have seen the most leadership out of your sister since this meeting began."

I simply just stared at the assistant sponsor. I had no one.

"I'm not apologizing specifically for that comment, but if I said anything to offend you, I do apologize."

They continued to suck their teeth and cut their eyes at me as my little sister continued.

"And then you told your crabs not to talk to us."

"I have never told them that and we can call them in here if you would like."

I felt as though the team got together and came up with what they were going to agree on about me.

My little sister began to cry saying, "I just don't feel like we're a team with you", as she walked out of the room.

I couldn't take her serious. I thought long and hard of what I did to her, to any of them for everyone to dislike me so much. As the meeting concluded the sponsors decided to cancel practice and give everyone time to cool off. I walked out of the room with the assistant sponsor and followed her into a separate room with the sponsor still on the phone. The moment she closed the door, I sat down, and she looked at me.

"You okay?"

I looked at her, then looked away because I could feel the tears forming in my eyes. She continued to speak.

"They shouldn't have come at you like that. They could have said and done some things better."

I looked back to her and looked away again trying not to be disrespectful. It was okay for her to correct me in front of them, but whenever anything needed to be said out of defense for me, it was always behind closed doors. I couldn't trust them. I was starting to think that they put me in the position to humiliate me.

After I finished talking with the sponsors, I walked into the band director's office. He just looked at me.

He said, "What did I tell you?"

I knew he was addressing the situation based on what had apparently taken place between my crabs and my best friend. As I began to explain to him that I had no clue what was going on he cut me off.

"Do you think administration is going to believe that? The only reason you are still here and not out of your position is because your freshmen had your back. They said you were not present when the situations took place. An 'anonymous' person said something. Didn't I tell you that those girls don't want to see you here? That's all I'm going to say. You need to be smarter about the decisions you are making and who you are hanging around."

I walked out of the office and into the dance room to talk to my crabs, as I asked them about the situation.

"Why didn't you tell me?"

"We didn't know how you would feel about us coming to you about your best friend. We just didn't know how."

"I told you both, you can come to me about anything. You are my priority right now, so don't keep things like that away from me."

They nodded their heads as we moved away from the conversation.

"I wanted to ask you all a question? Did I ever tell you guys not to talk to the team?"

They looked at me in confusion.

"Not that we know of."

I decided not to go into the situation any longer because I took their word for it. They continued to speak.

"The team called us yesterday on a group call asking if you ever talk about them to us and we told them no, you just told us to form our own relationships but to be mindful."

I trusted what they told me, but all I could think about was when I was a freshman and when we would confide in the team about our captain when they came to us. I knew I didn't treat my crabs the way my captain treated me, but I could only pray they had my back with the team as much as I wanted them to. That night I called my best friend, hoping he was alone because I didn't know where my emotions would take me. The moment he answered the phone, I didn't wait.

"What did you do to them?"

"Someone is lying. I promise I would never do something like that. I know what you are going through and I would not put you in a position to get you in trouble."

He informed me that he was with them when I walked away, however he wasn't hazing them. They were just laughing and talking. He could tell I was angry.

"If that is your story, then that's what it is, but from here on out, stay away from them. Don't speak to them, don't talk about them."

I loved him, but this position was causing me to do things I didn't necessarily want to do, but I came to a conclusion that if he loved me and truly knew who I was, he would understand why I made the decisions I made. Little did I know it would be the last time we would talk that season.

The weeks always seemed to go by rather slow, but fast at the same time. It seemed slow because every moment I had to deal with something and fast because before I knew it, I was already heading to my next performance. I did my best to dismiss many of the things I would hear, but it was always so hard. If it wasn't someone bringing to my attention how the girls would look at me from behind in the stands, or the things the fans would say, I never knew what was next. The truth is I already saw it for myself, but something always held me back from expressing how I felt or reacting to the people who I believed did wrong to me because I partially thought, what good would it do for me? I figured each game would only become worse until I chose better. For this particular game, I had it in my mind I was going to continue to build. It didn't matter if I was better than the next, but it mattered to me if I was better than my last. By the last I mean my performance. Growth was my biggest goal. I had a vision prepared before coming in that I strived to accomplish, but my downfall was always my team members. Once we made it to the location for our second game, the team waited next to the bathrooms outside of the stadium because it was raining. The team stood huddled in a circle, my crabs stood off to the side, and I stood next to the sponsor who filled in for this game. I wouldn't completely blame the team because I could've walked over and engaged in whatever conversation they had going on, but who really does that? Who really puts themselves purposely in a situation to be humiliated? Those are the questions that came to my mind every time I thought I should step in. I'd think on dismissing how I knew they felt about me. Each moment I spent alone, it would only force me to learn how to stand in it securely, no need for friends, or a crowd. I wanted it because it seemed as though that's what you needed to succeed. They made it seem as though it was better with friends and helped if the crowd loved you. But my biggest thing was how was I going to go without that and still come out on top? Regardless of what anyone said, I didn't feel like I was succeeding.

The week of the first home game was upon us. I was most nervous for this performance because this would be my first appearance in front of my peers. No one is bigger critics than the students of your own school. I had already put the

319

dance together that we would perform from the choreography I was given from the team. This was my first dance I'd done on my own. I was excited for it because I was satisfied with the way I knew it would come out, but I should've known I wouldn't be able to start my week without expecting something to take place. Normally I would receive the final version of the music we would be performing to the week before the performance, but I had yet to receive it. As I made my way through the band hall doors, on my way to the assistant band director's office to see about the music, I heard the song playing in the dance room. I peeked my head in to see that some of the team members already had the music. I tried not to allow it to upset me. I walked to the assistant director's office.

"Do you have the music for me?"

Even though I tried to take his word that he was sending it in that moment, I had yet to receive anything. I stepped outside to call the assistant sponsor to tell her what was going on. I just knew it was done on purpose. The team was forming a good relationship with the assistant director and I was the only one who didn't speak to him much, just based on our previous encounter. So in my mind I answered my own question when I asked how did the team have the music before me, as the captain. As I took the moment to calm down, I walked into the dance room. Immediately my crab sister turned to me.

"My part is going to go here. We already put the majority of the dance together."

I stopped. In my head I laughed, but on the outside, I clinched my teeth. I guess it wasn't enough for them to just say someone else deserved the position, but instead it was pushed by forcing their way into my responsibilities. I had to make a quick decision. Was I going to continue to be nice about it and let them run me, or was I going to lead and grab a hold onto what I was given?

"Thank you for the help, but the dance is already put together. So if everyone can get ready so I can go ahead and let you all know what parts will be put where based on how I put it together."

No one said anything. Everyone was quiet. I watched them cut eyes to one another as they moved around me, huffing their breath and rolling their eyes. I continued to look at myself in the mirror and kept a straight face, as I began to teach the dance.

Later that week everything seemed to be going fine. I stepped out to meet with the band director only to come back to find my crabs sitting in the hallway. As I walked in the dance room, the same alumni dancer who always seemed to pop up sat on the floor amongst the team. The same one who I would always remember as the very first dancer within the organization to discourage me. As I walked in, she asked if I could come back. Why did they always want to talk when I wasn't present? I had no clue. I went back to the band director's office. For a minute I just sat there, until he asked why I wasn't practicing. I tried to keep it brief because I didn't know how he would take her being in the room with the team. I didn't explain anything to the band director. I didn't want to create an issue that wasn't necessary. I let him know I just wanted a moment to step away. As I walked back into the room all the girls got up. The alumni dancer walked up to me.

"Can I speak with you for a moment?"

I nodded and dismissed the team for break. As the alumni dancer and I sat on the floor she looked at me and started to speak.

"I just spoke to the team. Don't get me wrong, I love all of you, but something isn't adding up."

I scrunched my face and dropped my head to the side as she continued.

"There seems to be a lot of concerns amongst the team about you and that concerns me. As a captain you should care about how your team is feeling. Frankly, you were not my choice for captain. You are a nice dancer, but there are others here that I believe deserved it and a little more seasoned for the position. I support you because I support the team. I just want to know what is going on."

My heart began to beat fast as I gathered myself to respond. I wanted to remain respectful, but I felt like I was on my last straw.

"I appreciate that you are concerned but you don't need to be. How can you say you support me and then look me in my face and say that I don't deserve what I have? Regardless, that's your opinion, but what doesn't make sense to me is that you seem to have so much respect for your captain and her judgement, but your captain is also the one who picked me to captain this team. So if you have a problem with that, then you have a problem with your own captain, which means that is something that I think you need to take up with her."

"I will."

"Bottom line, I was picked, and I'm here to stay. It's not about if you like it or not. So thank you for your 'support', but I got this."

It was funny to me how someone who never graced the position had so much to say about how to be in it. As I walked out to call the team back in, I made my way back to the band director's office. This time I decided not to hold back and I let him know what happened. He immediately called the sponsor.

"No more visitors in that room from here on out."

Once he hung up, he looked to me.

"Let her know that she can leave now."

I walked back to the room to find her sitting back down with the team talking again. I walked to the radio.

"We have to finish up our practice. Thank you for stopping by."

They began to side eye one another as they all got up. On my way home the sponsor gave me a call. I knew she was upset at the fact that I went to the band director, but he was present, and he was the only one who seemed to handle the situations that were happening to me right then and there. I was starting to feel as though I couldn't trust the sponsors anymore.

The first home game was finally here. I promised myself I wouldn't allow anything to steal the joy I had of performing as captain for the first time in front of my school, but all the nerves filled my body as I walked through the gate. I waited for someone to cheer my name, but I heard nothing. I continued to strut to the beat of the band as I forced my mind to block out any negativity. As we made it into the stands, I felt a sense of calmness once I sat in my designated spot. I focused my attention forward. All my mind really thought about was the field show. I wanted it to be perfect. The words of the sponsors played on repeat in my mind. "This year we want fire field shows." This time it was on me. I couldn't blame the assistant sponsor because I did it on my own. "What if I don't meet their expectations?" Just as I began to allow my mind to take me into the negative, I heard someone call my name. I turned to the side to see my classmates holding up the school magazine with me gracing the front cover as the captain of the team. I hadn't felt the feeling I felt in that moment in a long time. I looked around. It didn't matter if I saw negativity because I believed this was God's way of saying, "Just hang in there. I got you. Allow me to prepare your table."

My first home game performance went better than what I expected. The field show was flawless, and I could feel myself warming up to my position in the stands. Time was moving and I was already in my third week of leading a game. The upcoming weekend was important to me because the weekend would take place in my family's hometown, so all my family would be present. That Monday I began practice as usual. I walked out for a moment to speak with the band director. I knocked on the door and to my surprise my big sister stood in front of me. The same one who chose to leave the team. I tried not to show the shock on my face. "I'll come back." As I walked back to the dance room, I tried to think on every reason why she would be there. She had stopped by the dance room the week leading up to my first performance, but this time was different since she was speaking with the band director. Almost an hour later she knocked on the door and asked to speak with the team.

"I just want to say that I'm sorry for leaving you guys. I know you needed me, and I just abandoned you all. I think about you all, but it was just so much for me. But I will always be that leader for you guys."

As she finished making her statement a team member asked, "Will you be coming to the game this weekend?"

I engaged in the conversation, but on the inside, each question they asked, I anticipated the answer. I wanted her to come because all I could think about was how I wanted to prove her wrong with everything she said about me, but then the other half of me didn't want her present because of the thought of how she would feel.

"No, I don't think I'm going to go. It's too soon and I know people will be coming there to see me and I don't want to do that because I want that moment to be about y'all."

I got use to feeling like it wouldn't be a valid visit if no one chose to throw shots, but I was learning how to dismiss it. Slowly, but surely I was learning how to mask the things that would bother me because they weren't worth seeing my struggle. Maybe in a sense that's why they saw me as lazy. I wasn't one to publicize the things I did, so what was evident to them was only what I allowed them to see about me. I figured from their perspective, not seeing my struggle made way for them to equate what I made seem simple, as lazy. When practice was over I walked to the band director's office.

"What was that about? Her in here talking to you and then showing up in the dance room."

"I had no knowledge of her going into the dance room because we did not discuss that, however she came to apologize about her behavior."

I didn't always want to seem as though I was making it about me, so I didn't say anything, but in my mind, I thought on why. She had said things about all of us, and personally to my face, but not one time did anyone ask to speak to me. If anything, I was still wrong in their eyes.

The next day as we prepared material for the battle we would have for that weekend, I chose to really pay attention this day. I always observed, but this time I thought to make a move on it. Everyone had their ways with me in the room. I even had ways of my own, but I thought to shake some things up. I was becoming more acquainted with my role as practices went on day by day. I was learning what role each team member played amongst the group they formed. Despite the attitudes I would see my teammates display from time to time, I noticed my crab sister did her best to help me in the room. I knew she had a problem with me being captain because I knew she saw herself getting the position. From time to time she made it evident there was a problem just by body language and facial expressions, but despite how she felt about me, for the most part, she did what she had to do. That night after practice was over, I stepped into another room to call the sponsor.

"I have an idea. Now hear me out before you decide. I think we should make my crab sister co-captain. Her attitude hasn't been flawless, but no one's has, including myself. Regardless she steps up in the room and helps when needed."

My sponsor didn't say anything for a minute, and I waited in silence for her response.

"I think that is a great idea. For one, it will let the girls know that we've been watching, and I think it's a good reward to someone who has been striving to adjust to the changes. I say go for it. I will let the band director know. You can tell her, but make sure she doesn't say anything. We'll announce it to the team once everything is finalized."

As I walked into the dance room my crab sister just so happened to still be sitting in the room. I knew she had been going through some family issues so I thought this would be the perfect time to bring a smile to her face.

"I know you've been going through a lot, but regardless, you've worked hard to do what you have to do in here, and you help when needed, so I wanted to know if you were interested in being my co-captain?"

She began to smile as her eyes became glossy. I knew she was holding back tears. As she expressed a little of the things she had been going through at home, she continued to thank me.

"Everything is being finalized right now, so please do not say anything to anyone until the sponsors announce it to the team."

We hugged and she left out of the room.

The next day for practice, as we all made our way into the band hall to dance with the band, I called my crab sister up to lead. I looked around to the team. I could tell they didn't know what was going on, but everyone smiled except for my former roommate. Once we made it back to the room, I set in place what songs my crab sister would be leading to. My former roommate's entire mood was off. She stopped dancing like she normally did, and every word that came out of my mouth she rolled her eyes. I could tell by her body language she was upset, and honestly, aside from seeing a better attitude from my crab sister, I wanted it to also be evident that you don't get to treat people any kind of way and still get what you want. I guess God made it more evident to me that He gave me the specific task to simply lead the team. He would be the one to fight my battles against whoever I was facing because the moment I left practice, almost fifteen minutes later, I received a call from my band director. I stopped to get food on my way home, and once I answered he immediately began yelling.

"That girl is not going to be co-captain. Administration called me and questioned why you gave her that position. Shut it down! I told you, we do not need this right now. If you can't do the job yourself then we will find someone else. Shut it down now!"

I didn't even want to go back and forth, but I immediately called the sponsor.

"What is going on? The band director just called me going off!"

"Apparently someone made a call to administration."

I knew exactly who it was.

"Is this even fair? You all took the position away from my former roommate, so how can they dictate who gets it? She didn't even want it! Since day one she's had the worst attitude and has been the ringleader of making sure I know that I don't have the team's support."

My sponsor was still quiet.

"Hello?"

"We actually never officially told her that she wasn't co-captain anymore. With everything going on, it slipped our minds."

My emotions quickly rose.

"I'm just going to be honest, lately I've been getting looked at as the troublemaker for decisions you all have made, and I am tired of it. It's like I'm taking the fall for you all's mistakes. You agreed to make my crab sister co-captain knowing you all had not yet said anything to my former roommate. I can't even blame her for being upset. While I don't agree with how far it has been taken, this whole thing was made out to look like my fault all because you all did not communicate what you said you were going to do. I love you and I respect you, but I want to feel like you and the assistant sponsor have my back, and not straddling the fence."

She was silent.

"You're right. And I do apologize. I will talk to your former roommate before the week is over."

I knew my sponsor was going through her own situations and problems with administration not appreciating her leadership as sponsor, and I hated it. She was the only sponsor I ever experienced and she was amazing at her job. I would never expect her to be perfect at the position because I myself was a walking figure of not being perfect, but who was? So I understood that she did things the best way she understood them to be done, however, I also knew that if I was going to be the leader they chose, I needed to continue to be the person they saw before the title, and then some.

It was now the day before we were to leave for the performance. I had just gotten off the phone with my mom. She was informing me that my former roommate's mother gave her a call that morning expressing what took place the night before. I wasn't surprised. What surprised me was the fact her mother couldn't believe I would do something like that to my former roommate because we were supposed to be best friends. Now we were best friends. I never wanted to hurt her, but it was becoming more and more obvious that our relationship only mattered when it was convenient for them. I called my crab sister outside to speak with her.

"Did you tell anyone about the position you were offered?"

"No... well I did tell just my crab sisters, but I can trust them, and they were happy for me."

"I told you not to tell anyone. I don't know who, but someone went to administration about me picking you as co-captain. It was brought to the band director and now they're saying there is only need for one captain. I hate this happened because I knew you were looking forward to leading, but I promise this was not my decision. I do apologize because I brought you the news of being co-captain and now it's being taken away. Just be mindful of the people you think you can trust."

All she could do was stare. I didn't know if she was trying to put the pieces together or if she was still in shock. I wanted to use that moment so bad as a chance to throw my former roommate under the bus, but honestly, I just couldn't. I loved her too much and I didn't like the fact I did. As much as I wanted to see her hurt, I didn't want to at the same time. What didn't make sense to me was that these were the same girls who posed to be so close in front of me, but they didn't know I was seeing that they weren't everything they presented themselves to be. Was I a threat so much that in my face they had to stick together to prove their power against me? Although it hurt, I didn't think they realized just how much they were helping build me. We returned back to practice. I sat the team down to inform them a little of what was going on from what I knew. I glanced over to my former roommate to see her plant a confused look on her face, looking around from team member to team member as I made notice of what was going on.

After practice I asked for my former roommate to stay after. We sat in front of each other as I began the conversation.

"What's going on between us?"

"With what?"

"We have not talked since the last conversation on the phone, and ever since, you've had an attitude. I just want to try and get things worked out."

"I'm good."

"I'm asking you."

"I'm good."

I looked away for a moment. At that point I knew what I thought would be a conversation turned out to be one-sided.

"Okay. Well, I've tried. From now on can you please let the attitude go in practice? However you feel about me outside of this room is on you, but inside, we have a job to do."

As she walked out, she turned around before she shut the door.

"Bet that up. 100."

The day of the performance a lady who was said to be our new sponsor walked into the room. I knew about the talk of a new sponsor, however I didn't know it was officially set in stone. They hadn't given any information of who would be taking over or when, just "expect a new face ladies." I only knew because the sponsor felt as captain I should know. Once the new sponsor walked into the room I immediately recognized her. I didn't know her personally, but I knew her from passing. I could tell she was an alumni dancer because she was beautiful. She seemed quiet, but with every lesson I was learning, one was not to underestimate the ability of a person and what they are capable of.

We began the journey to our location. The moment we made it to our hotel we didn't have much time to get ready before it was time to head to the performance. As everyone moved around on the bus, dancing to the music playing through the speakers, I sat in my seat with my headphones in getting my mind right. This was our first real battle against another college. I wanted to make sure my head was in the right space. Plus, this was my family's hometown, so I knew many would be watching. We lined up to get ready to march in and my adrenaline kicked in. Before I could count the girls out my little sister got my attention. As I turned around, she yelled "Work 'em out," then winked. I didn't know if she was serious or not, but I felt like she meant it, and honestly, I could use it. It was the first time any team member encouraged me that year, so regardless of what she meant by it, I took it as something I could rely on. We marched in and people were everywhere. I could even hear them calling my name. I was ready. Everything everyone thought they were missing from me, I made it a mission to show it. From every stand to every routine, the performance seemed to get better and better. I didn't know what people were thinking. Because I was so focused on doing well, it didn't matter. As the event finished and we made our way back to the bus I felt good about the performance. Once we made it back to the hotel, my cousins met me in my room. As they sat on my bed, my crab sister was just getting out of the shower. My former roommate had already made her way out of the room. I knew my crab sister wasn't going to stay either. My cousins were the type who were always on guard. Because they weren't too fond of how I was being treated, they waited for any moment to let loose. I knew my sister could hear them because they purposely asked their questions out loud.

"Who's in the bathroom?"

"The one that I really don't talk to, but she is fine. She doesn't start any problems with me so please don't say anything." They

333

did just that. When my crab sister walked out of the bathroom she spoke.

"Hey."

My cousins ignored her as if they didn't see her. I looked at her, slightly smiled to acknowledge her, then put my head down because when it came to my cousins I knew it was better they didn't say anything.

The next morning I woke up to prepare for the parade. Before I knew it, it was time for the big game. Every time the game came, it was like a breath of fresh air. To go through so much during the week getting to the game felt like a weight lifted off my shoulders, at least for a minute. With my family there, the moment felt even better. Regardless of what fans or the team thought, I felt as though I was growing with each performance and God gave me glimpses of why He was doing what He was doing through each game. As we made it back onto the bus, I looked outside the front window to see my family surrounding it. I looked over to my aunt who mouthed, "You good?" All I could do was laugh because besides coming to watch me perform, every one of them was ready for whatever. I began to situate my things when the new sponsor called for all my crab sisters. They all walked off the bus together. As I walked off to greet my family, my crab sisters and my former roommate's mom stood behind me as she said, "These girls are with me," and pulled them off to the side. I looked over to them out of the corner of my eye as I congregated with my family. My mom could see the look on my face as she stood beside me.

"You were amazing tonight sweetie. Do not let that ruin your night."

My cousin walked up.

"Let them stay mad. They don't deserve to be in your space no way."

Even though I knew they thought they were encouraging me, it wasn't working. I thought I was growing out of caring what the girls did or thought, but I couldn't figure why I continued to let them get to me. Once I, along with the remainder of the team and the band got on the bus, we made our way to where we would be eating. As we got off the bus, I stepped aside to call the sponsor.

"Did you ever speak to my former roommate?"

"Yes I did speak with her. I let her know why we decided not to continue with her being co-captain and that I hated that it has separated you two. She said that she knew you were strong and that you didn't need her."

It was hard to believe she said that, being that since the beginning I heard nothing of that sort. If that was how she felt, why did no one want to say that to me? Maybe the roles were now reversed, being that I always treated her as if she should know. Maybe she unconsciously took on that same understanding.

It was now one of the biggest weeks of my time as captain. Homecoming. Everyone came around. I knew it would be a lot. From the team being on point with every move dealing with stands and the field shows, to the alumni dancers. Despite the outside drama, practices were going smoothly. I guess for me in some sort of way it was because of the guy I was talking to.

He kept a smile on my face and the majority of the time he caused me to dismiss a lot of other things I dealt with on a regular basis. He seemed to add balance to my life. In a world where there was nothing but chaos, he contributed a sense of calmness with me. He flew into town that week for homecoming, so I made sure I got everything done for practice ahead of time so I could make time for him. Despite him not being physically present with me all the time, he spoke to me and encouraged me every moment of the day. He listened to me cry enough times to where he made it his mission to keep a smile on my face regardless who did what to make me feel the way I felt from the beginning. He also prayed with me. Even though he had never been in my position, I felt as though he understood me.

I was growing a good relationship with the new sponsor each day. One would think I talked with her a lot about the team, but the majority of the time I would talk about my new guy. She never seemed to have a problem with it because he was motivation for getting things done. I was beginning to really like her. It seemed as if I could trust her and she trusted me. I knew she heard about the things going on with the team, along with some of the things I expressed to her. She allowed me to lead, with small direction whenever she saw fit, which was very rare. We had a good understanding, and it was important to me that she didn't have to worry about me doing the job I was given. She was different. She was more direct and assertive. So when it came down to issues, she didn't care so much of how it was handled, but the fact we were grown women and if we didn't know how to handle it, then what were we doing there?

It was finally Homecoming. It was good just to be surrounded by all the former dancers. As we moved around the room, finishing last minute make up touches and hair, alumni dancers walked in the room one by one or in groups. I was sitting on the ground putting on my character heels when my very first big sister walked in, along with the teammate who was cut from the team. All of my team members surrounded them as they hugged and laughed. I got up to greet them. My big sister hugged me. As I stepped up to my teammate saying her name and reaching for a hug, she walked past me. I dropped my arms quickly hoping no one saw, but I had a feeling some did. I tried not to let it bother me. Other than the small feeling of humiliation, I knew there was nothing I could do about it. I had a game to slay and I had every intention of doing so. The game was moving by fast. We began to make our way to the fieldhouse holding hands as we walked to get dressed for our field show performance. I looked over to see the guy I had been talking to staring at me off to the side. I tried to pretend like I didn't see him, but I couldn't help the smile that was plastered on the front of my face. We made our way to the sidelines. Normally I would get nervous during field shows, but I wasn't. To me it was like theater. I made it my goal to create a dance that told a story rather than it being just the next performance. So in my mind it was both easier and fun. The only downfall that seemed to occur was that it was raining. We blessed the field. Right before I lifted my hands to count the team off, I sent a quick prayer up, and then we took charge of the stadium. We were halfway through. Normally the crowd would react once the dance was over, but in this very moment, the crowd went wild. I had never, out of all the years I was a part of the team, heard the crowd react the way they did; at least not in the middle of a dance. I was feeling good about what had been accomplished so far. Stands was the last gig of the night. From my seat I looked out in the crowd to find my first big sister looking at me. Although I had yet to speak with her since she last was cut at auditions, I still felt like I wanted to

337

make her proud. The truth is, I wanted somebody. Besides my actual captain, when things were going wrong with her my crab year, my big sister was like my captain. So despite her not reaching out to me, or even feeling like I had her support, I still wanted her to see who I became and who I was becoming. Other than my big sister, I didn't care for anyone else in the crowd except for the guy I was speaking to. Although he was far away, he seemed so close, and I watched him. He didn't take his eyes off me once. Every move I made, if I kept his attention, I knew I had reached my goal for the night.

It was our first bye week of the season, which is basically when a week passes without a game or performance. It was also the week before my birthday. The guy I was speaking to planned to fly me away for the weekend. Normally it would be considered a choice to practice, but I always made sure to have things prepared for the team ahead of time whenever I felt the need for a break. I liked the new sponsor because she always seemed to trust I had things under control. So for the most part whenever I asked for moments such as this, she was okay with it. The next week when I returned from my birthday trip I was ready to get back to business. It was the day of my birthday. Because my new guy did such a great job with keeping a smile on my face, I wasn't too much worried that my day wouldn't go well. Only I should have known that just because it was my birthday, didn't mean my problems stopped. That same day it was brought to my attention that the team was being looked into for hazing my very first crab who quit. Apparently, it was stated that the situation was being escalated and I was due to be interviewed the next day with by a school official. As I walked into the dance room for practice, some of the team was already present. I sat down in my normal spot and no one said anything. They continued to talk as if they didn't know it was my birthday.

338

I engaged in conversation with them about the interviews we were due to have separately, trying to show that them not saying anything to me didn't faze me. My little sister walked in, hugging me as she wished me a happy birthday. I tried to give the team the benefit of the doubt, thinking maybe they forgot, but even after she approached me, still no word from anyone. As my crabs walked in with a box of cupcakes, running to hug me, I figured I could always count on them. They constantly reminded me who and what I was there for. I was becoming more prone to the attitudes, but I'd be lying if I said it never bothered me. Nevertheless, I was good at masking the pain. I spent every minute of my time talking to God and being encouraged by people who really cared about me, so I knew I couldn't give up, but it was hard to know whether or not it was working.

The next day my dad met with me to attend the interview. I always tried to believe the school was on my side as a student, but the more involved you get, you start to realize that after a certain point or a certain situation, you just become another number. My dad and I sat next to each other at a desk, with the school official sitting across from us. She began asking about what my tenure as a dancer was like for the past years I served on the team. I knew she was trying to trip me up with her questions, but it didn't start to become as evident until she began to ask about my crabs.

"Can you explain what happened to the young lady during the incident that took place during the team's camp?"

I began to go through from beginning to end what took place, as she continued to ask questions pertaining to that particular day. Because I was trying to answer her questions with no hesitation,

I didn't really think about some of the things she was saying because I looked past it. I looked to the school official.

"The most she had when she left us were a few scratches on her leg and a bruise on her arm from the doctor taking blood."

She didn't respond as she resumed in asking more questions.

"It was brought to our attention that you all refer to the new ladies as crabs."

"They are freshman."

I knew she was right but being that our new sponsor was also a part of administration, she made it very clear upon her coming in that the ladies would no longer be referred to as crabs, but as freshman. Of course it wasn't something I could get use to overnight, however I did have to change my approach on the name immediately and I had no problem with that.

She then asked, "What happens if they don't perform to standard?"

"If one doesn't do what is supposed to be done, we all engage in a workout that is a statement to show that we cannot continue to make the same mistakes."

"Did you attend the hazing seminar? Did you hear what it's called when someone does not perform to a certain standard and you have them do something based on what they did not do."

"Yes, I was present and you said 'someone,' I said 'everyone' does it."

"But you're punishing everyone. Why not just reteach?"

This was always my concern with people from the outside looking in. It seemed simple to them. Solutions were easy, and what they "heard," in their opinion never required much thought. But circumstances such as this also showed me it was easy to pass judgement on things that have yet to be experienced. My dad immediately stepped in.

"What you consider punishment, someone else might not consider punishment. When a football player gets a penalty, is that one person penalized or is the entire team penalized? Now, you used the word punishment, and what my daughter is saying is that the team is doing everything collectively, that means that if she's hazing, then she's hazing herself. Am I correct on that? Think about it. We're going by what you just said."

She began to stammer. I understood exactly what hazing was, and by no means was I trying to justify that it was right, but why did I get the feeling that the motive was not to discuss hazing but to try and catch me in a lie. She moved on.

"What is your relationship with the other team members? Any concerns regarding any of them?"

"No."

Preferably, I didn't feel as though that was any of her business. How I felt about them or how they felt about me was something I grew to understand couldn't be changed if one didn't want it to be.

As I returned to practice, I stopped in the dance room to hear everyone discussing how their meetings went. It appeared we were all on the same page until I made my way to the band director's office. As I spoke to him about the different things I was asked and what the team told me they said, he listened and stayed quiet for a moment and then began to speak.

"Those girls didn't go in there and say what you think they said or even what they are telling you they said. You need to be careful what you say around them."

I said nothing.

Partially because I didn't want to feel played in that I engaged in conversation with them thinking we were on the same page when really, they knew differently from what I knew. And even though my band director seemed to be the only one who had my best interest the majority of the time, I still hesitated on trusting everyone I encountered.

The very next day I began practice as normal with stretching. The sponsor had yet to make it to practice, but it was normal for her to show up a little later after we got the basics of practice out of the way. As I made the announcement to stretch, my crab sisters huddled in a circle, lightly stretching and talking amongst themselves. I looked over.

"Can you all spread out please?"

My crab sister looked back to me.

"For what?"

"Can you just spread out? Thank you."

I immediately got up and walked out. Because we were now under new leadership, it was hard to know what to do and how to handle certain situations. I couldn't just jump and react anymore, and I wasn't sure if I could give a "punishment." The original sponsors were more passive. They taught me to go about problems by talking it out or letting it go, but I was tired of that way. It wasn't working and I felt as though until I met at least one at the level they expected me to get on, they would continue to press any button they could. I stepped outside to call the new sponsor as I explained to her what took place.

"You are the captain. You oversee how things go in that room. If someone disrespects you, you need to nip it right then and there. Bottomline, what you say goes, so let her know she has 200 kicks and if she chooses not to do so then she will sit out for stands on the next game."

This was the approach I believed was needed. Now that I knew I had the new sponsor's support on it, all it needed to do was be implemented. Of course I prepared myself for my crab sister to refuse the punishment and I was spot on. I peeked my head into the room and called her outside.

"I just spoke to the sponsor. Because of your comment in the room you have 200 kicks."

She lost it, rolling her neck and raising her voice as she said, "For what? I'm not doing none of that."

I remained calm, but I could see my hands shaking as my heart beat fast.

"Okay, well since you refuse that, you will have to sit out for this weekend's game in the stands, per the sponsor's decision."

She began to walk outside.

"I want to speak to her! Where is she at. Get her on the phone!"

I continued to stay calm as I gave the sponsor a call and put her on speaker. My crab sister began to express to the sponsor her side of the story and her concern for the punishments that were presented. The sponsor responded.

"She is the captain and what she says goes. If she asks you to do something, you do it. Simple. Now I'm going to say that both of you do the kicks because you should have listened to her when she told you what to do."

Then she directed her next comment to me.

"You should have nipped it that very moment."

My crab sister folded her arms as she said, "Okay, I'm good with that, but I think me and my crab sister need to have a talk that's long overdue."

I agreed. I knew we had many problems in the past. Although she wasn't as vocal about her issues with me, I believed the moment was long overdue myself. We sat next to each other on the cart that sat outside of the band hall as she began. "No one is going to tell you how they feel about you so I'm just going to be the one to speak for everyone when I say I don't care for you. You're fake and you don't do nothing. We do most of the work and we just tolerate you for the sake of having to be here." I had

344

had it. Honestly, the new sponsor gave me the green light to utilize the person I truly wanted to come out. Ever since the season began, I tried to suppress the way I was handling situations based on what the original sponsors told me, and to a certain degree it was okay, but it wasn't me. Whatever I did, the team was never satisfied. If I didn't include them and choreographed on my own, I was leaving them out. If I did include them, they were "doing all the work." Forget the fact I put the field shows together alone, yet I did "nothing." Not once were things out of order or not done in time, yet, I was "lazy." So I gave her exactly what I figured they were waiting on.

"Because I'm talking to you, I'd prefer if you'd speak for yourself. We used to be so close, and along the way, some things took place, but I have tried. I treat you like the rest of our crab sisters, but for some reason you seem to just have a problem with me. We've talked on multiple occasions and you say the same thing each time, yet we barely talk in between for me to even have the chance to do anything to you. At the end of the day, you're going to think and say what you want about me. I know I do my job whether you want to acknowledge it or not. But I'm sick of the disrespect. When we're in the room, we have to lead a certain look because we all represent the organization, but outside of that room, it's free game and if you have that much of a problem with me, we can take it right behind that wall over there and handle it however you would like."

She opened her eyes and sat back. I didn't know if what I said in the moment was good or bad, but I knew I was fed up, and it seemed as though I could never get across to them until I took it there. She began to respond.

345

"Look, I don't want things to continue like this. It's just certain things I feel you can do better."

"Well talk to me about those things, and I will do my best to work on them, but you have to give me that chance."

We ended the conversation by agreeing that regardless of how we chose to feel about each other, when it was all said and done, we would be straightforward with one another. We also agreed there was no need for either one of us to do any kicks, so we left the issues right there where it was.

The next day was her birthday. As I walked through the door I went straight to her to give her a hug and wish her well on her special day. I didn't do it because I wanted to push to be friends, but because I wanted to show her that, regardless of how she chooses to treat me, I would always try to be the bigger person. The week seemed to be filled with so many surprises and unexpected moments. The next morning I woke up to a message from my first big sister. "Hey ma'am, I'm going to give you a call later today!" Homecoming was the last I saw her, but we had yet to speak. I waited in anticipation until the afternoon, anxious to see what she had to say. The moment I saw her name come across my screen, I took a deep breath and said, "God, please let this go well", then answered. We exchanged normal conversation as she asked how I was and how the season was going until the real questions came.

"My boyfriend and I were sitting talking. I know we haven't talked to you for a while, but we realized that it wasn't fair to you to not get your side of the story about how everything went down with you becoming captain. We felt as though, based on everything people were saying about you, it wasn't true because you're not the person to intentionally do something to hurt someone."

I immediately knew she was talking about what was done to my other big sister who quit the team as a result of not receiving the captain position or for reasons surrounding the particular situation. I laughed in my head. I didn't know I owed my big sister, her boyfriend, or anyone else an explanation, but because she felt the need to hear it from me, I was much obliged to respond. I wanted her to hear what I had to say being that my season was almost halfway over and this was the first time I was hearing from her. I explained what took place in how I was picked and that I didn't know anything upon receiving the position since she chose to compare my other big sisters' situation with her own. In my mind there was no comparison. I could see why she would be hurt for her own situation, but to choose not to speak to me because of an assumption of what was done to someone else, essentially put her in the same category as everyone else when it came down to me seeing who played what side. Granted, it's no secret that everyone takes sides, whether they realize it or not, but the problem with my big sister was I tried so hard to see her as better than. Again, that was my fault. I placed my own expectations on not just her, but others, who I didn't know whether they could meet them or not, but I still expected them to. I was beginning to feel that the call wasn't to make sure I was okay, even though she ended the conversation that way, but I wasn't ashamed of my story or the way things took place. I knew my blessing, and I knew my faults. I was far from perfect from anything I did, but I also knew God didn't make a mistake when He chose me.

The game that weekend went by quickly. It was great, but I had a problem of my own I was dealing with. Even though comments started to affect me a little less, it was one thing that still got to me: my size. I saw many comments about how small I was, and how I wasn't thick enough, or how my body type didn't match the team. I wish I could say it didn't matter to me, but it did and I wish I could say the random people commenting on my size didn't know what they were talking about, but I allowed each word to get in my head, ultimately causing me to think twice about my appearance. I never would've thought it would come a day where I longed to be bigger rather than small. I guess thick was the new thing. I began looking online for ways to gain weight quickly, not thinking you don't have immediate control over where your body fat goes, but I didn't care. The only thing that clouded my mind was the fact I was ashamed of my size. I didn't want to tell anyone, especially my parents or the guy I was speaking to. I knew they would try to stop me. My mind was made up. I knew they would think I was allowing the pressure to get to me, and in some cases I was. Well, in this case. I figured this was something I could fix on my own so I went online and researched anything that would help me gain weight quickly. I found a supplement and received it the very next day. It caused me to eat consistently throughout the day while lowering my metabolism which then caused me to become tired frequently. I did my best not to let the changes interfere with my captaining of the team. I did well hiding the symptoms, but the weight began to catch up to me quicker than what I thought. It scared me honestly. Not so much physically, but the idea of what I was doing. Everything seemed so hard. I found myself in a place where it felt as though I was getting everything wrong. I wanted to get something right.

We were headed to Texas for a weekend of a battle and a game. That Friday evening we prepared ourselves for the battle. For some reason, I didn't feel the same adrenaline as what I felt

348

for the last battle. My body felt fine, but the same feeling I felt the first time, I didn't feel. It seemed strange, but I had a job to do so I looked past it. As the battle came to a close, and the band played their last few songs, I watched as my captain walked in. Besides for some others, she was the one I felt like I needed to prove myself to the most. I saw the way she excluded me and treated me publicly, but that never stopped me from caring what she thought. I just wanted one compliment. I wanted one time for her to boast about me like she did for everyone else, just as I spent so much time boasting about her. Before every count I would look over out of the corner of my eye just to see if she was watching me. Every time I saw her pick her phone up it sent a small feeling of excitement in me thinking maybe this would be the breakthrough point, only to get back to the hotel to find I was not who she focused on. Social media brought out the worst part of me. It's almost as if it forced me to care. I couldn't help it.

The next afternoon at the game, the battle stayed on my mind. I replayed seeing her stand off to the side, as that vision became real in that moment. We sat in the stands, waiting to perform, and again I watched as she made her way to sit right across from me. The team huddled together as we laughed and joked around, not planned, not forced, just happened. I peeked my eyes over to see my captain sitting to the side watching us. The game came to a close as we began to dance back to back with each song the band played, and again, every comment she made and every count I threw, I slyly looked towards her just to see if she was watching me. I was getting tired of caring. Even though I knew there was a reason for my being in the position I was, I still had yet to figure out why everything was happening the way it was, and why I still felt the way I did.

The next morning we got ready to head to church. This was something I looked forward to. It seemed as though church always made things better. I know it did for me. The entire band packed into the balcony, while the team sat together on our own row. I moved in and the sponsor sat on one side of me and my crabs sat on the other side of me, followed by the rest of the team. The Pastor came from Hebrews 11:3; 8-12. Immediately he dove into what hit me. "If the enemy can't attack what you believe about God, he will attack what you believe about you." He instantly had my attention. I grew up on the Bible and faith was important to me, but even I grew to believe people don't take faith for what it truly is. By people I'm referring to myself. I didn't have to say it to know I was losing it, just by allowing the things the fans said, the way my captain felt, and the way the team saw me, get to me. What I was for sure of, that the preacher solidified, was that without faith, it's impossible to please God. My parents always told me before every game, "Everything you do, do it unto Him," and if I was losing faith, was I really pleasing God? Were the things I did really for Him? It's just I knew I was put in a position of having to prove so much of who I was even though the world and the people around me already saw me for what they wanted to see me as. But I heard God say before, "Who told you that you have to prove yourself to them?" I felt like there was no one in the room and the preacher spoke directly to me when he said, "I feel like I'm speaking to someone in here, but God says, you're going to wander around in the land of your promise. You're going to feel uncomfortable and strange at first, but just because you feel strange, doesn't mean it's not yours." Tears began to fall down my face as I internalized every word. "It's not about it fitting you, it's about you fitting it. Whoever I'm talking to, this shift is not about you. God is shifting you so that the ones that come after you will feel familiar in what felt strange to you." I didn't care who was around me in that moment. I had made the decision this wasn't going to defeat me, this time believing it. "Repeat after me. I'm coming out with great substance. It's my turn now."

Chapter 13
Coming Out with Great Substance

After that weekend I had plans to better myself overall. Whether it was the way I thought to handle certain situations or just bettering myself overall as a person. This week of practice leading to the performance was extremely important because we would be playing against one of our biggest rival schools. I had plans to shake my crabs up a bit because the season was getting closer to the end. It was almost like tradition that around this time, the process got tougher, so any moment I could use to build their strength, I took it. Practice was ending and we had just finished practicing the field show. The new sponsor normally left practice early because for the most part, I had everything she expected taken care of. My two crabs stood facing the mirror in the middle of the room. I was good for giving more lectures than actual physical punishments because I believed if they were always engaged in something while I spoke they would hear the sound of their feet hitting the floor or their inner thoughts about whatever they felt in the moment, and less of me and the words I spoke.

"What is the motto?"

As they began to recite it, I could see they were nervous as sweat rolled down their faces.

"Again. And louder with confidence."

Once they finished, the team began to interject with things they wanted to say.

"The way y'all performed this weekend was not it."

My crab sister continued to speak. "You were too wild and sloppy."

I continued to analyze the countenance of my crabs as my team members continued to speak. I stood in front of them, then sat down before I began speaking.

"I know you all get excited when the band plays, it's natural for all of us, but I want you two to be able to control the energy you put forth."

The team continued to make comments.

"You're not on your old dance team no more. We don't dance like that and if you want to dance like them then you don't need to be here."

I could tell the energy began to shift to singling out one of my crabs when another team member said, "And you have a crab sister next to you who you should be helping because I heard you don't."

I looked over to my other crab. She had spoken to me once before about how she felt as though she was alone and didn't have help from her sister. I thought she only shared it with me. I wasn't aware she expressed her concerns to the team. Regardless I chose to never discuss either of my crabs when only speaking to one because I strongly believed in them being as one. The way I saw it, one without the other was no good, and regardless of them being like my babies, they were still grown. They needed to figure out their relationship on their own. I didn't want it to seem forced, so when she confided in me alone, I told her just that. I still stood in silence, allowing the team to continue speaking as I observed my crab's behavior. I didn't realize how far it had gotten until my little sister said, "If our old band director was here, he wouldn't have even picked you to be on this team, because he could care less about your status." I stood up and looked over to my crab whose face was filled with tears.

"You are here for a reason."

I directed my attention to both.

"I don't want you to ever feel like you don't belong here because you wouldn't be here if it wasn't meant. Look into the mirror at yourselves. Those girls are worth it. Those girls are beautiful. Those girls have potential."

I watched them as they looked into the mirror. The one whom most of everyone's comments were directed to cried her eyes out as she did her best to hold it together. I looked to my other crab.

"I don't want to hear no more talk about what the other is and is not doing. If one is lacking, pick up the slack, and talk to one another. You don't like something she's doing, you talk to her and vice versa."

A tear rolled down her face. I knew both of them understood because they were extremely intelligent and I always made sure they knew that everything I said or did was out of love, but I wanted to give them the chance to sit and think on some things that were said. I wouldn't be present every moment of their lives to explain the good and the bad, so I wanted them to grow an understanding on their own of how to take what was for them and leave the rest. We said a prayer and practice was dismissed.

Once I made it home I went straight to the couch to call the guy I was talking to. It was about 10:00pm and I had no intentions on moving until I planned to make my way to my room to get ready for bed. Almost an hour or so later I received a call from the original sponsor. I figured she was calling just to talk and check in due to the time. The minute I said hello and listened to her response, my heart dropped.

"We need you to make your way back to the school, now."

"What is going on?"

"You need to get there now."

She hung up. I had no idea what for, but I was anxious to know. I rode all the way back to the school in silence thinking of every possible thing that could be wrong. Once I made it and walked to the band director's office I was under the impression it was just me until the rest of the team walked in together, excluding my crabs. For a moment, the band director looked at each team member individually and it felt like for the longest he stared at me.

"What took place earlier before you all ended your practice?"

The girls stayed quiet, looking around at each other. I began to explain what took place.

"I didn't have them engage in anything physical. I just spoke with them and others said a few things as well", as I explained the things I said to them.

"It doesn't matter if you had them doing anything physical or not, certain things that are said could be considered a form of hazing as well."

I knew not to respond, or even try to go back and forth with him because it wasn't the time and he was absolutely right.

"Who made the comment about one of the freshmen not belonging to the team?"

For a minute no one said anything. I looked over to my little sister who stayed quiet, looking around. The band director looked around.

"So no one said anything?"

My little sister spoke up. "I'll be honest. I did say that to her."

As the band director finished his lecture to us, everyone walked out of the room and I was the last one to leave as he said, "We will speak tomorrow."

We all walked out of the front door of the band hall. I looked to the side to see my crab and her mother standing off in the distance. I figured the tension was already too high and I wanted to make sure I was very strategic in approaching the situation.

The next day I met the band director in his office before practice.

"You know you were this close to losing your position last night."

"How? I didn't say anything bad to them."

"But you allowed the team to. You let it get that far. The only reason you are still here is because your freshman said you didn't say anything, but that still does not change the fact you are the captain. You are responsible. I don't know how many times I have to tell you, you specifically have to be careful with everything you do because there is so much against you and you will be held accountable even for their doings simply because you are the captain. Your little sisters shouldn't even be allowed to give their opinions. You need to take charge of the situation, because the next time I have to step in, that's it. Handle it."

As I walked out, I saw my crab sitting outside of the band director's door. I called her over to sit next to me. She came over and put her head down.

"Look at me. I am truly sorry for allowing you to get to the point where you felt like I didn't care."

Immediately she fell in my arms and began to cry. She laid her head on my chest as I hugged her. I allowed her to get everything out and it didn't matter how long it took. Once she finished she sat up. I looked at her as she whipped her eyes.

"I promise I will never allow it to get that far again. I should have nipped it and I take full blame. Even with that I still want you to get to the point where it doesn't matter what anyone says, you know who you are. You and your sister are two of the most talented girls having stepped in that room. Don't let the words of others dictate who you know you are."

I really was preaching to the choir.

"Is there anything in particular that I said or did that hurt you?"

She looked into my eyes and shook her head and finally responded.

"I appreciate everything you do for me. I'm just sick of people telling me what I don't deserve simply based on where I came from."

I was living what she was feeling and all I could do was hug her again.

As I held her I said, "We're in this together, and me, you, and your crab sister are going to make it out better and stronger than anyone."

After practice that evening I sat everyone down. I looked at my crabs.

"I know I spoke to you earlier in private, but because the situation happened amongst the team, I want to apologize to you amongst everyone."

I reiterated what we spoke about in private.

"Does anyone have anything they want to say?"

I looked to my crab sisters. No one said anything. I looked to my little sisters, nothing. I looked back to my crabs.

"Well, being that no one has nothing to say, I'm going to apologize on behalf of the whole team. Some things that were said were wrong. In this room, it will not happen again."

I then looked over to my little sisters.

"And from here on out, if either of you have an opinion, you may voice them to me and I will speak on it if it is needed for the team."

With that, practice was dismissed.

The next day as we headed outside that evening to practice our field show dance, the new sponsor called me to ride over to the practice field with her. I knew she was disappointed about the situation that had taken place.

"I apologize for the incident that happened. My intentions were not to hurt anyone, but regardless, I know you trust me and I don't want to lose that."

As we walked to the field, she waited a moment, smiled, and then responded.

"You are a good captain. Ever since I came, you do what you're supposed to do. Don't make me regret trusting you. Your crabs really admire you. Don't worry about how the team will feel when it comes down to including them. Those are your freshman and because the trust was put into you to build them, you are held to a higher standard than anyone."

I smiled, looked at her playfully saying, "I won't let you down," as she laughed, and we walked onto the field.

We continued to prepare for the game as the days drew closer and closer, until it was finally here. It seemed so surreal to be leading one of our biggest games, but with each game I felt more and more accomplished. I was tackling my goal with field shows and performed every stand, not by what someone else gave in the past, but what only I could give. I looked in the crowd to see my captain standing at the very front, but this time it didn't bother me like it did before. She was just another person in the crowd. I knew I still loved her, but it's something about growth I was realizing- as you reach new heights, not everyone grows with you. After the game, we strutted back to the dance room and I packed up my things to head home. As I walked through the door to get to my car my former roommate stopped me.

"Can I talk to you?"

We walked off to the side.

"I wanted to know if we could get together to talk."

I agreed to it. As I walked off, once I made it to my car, I sat there for a moment and then looked up. I smirked as I said, "God, what You got going on now?"

I was looking forward to meeting with my former roommate. Although the season was almost to the end, I tried to think of it as better now than never. I couldn't remember when the last time we sat down and spoke. When we met in front of the building of where we would sit down and eat, I didn't say too much. It wasn't because I didn't want to, but with so much that happened, I didn't know what I could and couldn't say to her anymore and honestly, I didn't trust her. Once we were seated, we started with brief conversation, then it was a pause.

She looked at me and said, "So how are you feeling?"

I slightly laughed, "What do you mean?"

"I mean so much has happened and it's just been a lot."

I decided not to hold back. "That's what I've been trying to figure out from you for the longest. I don't have to go through everything because you know, but we were best friends. If no one ever had my back, I always expected you to be there just as well as I was there for you. You just chose to side with everyone else, not trying to talk to me about it, just assuming whatever. Even after I tried to work with you and partner with you, that did no good. I got to a point where my whole image of who I thought you were changed. I used to wish things didn't happen the way they were happening, but now I'm starting to feel safe in what God is doing for me, so I forgave you, even when I didn't receive an apology. And I also apologize because within me hurting, I know there are some things I could have done better towards you as well."

I watched her demeanor as she began to explain her side. What stood out to me is when she said, "I do apologize for the way I treated you and handled some things." It didn't stand out because I was shocked. It stood out because I wanted to believe that very statement so bad, but it was like my heart didn't allow me. I accepted it. I just didn't believe it. I looked down for a moment and then looked into her eyes.

"It's okay."

The moment I looked away she began to cry as she said, "I don't know what happened between us."

I grabbed a tissue and handed it to her as I watched and waited for her to finish crying. I wish I could say I cried as well, but I didn't feel it. I loved the fact she wanted to talk and maybe everything she said to me was sincere, but to me, love was more than just the words that came out of a person's mouth. I wanted to give it a chance simply because it wasn't all bad times with us, but the good times ended when it didn't have to. Nevertheless, our short moment together was good. It was a good start. Even though it was towards the end, I guess you could say it was a new beginning.

The last home game flew by quickly and the weekend I had been waiting for all season was now upon us, Bayou Classic weekend. It was mind-blowing to really experience something that seemed like a dream. The adrenaline kicked in overtime as we lined up in the tunnel to enter the big dome for the battle of the bands. To know I was leading in the band amongst thousands of people, to see all the lights and hear the people calling my name was surreal. I had been here before, but not like this. Not in this position. From where I was standing, the view was different. The view was better. After the battle we strutted back to the bus and my entire family was waiting for me. Getting to see my family at every game, like most of the team, was rare for me. So seeing them made everything complete. I didn't get much time to hang out and enjoy the streets of New Orleans because we had to be up for the biggest game of the season the next morning.

As I walked onto the field in the arena the next morning for practice, I looked around as a tear rolled down my cheek. All I could think was that I made it. Before I knew it we were in those stands for the game. The field show was perfect and I was just waiting for the clock to hit 0:00. It almost made me feel like a crab again. I looked back to my crabs who I could see already had tears in their eyes. It was a few seconds away from our team winning the game. I counted down in my head as tears filled my eyes. 5...4...3...2...1! The buzzer sounded and the crowd went crazy. As we stood to do our alma mater, I couldn't help the tears that consistently fell from my eyes. I did it. I made it. Every problem, every situation. This was my breakthrough. My hand was lifted in the air, one finger pointing to the sky, but in my mind, I was pointing to the One I couldn't do it without. Those tears were for His glory. Without Him, I wouldn't have made it. But the moment was bigger than me. I called my crabs over. They sat in my arms crying. WE did it. WE made it. I continued to wipe my eyes, but the tears didn't stop. All I could hear God say was "Your table is set", because what He had in store for me was just beginning.

Chapter 14
More Than Enough, Still Never Enough

I couldn't believe I had made it. I mean, I knew I was capable, but it seemed so far away from the finish line. Still I didn't believe I was anywhere close to the end. I knew I had faced a lot, but I also knew it wouldn't compare to what God was getting ready to do for me. I just didn't know in what form my blessing would come. I felt accomplished and ready to take on anything. Although I wasn't promised another year, I was already prepared to take on the upcoming season. The year started off right. I had a new boyfriend and our performances were already showing me I was fully capable of continuing the tasks of the role I played. It was now parade season and practices still continued. I could see my growth in many areas. Attitudes began to subside from some of my team members and the others I didn't really give the time of day to because not only did I stop looking, but I stopped caring. I also had my babies who were no longer crabs. Making it through my first season as captain gave me the very strength I needed. We came to practice briefly one evening for a meeting. We all sat in the dance room talking amongst each other when the alumni dancer, who seemed to always show up, came walking through the door. I had no urge or eagerness to speak simply because it was always something when she came around. However, seeing there was nothing more she could say to me that was worse than the last conversation we had during the season, I didn't mind speaking. When I actually thought about it in the moment, I liked the fact she got to see me and I got to look her in the eyes. I sat down in my own area, engaging in the many conversations going at one time in the room when she looked over to me and said, "You proved me wrong. I know not to doubt you anymore. You still short though." Whether it was a joke to her or not, or whether she was serious or not, I chose not to engage in a response. I looked at her, raised my eyebrows and smiled, going back to focusing on what I was doing. I didn't smile at her comment because she didn't tell me anything I didn't already know. I smiled because she didn't even realize who she was dealing with and what she did. I had now put her in the place where everyone else was who doubted me. The pressure of what I was beyond capable of had yet to be applied, and she was a part of the many people who would have to sit back and watch as I surpassed the place many thought they could put me in.

Throughout the spring semester, besides dealing with the team, everything seemed to be going well. My former roommate and I began to speak often. Most people who knew me told me it was a bad idea. Did I have my doubts? Definitely. The truth is, I didn't want to feel naïve. She had already proven to me that our friendship in the past was only to benefit her, so I could only think I would be a fool to believe this time was different. Among specific relationships, I was continuing to grow a very close relationship with the sponsor. I would visit her office on campus almost every day to just sit and talk with her. Because I trusted her, I confided in her with almost anything on my mind. I didn't know she already knew about my former roommate and I being close in the past, but I decided to pick her brain on the issue and see what she thought. "I think you should work things out with her. She may not say it, but she needs you. I know. She may have made some mistakes, but the way I see it, neither one of you are perfect." I didn't deny anything she said. I just sat in silence wondering. Why did it seem like I always had to be the bigger person when others did me wrong? It was always, "They feel this way, they're not as strong." Why were they never held to the standard everyone held me? Regardless, I chose to give it a try. I guess the way I saw it, God took me through too much, and brought me through just as much for me not to trust that even if I showed myself friendly He wouldn't protect me. My biggest motivation was that if I was going to come back as captain, the strive was to come back better all around. I tried not to look at it as being naïve because at this point, what else could they do to break me?

As practices continued I honestly hoped things would have gotten better with everyone on the team. When I realized it didn't, I just continued to see more and more that no matter what you do, if people don't want to like you or accept you, there is nothing you can do unless they want to change. The spring semester was now over and we were a few weeks away from summer. I received a call from one of the school videographers a few weeks prior telling me how he was looking forward to putting my spotlight video together. Spotlight videos were normal and exciting videos of our highlighted moments of the season. Each member of the team receives one. So naturally I couldn't wait to see the finished product. Eleven minutes. This was the first time any footage this particular videographer had of me reached this length of time. As the music played in the background of the video, tears rolled down my face. I saw my growth, my pain, my happiness, and my strength all in one. After the video concluded, I scrolled down to a long paragraph he had written. Every single word brought tears to my eyes, but it wasn't until he stated, "She realized that the critics she had didn't carry any credentials," that made my tears stream down my face. It was the reflection of everything I had gone through flashing in front of my eyes. After I gathered myself, I gave him a call. I needed to thank him. As I expressed to him my gratitude for his hard work and all of his kind words, he immediately responded. "I'm glad you appreciate what I did for you. I received a message from your captain and your crab sister with words about how I showed you favoritism by making your video long. I just don't get it. I did the same for your captain last year." I was happy to know that him telling me this didn't necessarily bother me. It just continued to reveal who people were and whether his statements were true or not, one thing was, "she realized that the critics she had didn't carry any credentials."

It was a few days after the release of the spotlight video of myself when my captain messaged me asking if we could get together and just hang out. Around the middle, close to the end of the semester, I began receiving messages from my captain. While we spoke on more of a business level, after everything which took place, I didn't expect her to reach out to me as if she had done nothing. Nevertheless, she did. Because I was doing my best not to hold grudges, I tried to ignore, but after finding out her comments about the spotlight video of me, I could see she still hadn't changed. She was still trying to control the way my life went behind closed doors, but it was a different story when communicating directly with me. Although I was still sort of surprised when I received this message, I read it over and over again. I didn't trust her. Even though part of me thought maybe she wanted to talk about everything, a big part of me thought the complete opposite simply because this wasn't her first time reaching out to me. So if she wanted to talk, I figured she would've made it happen when she first reached out, instead of pretending as if she wanted a relationship with me. I read over the message a few more times, gave it more thought and responded. Even though I chose not to meet up, I still looked forward to at some point speaking with her. No longer was I in need of an explanation, but I thought it would be nice to hear an apology from at least one person. I also prepared myself in knowing it probably wasn't going to happen, but I guess it didn't hurt to hope.

It seemed as though summer was coming and going in the blink of an eye. Before I knew it, we were preparing for high school band camp. I looked forward to it because it was almost like a practice course to me. If I could handle being responsible for the team and overseeing hundreds of young girls, I was capable of running a season. I took everything as preparation for the next level, not really knowing what was in store for me, but being prepared and having a plan in place. The days were quickly drawing closer and the team and I pressed to get things in order. My former roommate and crab sister left for the summer so the team consisted of one of my crab sisters, my two little babies, and one of my little sisters. The new sponsor continued to solidify her role by setting rules in place and creating a visible structure for the team. It was needed. She made it very clear that participating in the high school band camp was not an option and every girl needed to be present for the event the day it began or they could forget about being a part. She was always very adamant with anything she said.

It was now Sunday, the first day everyone would gather to meet with the campers. As I moved around getting things situated for the week, I pulled the sponsor to the side to speak to her about my crab sister not being present. "You already gave them the information I told you. So if she does not show up today then she can't participate. If she does show up tomorrow, I will leave the decision up to you to allow her to stay or not." Listening to my sponsor, I figured her allowing the decision to be left in my hands was a great opportunity for me to have a conversation with my crab sister. We had yet to speak about what took place during last season. I saw it necessary to address any unforeseen issues before moving forward as teammates into the upcoming season. Once I told the idea to my sponsor, very nonchalantly she shrugged her shoulders saying, "It's up to you," and walked away. I didn't have enough time to think about why she brushed the idea off the way she did because things were moving quickly with the schedule that had been created. The band director came up with a structured schedule of how the week would go with the campers and I made it a point to review so I could break up tasks for my team members. I headed over to the dorms where the team, along with the campers, would be staying for the week, when I received a call from my former roommate. We had been speaking almost every day now, and despite the past, part of me hoped we could possibly get back to how we used to be. Yet again, I ignored the faint, but sharp feeling that poked at my heart telling me to keep things brief.

"Keep me updated on how the camp goes bud. I want to feel as if I'm there. I know it's going to go great."

The first official day of activities had begun. All the girls made it downstairs at the time they were asked so we could all walk to breakfast together, but upon us making it to the meeting hall we found the doors were locked. It was 7:00am. I made sure to follow the band director's exact orders in being on time. I moved to the side to give him a call.

"Hey, I'm here, where you told me to be with the girls and the people are not ready to serve breakfast."

"That's because I did not tell you to be there at that time."

I took the phone from my ear, looked up to make sure I wasn't tripping, and then put the phone back to my ear.

"This was the time you gave me yesterday, that's why we are here. I'm positive this is what you told me."

"How are you going to tell me what I came up with."

"I'm only reiterating you what you told me."

"And that is not what I said ma'am."

As much as it frustrated me, I knew it would get us nowhere going back and forth on who said what.

"Okay, so what time would you like for me to have them here from here on out."

"You can have them there for 7:30am."

As I hung up from him, I immediately called the sponsor to let her know what took place.

"I don't know what he is talking about. I will give him a call. Just let the girls sleep in for maybe another thirty minutes more unless he tells me otherwise."

I made my way back to the girls as we got ready to walk in and eat breakfast. Minutes later I received a call from my crab sister saying she was outside and prepared to join us. I knew what I was about to do, and I wanted it to go well. Once I made it outside, I immediately addressed the concern.

"You know the rule the sponsor gave about you not showing up on yesterday."

"Yes, but I could not help that I wasn't able to be here."

"I understand and I don't mind you staying, but I want to ask you a few things since we have this moment alone to speak.... What was up last season? What happened to us? Why did you say all those things you said about me?"

"To be honest I really don't remember anything I said. It was just a lot going on, but I don't remember what all really happened."

I began to list some of the things that took place and the things she said about me.

"I mean, it was just a lot that happened. Like I said, I really don't remember, but that's the past and I'm good."

I had one or two options: be petty or be the bigger person. Lord knows everything in me wanted to retaliate for everything they put me through, but every moment I had to "get even" something always reminded me my purpose was greater, and it wouldn't work even if I tried. I waited for a moment, as I could tell by the way she looked at me, she anticipated my response.

"Regardless of what happened in the past, what we remember and what we can't remember, regardless if we find our way back to how our relationship used to be or don't, we're on this team together and we should love and support each other. I know you wanted captain and I know it bothered you, but that shouldn't have changed the fact of how you treat someone. That goes for both of us. This will be our last season and I want to finish strong...with my sisters."

She agreed, but before we could finish our conversation, I was needed amongst the girls. We gave each other a hug and walked in to be with the team. I didn't know what it would bring or change, but I knew I felt good within myself because I felt like the captain I wanted to be in my first season. I was also realizing it took them and the situations I went through for me to be able to experience the feeling of growth. After we wrapped up breakfast and walked the girls to the gym to begin practice, I gave the sponsor a call to let her know about the conversation between my sister and I.

"I didn't say much yesterday because I wanted you to make the decision on your own and as a captain I am very proud of how you handled the situation. You're showing that you can handle these types of issues and that is important. Regardless of what I stated, I gave you the choice and as the leader you handled it very well and I'm glad you all were able to speak."

The first day went by smoothly. We prepared to go into our next day of camp. I followed exactly what the sponsor instructed me to do, allowing the girls to sleep in an extra thirty minutes. When the time came, we all met again to begin walking to breakfast when I received a call from the band director.

"Why are you not at breakfast with the girls?"

"You told me to come later."

"No I did not say that. You don't listen."

Now I was confused and on another level of frustrated. I didn't know whether he was serious or whether it was a joke but either way it went, it left me in a position of not knowing what to do. I didn't want to be disrespectful, but it seemed like everything I thought or said, he made it to go against what he wanted. Once I hung up from him, I gave the sponsor a call explaining again what had taken place and the confusion.

"I forgot to call him yesterday, but don't worry about it. I'll take care of it. Just go ahead and get the girls to where you all need to be."

I didn't know what was going on with the band director. We always seemed to have a good form of communication, but now it was different. It was hard to tell if it was me, or his frustration with camp overall. Besides for the miscommunication with the band director, everything was going well. The campers seemed to be having an amazing time and the team and I worked well together. That evening all of the campers met outside on the yard of the school for some activities, music, and fun. I watched the band directors drive up as I stood amongst some of the campers. I walked over to him in hopes to break the ice.

"So for tomorrow, what time would you like me to have the girls ready?"

He stared at me with no expression on his face and as he gave the time he said, "I told you that the first time but you don't listen."

"When did you relay that message to me?"

"I told your team members to let you know."

Now I was really confused. These were the same girls he told me all season not to trust, but he seemed to trust them with information that never made its way to me.

"Why didn't you tell me?"

I tried smiling and laughing a little to lighten the moment but still he stared at me with a blank face and responded saying, "That's not my problem."

I had no idea what was going on with him. It seemed like such a drastic change. I was trying to see what took place in between for it to happen this way. Just last season he was the closest to me and always professed to have my back, now anything I said or did seemed to be a problem.

It was now Wednesday. Two days closer to the big camp performance. Over the past few days from the start of camp, I prompted the campers to drink lots of water because on this particular day we would go outside to practice. The band director gave me the time and the girls strutted to the field. As we split them up into their dance groups, I noticed some were becoming tired or faintish. The team and I began to tell the girls to take it easy and get some water when one girl passed out. Next thing I knew, the ambulance was on campus and the band director and the sponsors were on the field. As I stood next to the young lady to make sure she was okay, I looked over to the band director as I watched him cut his eyes at me then look away. I tried not to give it much thought in the moment. I wanted to make sure the girls had my undivided attention, but the moment we made it back into the gym I decided to ask. The old sponsor was present that day and as she stood to the back of the gym, helping to bring water in for the girls, I walked up to her.

"Is the band director upset with me about this?"

"Why would he be upset? You couldn't control what took place and you did everything you could."

That's exactly what I thought, but his facial expressions towards me showed otherwise.

As I showed her how he looked at me she laughed saying, "He was just concerned about the girls that's all. I'm sure it had nothing to do with you. Just let it go. The good thing is the girls are fine and there have been no problems. You've been doing a great job."

It was hard to hear anything of that sort when the main person in charge didn't seem as though he was pleased. It bothered me because everything was going so well, but I cared so much about why he was acting the way he was towards me.

The next day was the day everyone would go out onto the field to practice together, camp dancers and band members. The new sponsor left, as well as the old sponsor, and an alumni dancer came to oversee as a fill in sponsor. I liked having her there. She reminded me a lot of the old sponsor and we had a great relationship so it was easy to communicate anything I needed. As I sat the girls down on the track to get them ready to perform, some of them began to ask if they could use the restroom. I knew it was coming due to the fact we had them drinking a lot of water. I asked one of the team members to check the restrooms under the stadium. The doors were locked. I then prompted her to check the football locker room, where the team normally got dressed for performances, to see if it was okay for the girls to use the restrooms there. Once she cleared the room, we sectioned the girls off in groups with a team member. The band director stood up on the podium as I directed the first group of girls who were present to get ready to perform their dance on the field.

As I stood next to the podium counting the girls off, the band director looked down, calling for my attention yelling, "Go get them girls out of there! Who told you to do that?!"

"They had to use the restroom."

"I don't care! Go get them!"

I felt like someone had tied a rope to both of my arms, pulling me in opposite directions. The girls were about to perform and I didn't want to leave them, but the band director told me to get the other girls out of the restroom. As I began to walk towards the football locker room where the girls were, I looked over to the fill in sponsor who walked down from where she was seated asking if everything was okay.

"I don't know what is going on with the band director but he's telling me the girls can't use the restroom and I need to go get them."

"You handle the girls out here. I will go and see about the girls in the restroom."

I walked back to the camp dancers to see they had just finished and the band director came down from the podium. As I began to gather the girls to line up, he called me to the side.

Yelling amongst the girls and the band campers he said, "I told you I didn't want those girls in there!"

"All the other restrooms were locked and I didn't want to make them hold it."

"I don't care, I said no!"

"You left me as the leader to make decisions such as this and I was not going to make those girls do such a thing."

As I stood there explaining myself, he walked closer to me, rose his hand, pressing his finger into my shoulder three aggressive times saying, "I'm in charge and I told you to get those girls out of there!"

I looked down at my shoulder and then back to him, raising my eyebrow as I said his name shaking my head. I tried to keep my composure simply because we were surrounded by kids and parents, but he had gone too far. I looked into his eyes.

"I'm going to walk away now and we can talk about this when our attitudes are better."

I knew he watched as I walked away, holding my tears back. It hadn't been a minute before I could completely leave when I looked over to see one of my camp girls laying on the ground crying. I immediately ran to her as her head lay in the alumni dancer's arms.

"What happened?"

"She was stung by a wasp."

As I called a few of the band members over to carry her, the band director walked over. I expressed to him that the camper was stung by a wasp and had an allergic reaction.

He looked at her, then looked at me, and without asking anything for the dancers' behalf he said to me, "Come over here."

We walked off to the side as he began talking.

"Now I have my reasons for why I said what I said to you. There are men in that locker room and anything could've happened to those girls. I saw some football players out on the field and those boys could have done anything to those girls."

"There was no one in the locker room. I had it checked before they went in and the team members were with them."

He continued to raise his voice and step closer to me as I watched the other band directors watch us from afar.

"It doesn't matter. If administration saw something like that, it would be my job on the line and then what?"

"I wouldn't do anything to jeopardize your job, but in that moment I had to make a decision as the leader whether it was right or wrong."

He continued to raise his voice and walked closer as he said, "I'm in charge. You don't have no authority. You listen to me."

As I backed up I looked into his eyes. It wasn't the same man I knew, or maybe it was and I just never saw this side of him.

378

"Okay once again, I'm going to walk away because I don't like how this looks or how it's going."

"You walk away again and you can cancel Christmas."

I didn't know exactly what he meant and although the first thing that came to my mind was my position, I continued to walk away. My integrity was more important than my position.

As I walked off tears uncontrollably began streaming down my face. What made me even more upset was the fact the team saw. Despite everything going well, I still didn't trust them. In my mind, it was moments like these they were waiting on to use against me. Nevertheless, I had no choice but to utilize them in the moment. I directed them to take over in leading the girls back to the gym as I stepped aside to call the sponsor. She knew I was crying by my shallow tone and heavy breathing.

"All week he has found some type of issue with me", I said as I explained to her what he did and said to me.

She immediately hung up from me to give him a call.

Minutes later she called me back, took a deep breath saying, "Calm down. Clearly both of you all's emotions are high and both of you were wrong to a certain degree. You should have just listened and went and got the girls and he should not have made a scene with you the way he did, but it's okay. You both just need a minute. It was just a misunderstanding. I'm sure it is not that deep. You have been doing a good job with the girls and you have one more day so clean yourself up and finish the camp strong."

As I hung up from her, I was still angry. I thought to call my family, but I didn't want to escalate the problem. I thought to go to administration, but I cared too much for him to see where that decision would lead. I made it into the gym with the team and all the campers. As I stood next to my crabs, I watched as the band director walked through the door on the other side of the building. With absolutely no control over my emotions, I began to cry. My crab grabbed me as she put my head on her shoulder. My other crab came behind and hugged me as they both whispered, "It's okay. We're here." The fill-in sponsor motioned to speak with me as we walked outside together.

She hugged me saying, "You didn't do anything wrong," as I cried in her arms.

"Would you like for me to speak to him?"

"Thank you, but no. This is my situation and I need to handle it on my own."

I stayed away for a minute to get my mind together, but really to argue with God. Every single moment I thought He was helping me, He allowed a situation of this magnitude to take place. I isolated myself far enough to speak out loud. "Why do You allow these things to happen to me? Do You even care or do You want to see me humiliated? You told me that You would see to it that they watch me eat from the table You prepared, instead their watching me fail and suffer. That's what You want?" I wiped my tears, gathered myself, and returned back to the gym. I was standing off in a corner because I didn't know if the tears would come back again or not, when someone tapped me on my shoulder. I turned to see it was my captain. She asked to speak with me as I followed her into a secluded room. We stood there, a few feet apart. I could feel her staring at me as I looked down fighting back tears.

"You okay?" I lifted my head, nodded, and smiled. My eyes were bloodshot red and puffy.

She dropped her head to the side and said, "Despite the past, you can come to me. I will always be here."

I began to cry again. I couldn't help it. It wasn't her, but at the same time it was. I still didn't trust her either, but I just knew the team had told her what happened. She wrapped her arms around me as I stood there with my head on her shoulder crying.

"Captains go through struggle, but you are one of the strongest people I know, and regardless of what happened, God obviously knew you could handle it. And besides, I've never seen you back down, so don't you dare drop your head on me now."

She pushed my shoulders back, tilted her chine down, and smirked. I looked at her with a slight smile and then hugged her. It felt good to have my captain with me; even if it was just for a second.

I spent the night putting myself to sleep with my tears, hoping that anything good would come out of the situation, and thankfully something did. The final high school band camp performance was nothing short of amazing. Every dancer, parent, and even team members were pleased. What I set out for my end goal of everything had been accomplished. In many ways I felt as though God was teaching me to stop expecting things my way and start believing in His way, even if it didn't make sense; and it didn't make sense, but I would always end up surrendering to Him. The day was finally over. As everyone packed up their things, I found myself to be the last one still sitting in the parking lot of the dorm rooms. I laid my head on the wheel contemplating calling my parents. I took a deep breath and called my mom.

"Hey sweetie! How did it go?"

"Is daddy with you?"

"No what is going on?"

I immediately began to explain everything that took place. "I'm about to tell your father."

"Mom no! Please don't."

"No we need to come up there, and I will be scheduling a meeting with administration first thing tomorrow."

"Mom, I don't want to do that. I just want to talk to him and see what happens. Even if you go to administration, I'm grown. They're going to want to hear the situation from me. If I don't say anything, it won't matter what you all say."

"Sweetie, I'm not going to give you an answer on that because this is something that has gone too far. Your daddy needs to go up there and say something to him. I'm going to have to think about this because as of right now, I will be telling your dad and making a call tomorrow."

She was angry. There was no doubt about it based on her tone. I didn't know how to tell her I wanted the situation to be handled, but something kept telling me to wait. Not, "Don't do it, don't retaliate," just...wait. After I hung up from my mom, I called my two mentors to let them know what had taken place as well.

"I want to go and speak to him right now, because I hate to let this situation sit. What if he takes me out of the position because of this?"

"If he didn't take it away from you in the moment everything happened, then you are fine. Because he does have the authority to do that. Every captain gets into it with the band director. Most of the time that's how you know you're doing your job because you both won't see eye to eye about everything, but I say leave it alone. If he reaches out, you all can talk, but what's done is done and there is no changing it. I haven't heard anything being said about you so I believe you will be okay." As much as I wanted to listen, I was still on the fence about how to handle the situation. I didn't know what "wait" meant? Did it mean just what my sponsors said, to leave the situation alone, or did it mean don't try to make any moves right now. Was it God, or was it just my conscience?

Once I made it home my former roommate called. Seemed like it was right on time. I laid down on my bed as I answered the phone.

"So bud how was it? Tell me everything."

As I began to explain each day from start to finish, I hesitated in telling her the situation between me and the band director, but before I knew it, I was halfway through the incident.

"He's lucky I didn't take it further because I can. I just wouldn't want to do anything out of spite."

She stayed quite for a moment and then said, "It'll all be okay.

But I'm with my mom right now so I will talk to you later."

That very instant as I hung up the phone, a feeling of regret hit my body, but because so many issues were taking place all at once, I couldn't tell what the regret was towards.

A few weeks had gone by and I decided to stop by the sponsor's office to discuss some ideas for the upcoming season. I began by asking if she had heard anything from the band director about the incident that took place during high school band camp. "I'm sure he is over it. There is no need of talking about it now. Your focus should be auditions because this year we're buckling down. Any of you all come in there lacking in any way, you won't be on this team this year." Part of me was listening, and the other part of me listened too much and over thought everything she said. Until that time I was still a captain so I automatically knew I wouldn't be looked at the same as everyone else, but I just couldn't shake the unresolved problem between me and the band director. I tried to dismiss it as I continued to talk about my ideas.

"Did you have some ideas for uniforms?"

"I'm actually supposed to be meeting with your former roommate's mother tomorrow to discuss some ideas."

I don't know why the comment made my heart jump, but something just didn't feel right, and I couldn't put my finger on it.

The days drew closer and closer to audition time. Each day that came closer, I felt more and more uneasy and didn't know why. My former roommate was reaching out to me more than ever, and slowly, I wasn't hearing much from the sponsor or anything from the band director. I knew I needed to stop allowing it to get to me, but the feeling only got stronger and stronger. It bothered me that I had no clue what it was. I had a feeling I wouldn't find out until whatever it was actually presented itself. The day before auditions my roommate asked if we could get together to practice. I could only hope that every moment was as genuine as what I wanted it to be, but every moment I couldn't help but see everything that took place surrounding me as a puzzle. I was trying my hardest to put the pieces together.

Chapter 15
Favor or Retribution...You Decide

It was now audition day. I woke up early that morning to a call from my former roommate. It kind of surprised me because even though I wasn't trying to hold on to the past, my heart and my mind wouldn't let me forget. As I made it to the school I watched as my former roommate pulled next to me. I was just getting my last prayer from my family when she opened my door and sat in the passenger's seat. Once I hung up the phone she said, "My dad wants to pray with us." As he began to pray I couldn't bow my head or close my eyes. I simply just looked down. The moment almost scared me. As he said Amen I looked up with a slight smile and then looked out of the window. Something still just did not feel right.

The former team gathered in a room amongst other dancers who were auditioning. I received word during the summer that one of my crab sisters would not be returning. I seemed to find out it was true when she didn't show up, but my other crab sister walked in just before they called us into the room with a brace on her knee. My former roommate and I looked at her asking what happened. The day before auditions and she had injured herself. All I could think about were the words of the sponsor. Auditions began to take place as normal. Once we made it into the band hall to begin the technique portion, I made my normal scope of the judges and the room. I saw my mentor amongst the judges and as I panned the room my big sister, who quit last season, stood amongst some of the dancers on the opposite side of the room. She stood at the front of the line. I wasn't surprised she was back. I heard many rumors about her returning, but I knew I would find out for myself when the time came and here it was. We began technique and I felt good about it. My hair and makeup were done to perfection, my body felt good, and my technique worked in my favor. As the line moved forward to showcase the next technique, I looked behind me to find my crab sister standing next to the door. I could tell her countenance was down. It was all over her face. I walked next to her and said, "Pull it together sis. You got this." I knew she was scared to perform on her knee. As I watched her go across the floor, she barely performed the technique because she couldn't. I surprised myself because all I did was look at her and pray she made it. I guess I was surprised because I didn't think it would be that easy to pray for someone who was once so against me, yet in that moment I didn't think twice about it. I just wanted her to do the best she could. I watched as my big sister went across the floor. She always did amazing when it came to dancing and a big part of me was glad she was there because in a way, she forced me to stay on my game.

This time they went about cuts differently. After we waited briefly, they called everyone back into the room. One by one they called the numbers of the girls who had made it. Everyone from the former team was called back including my big sister. The ladies who did not get their numbers called left the room. We immediately began the next part of auditions which was choreography. This is when the feeling I was experiencing for the majority of the summer came back. As I studied the movements the choreographer taught, I looked up into the skybox towards the top of the band hall to see the band director standing watching us. For some reason I felt as though he was looking at me. The situation began to pound at my head. Everything from the last season up until now clouded my mind. I tried my best to hide my true emotions, but something just wasn't right. The moment they dismissed us for a minute before they would call us back into the band hall, I walked fast into my assigned room to try to calm myself down. I didn't know what it was. They finally called my number to perform the dance. I stood in my pose replaying the dance in my head over and over again. The choreographer counted us off and as my body began to move performing the steps taught, I felt like I was making it, until my mind drew a blank. I lost it for one whole eight count, and it was noticeable. It felt like the longest moment ever. Once I caught back to the choreography it seemed as though it was too late. I knew myself that my energy was off. We walked out of the room and as I made my way to sit with the team I stayed quiet. I could hear most of them say they messed up, but it didn't make me feel any better. As we all sat there waiting, the sponsor walked out to the lobby where everyone was seated. "Ladies, if we call your number please return back into the band hall to perform the dance again." My heart started to pound because I just had a feeling I would hear my number. Sure enough I did, along with one of my little sisters. I rubbed my hands together as I walked back into the room, trying to wipe away the sweat. I stood towards the front as I looked each judge and sponsor in the eyes. The minute the music started, I danced for one eight count and the sponsored pointed to me, "Leave." I quickly walked out. My heart continued to pound. I didn't know what it was about, nor did I even try to guess at this point.

They called every girl back into the room. As they began to call numbers my hands began to shake. I still stood amongst the dancers who had yet to be called when the sponsor said, "Thank you ladies, please try again next year." My heart dropped to the floor. I looked to the team and then to the judges. I couldn't move. Other dancers who had made it reacted in disbelief. I tried so hard to hold my tears back when the sponsor yelled, "Wait! We missed a few numbers," and then they called mine. This was the second time of the audition they hand done this, forgetting my crab's number during the first round. I couldn't tell whether it was truly by mistake or if something was going on, nevertheless I felt relieved. As the audition made it to the last round, which were interviews, the remaining girls sat outside of the band hall waiting for their number to be called. Every former girl who was on the team was still present including my big sister. My former roommate sat close to my side until they called her name. It wasn't long until she returned, but judging by the look on her face I couldn't tell how it went.

"You okay? How did it go?"

"They said I need to lose ten pounds."

The moment she said that the same feeling came back to me. This wasn't the first time she mentioned her weight to me and to hear it again and feel the same sting in my spirit didn't sit right with me.

"You'll be fine. You have time to lose it. You just have to keep working like you've been doing."

Minutes later they called my number. I walked in and sat in front of the judges. The band director stood at the end of the table staring at me with no expression on his face. Immediately I felt like I had to guard myself. The sponsor began to speak.

"What is something you learned from last season and what would you do differently now that you know?"

"I learned to persevere. And in going through everything, I've learned to treat people right even when they do you wrong."

389

I looked over to the band director and then back to the sponsor and the judges. As she asked a few more questions, I kept each answer brief. I didn't know what it was, but I just held back. I walked out of the room not feeling good or bad about my interview, but I knew it wasn't my best. All fifteen finalists returned back into the band hall. This would be the first time since I first auditioned they would pick the team as the final moment before the day ended. They called my number first and when they finished the sponsor said, "Congratulations, you all have made the team." Everyone hugged one another. We crowded around the freshman as we greeted them, along with my big sister who made the team again. I tried to read the room in the midst of all the commotion. I could see the sponsor didn't look too happy. She stopped all of us. "I am very happy for you young ladies, but I am also disturbed about news I am already receiving of people complaining about auditions." She didn't get into any details, but judging by her phrase I figured it had to do with possibly parents complaining that my crab sister made it all the way to the very end and every girl at auditions watched as she struggled to complete most of what needed to be done. If that was the case, looking from that standpoint I could understand, but at the same time, every year something took place that didn't make sense to someone. Nothing really came as a surprise anymore. I honestly couldn't open my mouth on that situation because I knew I had one of my own I had yet to figure out.

I didn't talk to anyone that night about how I felt about auditions except for my boyfriend. He was the only person I truly expressed the majority of what I felt to. I still kept some things bottled in. That next day I chose to go to my mentor's house. I knew my other mentor filled her in on how auditions went being as though she was a judge. The moment I walked in her home I could tell by her face she knew something I didn't.

I stood there looking at her, as she asked, "So, how was auditions?"

"I mean it went pretty good. I messed up briefly, but it was okay."

"So you want me to be honest?"

I knew she had something to say, and one thing was certain, I could always count on my mentors to be honest with me. I stared at her, indicating I was waiting for her to start.

"Your other mentor said she could tell something wasn't right with you."

I immediately got defensive as we stood there going back and forth. She gave my other mentor a call as they both went back and forth with me.

"You didn't do bad yesterday. Matter of fact your technique got a perfect score along with your big sister and one of your crabs, but after that something changed. You weren't bad, you just weren't the vibrant girl we all know you to be; and in your interview you seemed guarded."

This time I didn't say anything. I surrendered. My mentor looked at me because she could see the tears forming in my eyes. My mentors continued.

"We thought for a moment if it was your big sister who you let get to you, but we know that's not how you are. So what is it?"

They waited for me to stop crying. As I gathered myself, I walked outside to speak with my other mentor on the phone. I expressed my concern about my band director and how I had a feeling he was retaliating against me in some way. This was the first time I had expressed my true feelings. She remained quiet for a moment and then answered.

"He asked our opinion in who should be the captain and when we said you, he was against it. He wouldn't say why, he just made mention of another option. Here's my thing. Don't worry about that. It's still your position to lose. I say reach out and see if you all can speak."

"I'm not going to beg him for a position. I feel as though he wants me to do that."

"You don't have to mention anything about a position. You both just need to clear the air on the incident that took place between you two."

The entire time I knew it was something. A tear rolled down my face as I thought on what to do. I pondered on if it was really me or was this His way of proving to me His authority. I paced back and forth contemplating reaching out, asking God what I should do. Again something told me to wait, but all I could think was that I did that the first time, and this is where it got me. So I decided to send a message. "I hope your day is going well. I wanted to know if we can please talk soon. I know a conversation is long overdue, but I wanted to focus on completing high school band camp and getting through

392

auditions. However, I'd like to have an opportunity to address what I feel is a misunderstanding." Minutes later he responded saying that we could talk but he wanted to meet off campus due to him being on vacation. I tried not to think too deep into it and agreed to meet with him.

I walked into a small restaurant and sat at a table close to the corner by the restroom. I tried to go over everything in my mind I wanted to speak on when he walked through the door. Once he ordered food, he came to sit across from me. The conversation began calm and cordial, and then he asked how I felt I did at auditions as he said, "I was expecting more out of you. The whole team looked bad. Some of y'all injured, some out of shape, and some of y'all just not bringing it. Y'all let that girl come in there and out dance y'all." I knew he was talking about my big sister. He continued. "And I know its rumors going around that she is the new captain, but that is not true. I haven't given anyone the position nor have I said anything to anyone about the position. Be careful who you listen to. You can't trust those girls." I was starting to think was it them I couldn't trust or him. I stayed quiet, listening to everything he said being that he had already pegged me as the person who "didn't listen." I then brought up the incident that took place at high school band camp. He was adamant about how he handled everything as he said, "I don't know if you thought you were running things, but the way you were talking to me from the very beginning seemed like you had an attitude, like you forgot who was in charge, but I let the situation go a long time ago because I'm a "man man" and I don't hold grudges." I saw no point in trying to continue to prove mine, but I was hurt. I trusted him. I knew something wasn't right, even being in the midst of him. I could feel the tears coming as I quickly got up and walked to the restroom. I stood to the mirror, looking myself in the eyes as I pinched my arm. I took a deep breath and walked back to the table. He waited for a moment and then said, "Why were you crying?" I tried my hardest to hold them back again as I pinched my arm under the table. I shook my head as the tears rolled down my face. "I just don't know what is going on. I completed a season that nearly broke me, with style and grace, and now to get to this point and question what I know I am capable of all because of a situation with you, the same person I trusted and it hurts. To hear I wasn't who you expected at auditions, hurts." He continued to indulge into his food until he responded. "If you want God to make something happen for you, just ask him and believe that." I heard the words that came out of his mouth and I already knew what he said was true, but I didn't feel it. I mean others had told me the same, and with them, it moved me, but this time with him, it made me want to pray, but not based on what he was saying. Something was just different.

Once I made it home I immediately called the old sponsor to tell her what took place as she said, "I'm not sure what is going on. Once the season was over, it was already evident you would return as captain and now he is saying that he doesn't know if he wants a captain and he's looking to go in that direction. At the end of the day, continue to carry yourself as the captain, as a leader. Get everything together and present it." That is exactly what I did. I began to get everything prepared for the season.

About a week later, after organizing everything pertaining to the team and practices, I reached out to the band director asking if I could meet with him to present some of my ideas for the season. It seemed to go well. He advised me on making certain changes and expressed to me certain things I could do for the upcoming season. "This is your team, so you need to make sure you have yourself together," he explained. Was that my answer indirectly? Upon leaving I felt good, but still in a way confused. I was doing everything they expected from a captain with no real knowledge of if I had the position or not. As I made it to my car, I called the new sponsor to inform her about meeting with the band director. She stayed quiet for a moment and then said, "I just got off the phone with him. He asked me if I told you to do everything you did because he didn't. There is no captain." My heart stung as it felt like it dropped to my feet. I wanted to walk right back into his office because why didn't he say all of that to me?

The very next day I received a call from the sponsor. "I just spoke with the band director and as of right now there is no set captain, but if he does choose, it will be out of you and your former roommate." I instantly put my phone down, shaking my head. It took that very comment for me to see things start to piece together.

I picked up the phone and said, "Where did this come from?"

"Well there are no other options and she is just as deserving as you. The way I see it, you both have things you need to work on. She needs to get a backbone and you need to learn how to remain confident in the decisions you make."

It was like a joke to me. They knew exactly how she treated me when it was my time, but yet she deserved the position? And the logic behind what I apparently needed to work on seemed to be a forced reason. When I stood my ground for the decisions I made I was looked at as one who didn't listen or was disrespectful, but now it was something they wanted? Part of me was more so angry with myself in giving so many people the benefit of the doubt. Every time I tried to allow myself to trust someone, something happened. All I could respond with was "okay," because the trust was gone.

Ironically, hours later I received a message from my former roommate. "Hey bud. I'm going to call you tomorrow. Love you!" I read the message and then laid the phone down. I began to think back on everything she did to me from the very moment she knew I received the position that she wanted. I asked myself "does she even think about it? Does she even realize or remember?" I figured she "forgot" like the rest of them or just didn't care because this was now in benefit to her. I wanted to treat her exactly how they treated me, but something said, "Be still." The words rang over every negative thought. As much as I wanted to retaliate, I couldn't. "I love you more my girl," I responded to her message with a tear rolling down my face. The sad part was despite everything, I knew I meant it more than she did.

A few days went by and we decided to get together to talk. Upon preparing to meet, I received a message from her. "I just found out that I have to be at the band hall in the morning to meet with the sponsor for a training. We can get together tomorrow." No one had called me. As unsure as I was about what was going on, I didn't want to ask too many questions out of fear I would be doing too much.

The next day we met. As we walked in and sat across from each other, the feeling just didn't seem right. It seemed like a moment of Déjà vu from when just this same time last year I sat across from my big sister. But as I played that scene in my head, I knew I didn't want to respond to my former roommate the way my big sister responded to me. My roommate began to speak.

"I don't know how to feel. I'm just excited and shocked. I wasn't expecting any of this."

I tried not to respond with my facial expressions, but I began to realize that clearly there was information that I didn't know. I cut her off before she could finish.

"What didn't you expect?"

"Them giving me the position. Well I mean, they said that I would be leading band camp."

My heart began to beat fast as I clinched my teeth tight. Still I did my best to hold back my emotions. I didn't know if she was saying too much unconsciously out of excitement, or if she wanted me to know, but I remained silent as I allowed her to continue speaking.

"I'm looking forward to us working together. I wanted to run some of my ideas for the season by you and also I wanted to say that last year was a lot, but this year is a fresh start."

Spoken in a shy faint tone almost as if she was afraid to speak to me. I let out a small breath and stared into her eyes for a minute. It seemed as though now that it worked in her favor, I was simply supposed to fall in line. She dropped her head and then looked back to me saying, "What you thinking?" I didn't take my eyes off of her as I said, "I'm thinking about everything you all put me through last year; how I overcame it, and how I'm going to continue to see the best in these situations." She looked down and with nothing more than these three words she said, "Yea. I know."

As we parted ways I immediately gave a call to the sponsor. It seemed as though I was getting the run around. The moment she answered I expressed to her what took place as she responded saying, "She will lead the first week and you will lead the second week and we will make our decision from there. You will receive the same training she received the weekend before your week to lead. I want to make sure you support her and stick by her side because she is going to need you." So much of me wanted to say, "Just let her have it," because the situation seemed so messy, and deep down inside, I knew it was going to be her, but one word continued to fill my spirit. Wait.

It was the day before the start of our team band camp. The team was scheduled to meet to discuss rules and guidelines for the season, as well as what would be taking place for the two week camp. I decided I would try to get to the school early for no particular reason, but something just told me to go. As I walked into the room, I watched as the sponsor and my former roommate quickly ended their conversation, planting big smiles on their faces as they said, "Hey! You look cute! You're here early." As uncomfortable as I felt, and as suspicious as the moment seemed to me, I chose to play along, trying not to show any emotions. "So what were you all talking about before I walked in?" My former roommate looked over to the sponsor as the sponsor continued to look at me saying, "I was just filling her in on how this week should go." Minutes later the new team walked in consisting of one of my crab sisters, my two crabs, my two little sisters, my big sister, and two new freshmen. The sponsor began going through the rules and guidelines of the team. After almost an hour of discussion, she looked over to my former roommate, then back to the team saying, "For this week she will be acting captain. You all will show her respect and support her." The tension was evident. I knew everyone was trying to figure out what exactly was going on. I kept a slight smile on my face. I knew the first place they would look for answers was through my expressions.

It was now the start of our first week of band camp. Despite everything going on, what I did and didn't know about, I was expected to stay by her side and support her no matter what. It almost seemed like the hardest task I had to endure. Nevertheless, I knew if I did it, I wanted to mean it, so my motivation was the simple fact I knew God was going to bless me and it would be greater than anything they could take away from me. Every moment my former roommate made sure I was by her side. Every moment I made sure I encouraged her.

The day practice ended the sponsor gathered the team and asked, "How was today?"

They hugged on my former roommate as they spoke one by one saying, "She did amazing. Everyone got along and we all just love her."

I continued to keep a smile on my face despite how the comments made me feel.

It was the second to last day of the camp for the first week. The sponsor made everyone line up in march-in formation with my roommate leading. She called the band director in to watch. As we began strutting in a circle, I glanced over to him and the sponsor out of the corner of my eye. Once we stopped, the sponsor looked to him saying, "This looks like a team. I like them just like this." He didn't respond, just continued to look our way. I felt as though he was only looking at me. My heart turned at the comments from my sponsor. I didn't know if she meant exactly what she said or if her words were directed towards affecting me. Regardless, I kept a smile on my face.

It was Friday. The last day my former roommate would lead before I would take over the following week. We had gotten back from lunch and as we all walked through the dance room door my former roommate told the freshmen to plank. I sat down in my space, looked over to my crab sister and asked, "What did they do?" She shook her head and shrugged her shoulders as we all sat waiting for my former roommate to come back from the restroom. Once she walked through the door, she sat down in her space. No one said anything. One of the freshmen began to cry and breath heavy as she struggled to stay up. My former roommate continued to look at them. Within that same moment the band director opened the door. My roommate began to whisper to the freshmen, "Get up, get up," but it was too late. The band director looked down to the freshman, to the team, and then back to the freshmen saying, "You two come with me. Everyone else, go home." Then he shut the door behind him. The room stayed silent as we gathered our things, but before we could leave the sponsor and the band director came walking into the room as she began yelling, "Did I not just read the rules to you all?! This is unacceptable!" She looked over to my former roommate. "And you are supposed to be in charge which makes you responsible and this is what happens?" Once we were dismissed again, my crab sister and I walked my former roommate to her car as we encouraged her. She began to cry as we continued to console her. When I made it back to my car I sat and thought. Because of this very reason, I knew it would tell me just what was going on due to the fact it was stressed that there should be no acts of what had just taken place, and if caught, it was grounds to being permanently put off the team. Why did I have the feeling this very rule wouldn't be applied for this moment. That night, I called the old sponsor to fill her in on everything that had taken place that week. "All I'm going to say is that they are testing you." What I couldn't understand was why? It almost seemed as though they pressed for me to want to back down. I wasn't built that way, but Lord knows it wasn't easy. It was the day before the start of the second week. I still had yet to receive a call about the "training meeting," just as my former roommate did, or an announcement about me leading for the week. I decided to just wait, so I left it alone.

The first day of the second week finally began and still the sponsor had yet to say anything. Before we wrapped up our workout outside, she sat the team down, looked at me and then directed her attention back to the team as she said, "This week she will take over as acting captain. She is in charge so please respect her authority." After the announcement we all gathered our things to head to breakfast. Immediately I looked over to see my former roommate had walked off to be with the team. I tried not to think too deep into it, but the very next day she barely said two words to me and continued to flock amongst the others. I continued to do what I was supposed to do by making sure everything ran smoothly. Towards the end of practice the sponsor called the team to gather around. "How has it been going?" Besides for my crabs and the new freshman, everyone shrugged their shoulders saying, "It was good...normal." I continued to move as the captain and leader I saw myself to be. There were no real problems except for one. My big sister cried almost every day. I didn't know if this was part of a plan or if it affected her seeing me lead. I thought every now and then how it would have been if she would've stayed. As comfortable as I tried to make her feel, I knew it couldn't be me. She had to settle for herself. Besides for a few of the upperclassmen, I was beginning to form a relationship with the new freshmen quickly. It felt good because my crabs were always my motivation. To be able to think I could be that inspiration to two more, made the job better.

It was the last day of the second week of camp. I let everyone go off and eat lunch on their own while the freshmen came with me to the cafe to eat. As we got ready to head out from getting to-go boxes, the band director passed us, looking at me, then the freshmen, then back to me. We all said hello as we continued to walk out the door. About an hour later everyone made their way back into the dance room when the band director called everyone into his office besides for the freshmen. "If you all are feeling over worked, you need to say something. Those freshmen looked tired. They are not used to working like this, so if you all are doing extra you need to say something because there should be a balance with your workout." I squinted my eyes and tilted my head to the side. I had no clue why he was saying this, but I didn't rebut. I simply listened. Once he dismissed us I came back to his office a few minutes later. "Would you like for me to dismiss practice early so everyone can get more rest?" He continued to engage in what he was doing as he glanced at me for a brief moment saying, "No, just needing to make sure the girls are getting the proper workout." He continued to confuse me because I created the workout and practice structure. The same workouts I used were implemented in the first week of camp from my former roommate and he didn't have a meeting with us then. I walked away shaking my head because I knew there was more to it.

The week went well, and regardless of if the team wanted me in the position or not, I felt good about how I led for the week. It was now the first day of the fall semester. I had just finished up my last class, heading to the sponsor's office before practice, when I could hear one of the new freshmen calling after me. I turned around as she ran up to me. "Hi mom! I missed you today." That one moment made me want to cry. Simply because they felt like my little babies already, but I didn't know how long that feeling would last. After stopping by the sponsor's office, I walked into the danceroom to find my former roommate already there. Because we had yet to get word on who would be the permanent captain, I continued to serve in the role from the week prior, as I lead everyone to begin stretching. We were all stretching and talking amongst ourselves when the sponsor and band director walked into the room. We turned off the music and the room became very still as the band director began to speak. "As you all know, we had yet to pick a captain, and to be honest I wasn't going to. But I do realize that the sponsor cannot be with you all 24/7. All of you ladies are wonderful and I'm sure you could all serve the position well, but unfortunately we can only pick one. There was a lot that the sponsor and I did not agree on, but we came to the best decision for this year's team."

He paused for a moment, looked at me, then looked to my former roommate and said, "You ready?"

She responded in a soft hushed tone. "Yes sir."

"She will serve as your 2019-2020 captain."

I kept my eyes forward as I discreetly pinched my arm trying to hold in my tears. I could feel the team's eyes on me. My former roommate sat to the side of me as I looked at her and smiled, but she wouldn't make eye contact with me. The sponsor began to speak as she addressed me in her comment. "This does not change the fact that she was an amazing, fierce captain. We just decided to go a different direction this year." As she dismissed us for dinner, the band director looked at me with a slight smile and walked out. I got up and walked to my former roommate as I hugged her saying, "Congratulations girl," then I left. I couldn't cry in front of them. They didn't deserve to see it because they wouldn't understand. Once I made it to my car I had yet to let out my tears. I drove to a secluded area and I called my mom.

"They didn't pick me." I broke down crying.

She stayed quiet for the moment while I cried.

"Sweetie, I know you don't want to hear this, but this is all a part of God's plan for you. Don't worry about if they were fair or if they did it to spite you, because you are anointed. God is working on your behalf and you have to believe it. The band director may have made this decision, but God is making a greater decision and no man will be able to stop it. They will have to watch as God begins to rain blessings down on you, but you have to trust His process. He showed you once that He can bring you out undefeated. This is a new level, and you got to go through and get what is for you. You get back to that dance room and don't let them see one tear. I don't care how your former roommate treated you last year, you treat her with love and respect because she is the captain, but you are a leader."

Once I cleaned myself up, I went back into the danceroom. Minutes later the new freshman, who saw me earlier that day, walked into the room. She had just come from class so she had yet to hear the news. She put her stuff down, came to hug me, and kissed me on my cheek. My eyes began to water and I did everything to hold them back. It sent memories through my mind of how every practice last season my crab would come in, hug me, and kiss me on the cheek every practice. Not because she was told, but because she wanted to. I thought I was almost another's inspiration, but who was I an inspiration to now?

I drove all the way home, holding back my tears. I walked through the front door to see my boyfriend sitting on the couch. I just stood there. He looked at me and said, "Babe." I walked to him and fell in his arms crying. He held me in his arms as I continued to cry. He picked me up, carried me to my room, and laid me on the bed. I continued to cry. God always seemed to have him around me at the right times because I needed someone. Physically I was weak and he was the strength I needed.

For the next few days of practice I didn't speak much. I did everything I was asked, but that was it. I made sure not to have an attitude, but I was still processing everything and I didn't know what to say, so it seemed better not to say much at all. Every day I pondered on quitting. So many reasons and questions filled my mind. Was I stronger if I stayed or I left? Was I giving in if I stayed or left? I didn't want my reason for leaving to be because I didn't get my way, but I also didn't want to stay and continue to experience the mess. I didn't want to leave either and have regrets. That Thursday I was late to practice. As much as I didn't want to speak with the sponsor about anything, I informed her I would be late. That evening we all went outside to mark the field show for next week's game. I could see the frustration on the sponsor's face as she watched us go through the dance. I could tell she wasn't pleased. I stood in silence while everyone moved around talking. The sponsor walked up to me presenting formation ideas on her phone. "What do you think about us doing this formation?" I kept my response brief. "I think it's fine." I then turned away to speak with my crab sister.

The next day I made it to practice early. My former roommate asked to speak with me. We walked to an empty room and sat across from one another. She began the conversation.

"I just wanted to see how you were feeling?"

Every moment reminded me of how she treated me in the past and I hated it. It drove me crazy because as much as I wanted to forget it, I couldn't. To them, it was simple to let it go, but that is exactly how I knew they didn't understand. Still I tried to internalize my mother's words as I responded to her.

"I'm good."

"I don't think you're good. You're just not acting like it," as she shyly responded to me.

"How do you expect me to act?"

"I'm just being considerate of your feelings or whatever."

I clinched my jaw to keep me from reacting how I really wanted to. She didn't care. She got what she wanted, but I was expected to cooperate. I knew she, as well as everyone else, was waiting on me to treat her how she treated me.

"I don't have much to say because at this point, it's out of my hands. I'm not going to be the one to have bad sportsmanship. My main goal is to do what I have to do and get through this year in a positive light. I don't want to feed into being negative because regardless of me having the title or not, it doesn't change that I'm a leader."

"Well hearing you say that, I have gotten a different vibe from you. Not negative, it's just I can tell you're holding back and I just wanted to see if everything was good."

Before she could finish, her posture changed as she tucked her chin into her hand and with a faint tone saying, "I did talk to the sponsor about it and you are responsible for five hundred kicks."

"For what?"

As we went back and forth, I ended my comments with, "I will speak to the sponsor about that."

"I just wanted to speak with you on a more personal level because I know we have a different relationship than everyone. We're building it and I want to continue to build it."

After she said her piece, I had nothing else to say. None of it seemed real, but at the same time, I was actually living it. Immediately I went straight to the sponsor's office to address what my roommate told me. We continued to discuss the situation back and forth. I began to walk out from ending the conversation as she said, "What's wrong with you?" Scrunching her eyebrows and dropping her head.

"I'm just here now, going with the flow."

"What is that supposed to mean? Ever since we announced your roommate as captain your disposition changed like night and day."

What were they expecting for me to do? I felt as though I was played. It had less to do with my former roommate and more of the fact I believed the decision was made all along and I just wished someone would have said something. It wasn't entitlement, but it was the simple fact the one man in control of the decision looked me in my face and made me believe I was the rightful person. I trusted him. He was a coward in my eyes. Why couldn't he just have told me? Instead, it seemed as though it was a walk in the park for everyone else. My roommate was angry all of my season for not receiving the position, only to get it. My crab sister was injured and my big sister bashed the organization and they were still on the team. I hated to compare myself, but what else was there to do. I didn't trust anyone. It seemed as though they won. The girls won. I was in the very position they wanted me in. So ask me again why my disposition was the way it was. I had every right, because judging by my perspective, each and every person knew exactly what they were doing. The sponsor watched as tears rolled down my face while I expressed to her what was on my heart, and then she responded. "I understand you being hurt, and while I agree that you have every right to be, the way you are going about it isn't helping. At the end of the day, myself and the old sponsor fought tooth and nail for you to be back in the position, but that is not what the band director wanted. There were things he said he saw about you that I never saw, but now I don't know based on the way that you have been acting. Do I understand his reasoning? No, but at the end of the day, this is his band, and he can do what he pleases. You chose to make the mistake in trusting him the way you did. You never should put your trust in a man like that because at the end of the day he will always let you down. There is not much I can do about it, but I can tell you this, your former roommate doesn't deserve the way that you are acting, even if you're not being negative, you're not being the girl we all know, because if we're being honest, every single girl in that room right now, except for your roommate, your freshman and the new girls, went to the band director and complained about how they didn't want you as captain this year. Forget the fact that they didn't get picked, they would have preferred it be anybody but you. Apparently it has something to do with your friend dating your captain's ex-boyfriend or some foolishness like that, but the truth is, you're different, and they are not use to someone like you. But I have tried. You were thrown in the fire last year and you came out blazing. You produced two of the most dynamic freshmen. I've said it all, but just as much as I believe you deserve it, I believe your former roommate deserves it too. I'm 100% behind her because she's the captain and I have to be. The only difference is I'm still 100% behind you. But you are better than this. I specifically told your roommate to lean on you because you are the most capable to run that room, but she can't do that when you give her the cold shoulder. It might seem like she's allowing others to dictate, but I guarantee, if you assert yourself she will depend on you before she depends on them, and they will back down. They never won. They never had the position. You did. Regardless of it being your former roommate now, it's not them. Assert yourself because that is who you are."

Chapter 16
Just Finish or Finish Strong?

Regardless of the things I disagreed on, she was also right in many ways. My former roommate didn't deserve it. Not from me. It wasn't my job to punish her for how she treated me. Of course everything in my mind made me believe she knew more than what she let on from the beginning, but what did that matter? What if she really didn't know. When it was me, no one believed I didn't have anything to do with it, no matter what I said. Now it was her turn. Whether she knew or not, it didn't change the fact that my job wasn't to ridicule her, but to uplift her. As far as my teammates, I knew all along. They would have done anything not to see me in the position again, but every thought of me quitting went out of the window when my sponsor informed me about what they were doing. Now, I had to stay. I wanted to make sure they had front row seats to witness me overcoming everything they thought they changed behind closed doors.

I finished the week off with a better attitude after speaking with the sponsor. Before I knew it, it was the end of the next week right before the first game of the season. Once practice ended, the sponsor asked if I could stop by her home to pick something up. As we talked about how the weeks had gone, she made mention of her disappointment of the field dances. I already made notice it was a frustration for her because she was now exerting energy she hadn't before. Although my attitude did get better, it still seemed as though my roommate depended on my big sister and my crab sister to do the majority of the task. I didn't want to force myself upon her. I knew creating a dance was my strong suit, but I strongly believed that was one of the biggest responsibilities of the captain. If the captain didn't do it, what were they truly responsible for.

The sponsor and I were on the same page that the dance was not where it should be, but I looked at her and said, "All I can do is contribute my ideas, and it is up to the captain if she wants to utilize them or not."

I knew something was up when she began to slightly smile.

"What if I give you complete control of the field shows? You'll be responsible for running everything when it comes to the dances, of course with your former roommate's assistance. I've spoken to the band director and he approved it and your former roommate is also fine with it."

I didn't respond immediately. I couldn't. As much as an honor it seemed like it was, it was an even bigger slap in the face. The way I saw it, I would run things, but my former roommate would be the face and she was okay with that. I would be left with the work while they got the glory. It seemed as though in their minds this idea made everyone look good. I didn't say much in response because I didn't want to say the wrong thing. I decided to think about it, because although I didn't want to feel like I needed a title to do a job, I didn't want to feel used either.

It was the day of the first game. No one could understand the feeling going through my mind and body. This would be the official reveal of my former roommate being captain and me dancing behind her. I wanted so bad to run away from the things I knew people would say and the stories they would make up. I honestly needed God more than ever. I sat next to my former roommate on the bus, so I couldn't speak out loud. I turned my head to the window and talked to Him in my mind. "God, I promise I'm working to get my emotions together, but can You be me today? If they see me, they're going to see hatred, anger, sadness, but if they see You in me, they'll see support, joy, and love." The minute I stepped off the bus, I knew He'd answered my prayer. As we all walked to the restroom to freshen up before entering the game, the sponsor walked up to me and looked me in my eyes, "Are you good?" I smiled. "Yes, I am." I genuinely was and it shocked me. As I sat in the stands, all the moms stood in front of me, calling my former roommate's name. I could see them watching me, waiting for me to act in the very manor their daughters did towards me, but it only made me put a better smile on my face. It didn't need to be bigger because God was doing it for me. So no matter what face I wore, they were seeing Him.

Once the game was over and we all made it back onto the bus, all the girls gathered around my former roommate commending her on how good she did. I could never help that I always had flashbacks to when it was me and no one said a word to me on my first game, but I also remembered they preferred it to be anybody but me. There was a part of me that felt it was done purposefully, but what could I do about it. I had to continue to wait. It was hard not to think why her season seemed to be starting off so good and mines started off the way it did. But immediately I realized the climax of my year, the barriers I broke, and how I surpassed everyone who doubted me. I didn't need to compare my time to my former roommate's because this was her time. Her moment was what it was because it was her, and my moment was what it was because of me. Nothing could compare. It was also good to know I still had my crabs and a sponsor who I believed supported me despite the decision. She was never the type to show much emotion or

412

affection, but for the first time, she did towards me. She walked up beside me as I walked alone. "I'm really proud of you," as she grabbed my shoulder and hugged me. She probably couldn't tell or didn't know, but it meant a lot to me.

Throughout the weekend and up until the beginning of the week, I pondered on my decision to accept the sponsor's offer to me. So many questions came to mind. What if this was what God wanted me to do? What if this was them testing me? What if it was exactly what I thought, nothing but a plan to make everyone else look good. I wasn't in it for me, however it was me who organized everything for the season with plans and structure only for it to be given to my former roommate. After giving it much thought, I made my decision. I believed that responsibility was for the captain. If she was going to be in that position, she needed to experience it for what it was in its entirety. I knew the sponsor was upset about my decision, but the way I saw it, she was no different than the band director or anybody else. She wanted things the way she wanted them and would do what she could to get it, whether it was meant for good or bad. It was up to me to stand for what I believed, whether anyone saw my decision as right or wrong. Despite me not accepting the offer, my former roommate did begin to lean on me more just as the sponsor said and I didn't mind helping. I would admit that part of what motivated me was to see the reaction from the team when my former roommate came to me for help, just like my sponsor said. But surprisingly it made me feel good to treat them right.

As the weeks went by, things seemed to get better for me in the sense of me actually feeling good. I was genuinely learning and growing a true understanding of being happy. I was noticing my roommate beginning to pull away from me. I almost got the feeling she resented asking me for help. Although the sponsor took over most of the practices, she seemed to never be pleased anymore. I was noticing her pulling back from me as well. Each practice before every performance she would get more and more frustrated. As we all stood outside practicing before the performance the next day, I looked over to her to see her head buried in her hands.

I knew she was frustrated with how the dance looked so I waited for a moment and then asked, "Would you like for me to take a look at it and fix some things?"

"Anything will do at this point."

I felt different; free. Despite the underlying feelings I felt coming from them, it didn't matter because my joy was stuck. I knew what it was. They didn't understand my joy, but they let me know I was doing exactly what God told me to do. "If your enemy is hungry, give him food to eat; if he is thirsty, give him water to drink. In doing this, you will heap burning coals on his head, and the Lord will reward you." I knew my reward was right around the corner.

The season was getting closer and closer to the end. I could personally say I felt better than everyone in the room. We were practicing our stand dances for the weekend's battle when the sponsor walked in and stood at the back of the room with a man and a woman. I could sense something was going on, but we continued to dance as if no one was there. Later on that night before practice ended, the sponsor sat everyone down to speak with us. She was excited to announce the band was selected to be a part of a music video for a well-known recording artist.

"There is a lead role that they are holding auditions for amongst you ladies tomorrow, so whoever would like to audition you need to make sure you are present. This is a real audition that is being ran completely by them. The band director nor I have any other information and will not be a part of the selection so good luck."

My heart beat fast the entire car ride home. It seemed like the right path for me because I always dreamed to pursue an acting career, but what made me nervous was I didn't trust the people around me. I knew the sponsor said they had no involvement, but it was hard to believe. I kept the news completely to myself. I wanted to keep my mind on the positive. I prayed all night in preparation for the next day.

As I walked into the school union, my palms began to sweat and my heart beat faster and faster. I didn't know who all from the team chose to audition, but I tried not to let that be my concern. As I walked into the room they directed us to wait in, I saw my former roommate sitting in an area alone. I sat next to her as we briefly spoke. For a moment, I thought maybe it would be just me and her, until our crab sister walked in followed by my big sister. All of the seniors. This was a moment to me. It finally seemed as though I was up against the three main people who felt like I wasn't capable. The director walked us through what the video would consist of. There was a lead and a co-lead role. It was easy to say it didn't matter what role I got as long as I got one, but I also knew I wanted the leading role. The four of us sat to the side waiting for the audition to begin when the director walked up to meet us and see how we were feeling.

"So who is the captain?"

My roommate raised her hand as she smiled, but then he looked at me.

"But you were the captain last year?"

As I nodded my head responding to him he said, "I saw a video of you leading those girls last year and I was sold. I said man. I have to have them."

I began to smile from ear to ear. Not that I was surprised, but out of all of us, he noticed me and it felt good. Once the audition began, he had each of us showcase our dancing ability. He played the song of the artist and one by one we danced. As we wrapped up the audition with a small scene of improvisation, he watched as we all played the scene to the best of our own understanding. When we finished, I noticed my heartbeat kept the same rhythm it had upon the start of the audition. I knew I couldn't be completely calm until I knew the results. A few weeks went by leading to our final home game and as excited as I was, all I could think about was the audition and when the results would be in. We were informed they would reach out to the ones who were picked, and I had yet to hear from anyone. I sat in my own area, quietly, trying to listen to the room to see if anyone would speak about it. I couldn't take it anymore. I walked up to the sponsor.

"Have you heard anything about who was picked or who got what part?"

She continued to engage in what she was doing as she said, "I don't know anything. All I know is that they reached out to your roommate."

All that went through my mind was the wonder of what part she had received and if they already made their decision. Who was the other girl? I tried to forget about it for the time being to focus on the game. It was traditional for seniors to lead on their last home game, but I wasn't sure because I hadn't heard anything from my roommate about it. I knew it was that time when she looked to my crab sister to lead. It made me happy to see my crab sister in the position she wanted, even if it was for a moment. I knew what it felt like, and that reason alone put a smile on my face for her. It seemed as though the moment moved in slow motion when it was my turn. Everything went through my mind as if it was my first time. Soon as the music started, my body settled in the position like I had been there before. The beauty in it was that I had. I prayed to God letting Him know if He didn't do anything else for me, to make that moment one to remember for the people who doubted me, and for the people who counted me out. I wish I could've looked every last one of them in the eye, but when the beat dropped, it no longer mattered. Regardless of anyone not believing in me, I believed in myself. I guess it was easy to say God was working in my favor because the moment I made it to the dance room to gather my things, I picked up my phone to see I received a message from the crew of the music video. I maintained my composure as I said nothing on the way to my car. I was still on edge because I still hadn't received any real information. I was asked to be present the next day and with just that little information I could only imagine what was next.

I made it to school upon the time I was asked to be present and to my surprise none of my teammates were there. Because I didn't know much, I wasn't sure what exactly was going to take place. I stood in the hallway talking to some of the crew members when the band director came walking behind me. I turned around to say hello with a smile on my face.

He just looked at me as he said, "What are you doing here?"

"They asked me to be here."

Before he could respond, my former roommate and her mother came walking through the door. I greeted them the same way I greeted the band director. I wasn't surprised when they responded the same way he did. I turned around to see him walking in the opposite direction from which he came. Their demeanor towards me didn't concern me so much because I was looking forward to knowing what was next. The director called my former roommate and I into the band hall along with the sponsor tailing behind. We all had yet to know who was given what role, but the moment of truth was now here. He looked towards both of us as he began to explain his vision of the storyline and then he looked at me. "Which is why I think you would be perfect for the leading role." He continued to talk as if he didn't just tell me I had gotten the leading role. I mean, I figured it didn't mean that much to him because it had everything to do with me. I had to maintain my composure because I wanted to run around the entire building. Once I made it to my car, I let out a loud scream as tears rolled down my face. I looked up to the sky. "You did it again. Thank you." The week of filming went by extremely fast. I made sure to cherish every minute of it. They placed me in the middle of the dance floor with all the lights and cameras on me. Every band member sat to watch and the team sat front row. The sponsor stood off to the side. The room went black and then the director said, "Action." The spotlight came in on me as I lifted my head to look into the camera. It was the best feeling, but I wanted to know one thing.

As we wrapped up, I began speaking to the director about my future then I said, "If you don't mind me asking, why did you pick me?"

He didn't hesitate.

"Besides for the way you danced, there was and is something special about you. You're a star."

It was the last weekend of the season. The weekend we all looked forward too. The biggest game of our season. Bayou Classic. I was still on cloud ten from shooting the music video, so anything else that took place could only enhance what I was already feeling. The weekend seemed to go by quickly and the moment we made it to the game, it seemed so surreal. This would be the last time I would strut through the stadium as a dance girl. The last time I would grace this field. The last time I would sit in those stands, and the last time I would lift my hand in the air in reverence to my alma mater amongst the team. But this time when I lifted my hand I could think of everything for the last time in the heat of the moment. Every lesson, every trial, and every blessing took over my mind and occupied the space of my body. God spoke to me. He said, "When you are satisfied with Me and Me alone, I will bless you beyond measure." I learned to trust Him, to lean on Him and to love Him like never before. He showed me what consistency and favor really looked like and the blessing in disguise was me. He used my life just so I could bring glory to His name. Everything He did, everything He allowed was needed. He prepared a table for me, in the presence of my enemies, and He said eat. I would look back to the very beginning, only to realize the true meaning of why He allowed me to go through what I did at such a young age. It was all preparation for a moment He knew all along, something that was greater than me. I received so many blessings even beyond this point. I endured so much, but in the end I only appreciated the trials because the end result spoke for itself. I could say my testimony didn't benefit just me. So when I lifted my hand, it was beyond my school. It was beyond my team. It was beyond me. It was to Him because He was the very reason I could lift it with all the passion that my body contained. Who was I an inspiration to? Within my four years He gave me the true answer just so He could show someone who saw their life through me to forget their troubles and simply just dance.

Galatians 6:9 Let us not become weary in doing good, for at the proper time we will reap a harvest if we do not give up.